C000246866

The NICEIC guide to

Domestic Periodic Inspection, Testing and Reporting

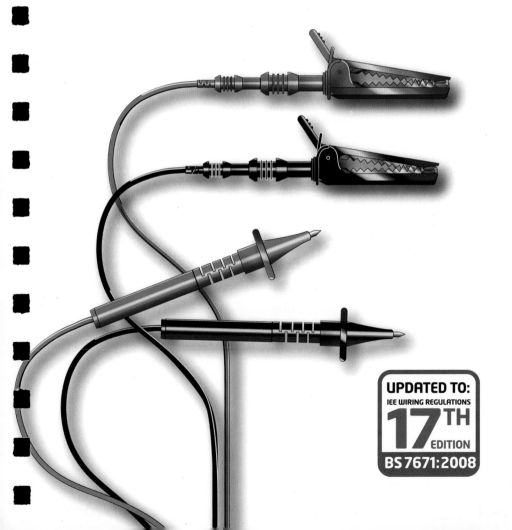

UPDATED TO:
IEE WIRING REGULATIONS
17TH
EDITION
BS 7671:2008

NICEIC

'NICEIC' is a trading name of NICEIC Group Limited, a wholly owned subsidiary of the Electrical Safety Council. Under licence from the Electrical Safety Council, NICEIC acts as the electrical contracting industry's independent voluntary regulatory body for electrical installation safety matters throughout the UK, and maintains and publishes registers of electrical contractors that it has assessed against particular scheme requirements (including the technical standard of electrical work).

The registers include the national Roll of Approved Contractors (established in 1956), and the register of NICEIC Domestic Installers that, since January 2005, have been authorized to self-certify their domestic electrical installation work as compliant with the Building Regulations for England and Wales.

The NICEIC Approved Contractor scheme is accredited by the United Kingdom Accreditation Service (UKAS) to EN 45011 – *General requirements for bodies operating product certification systems.*

The Electrical Safety Council

The Electrical Safety Council (formerly the National Inspection Council for Electrical Installation Contracting) is a charitable non-profit making organization set up in1956 to protect users of electricity against the hazards of unsafe and unsound electrical installations.

The Electrical Safety Council is supported by all sectors of the electrical industry, approvals and research bodies, consumer interest organizations, the electricity distribution industry, professional institutes and institutions, regulatory bodies, trade and industry associations and federations, trade unions and local and central government.

Published by:

NICEIC Group Limited
Warwick House, Houghton Hall Park, Houghton Regis, Dunstable, Bedfordshire LU5 5ZX

Tel: 01582 531000   Fax: 01582 556024

Email: customerservice@niceic.com Website: www.niceicgroup.com

ISBN-10   1-906091-06-4
ISBN-13   978-1-906091-06-4
EAN   9781906091064

Acknowledgement is given to the following for their help in developing this book (and many others not listed):

David Roydhouse IEng MIET LCGI MIHS
Martindale Electric
Megger
Socket and See Ltd (Kew Technic)
Terry Brown - Navigator Productions
Tony Cable IEng MIET
Photographs (unless otherwise indicated) courtesy of www.goodphotoart.com

**The NICEIC guide to
Domestic Periodic Inspection, Testing and Reporting**

CONTENTS

An NICEIC publication © Electrical Safety Council (JAN 2008)

CONTENTS

The NICEIC guide to
Domestic Periodic Inspection, Testing and Reporting

Compiling Domestic Electrical Installation Periodic
Inspection Reports

CONTENTS

The NICEIC guide to
Domestic Periodic Inspection, Testing and Reporting

INTRODUCTION

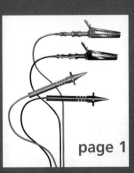

INTRODUCTION

1.1 Aims and objectives

This book gives practical guidance for NICEIC Approved Contractors and Domestic Installers, and others carrying out periodic inspection and testing, and preparing periodic inspection reports for electrical installations in domestic premises.

All electrical equipment deteriorates with age, as well as with wear and tear from use. Every electrical installation therefore needs to be inspected and tested at appropriate intervals during its lifetime to establish that its condition is such that, subject to the completion of any necessary remedial work, the installation is safe to remain in service at least until the next inspection is due.

Correctly compiled Domestic Electrical Installation Visual Condition and/or Domestic Periodic Electrical Installation Inspection Reports (supported by previously completed Electrical Installation Certificates, Domestic Electrical Installation Certificates and/or Minor Electrical Installation Works Certificates) provide the persons responsible for the safety of electrical installations (including contractors, owners and users) with an important record of the condition of the installations at the time they were inspected and tested.

Such reports and certificates also provide an essential basis for subsequent inspection and testing, without which a degree of costly exploratory work might be necessary on each occasion. In the event of injury or fire alleged to have been caused by an electrical installation, reports and certificates will provide documentary evidence to help demonstrate that, in the opinion of competent persons, the installation had been installed and subsequently maintained to a satisfactory standard of safety.

Every electrical contractor should employ at least one experienced person who has responsibility for inspecting and testing electrical installation work in accordance with the requirements of the national standard for electrical safety, *BS 7671 – Requirements for Electrical Installations* (otherwise known as the *IEE Wiring Regulations*). This includes the preparation, to a satisfactory standard, of the forms of certification and reporting associated with inspection and testing, in order to accurately record the results for the benefit of both the contractor and the users.

Practical advice and guidance which answers many of the questions commonly arising during the inspection and testing of electrical installation work, or during the preparation of the associated certificates and reports, is given in the NICEIC *Inspection, Testing and Certification* book.

Guidance to completing specialized certificates and reports, which includes fire detection and alarm systems, and emergency lighting installations, is given in the NICEIC *Completing Specialized Certificates & Reports* book.

1.2   Scope

The scope of this book includes the following **one star** ★, **two star** ★★ and **three star** ★★★ 'service levels' for preparing the following reports:

> ★ **Domestic Visual Condition Report**
>
> ★★ **Domestic Electrical Installation Periodic Inspection Report**
>
> ★★★ **Domestic Electrical Installation Periodic Inspection Report** (as a **two star** ★★ Domestic Electrical Installation Periodic Inspection Report' but to include **enhancements**, such as:
>
> > • inspecting, testing and reporting on a **higher** % sampling rate of electrical accessories (such as lighting switches) and lighting points, compared to **two star** ★★ inspection, testing and reporting, and/or
> >
> > • expanding the extent (or reducing the limitations) of the inspection and testing, to include items such as portable appliances or fixed current-using equipment.

The extent, limitations and % sample rate checks of inspection and testing recommended for service levels is given in Annex A. These service levels will enable the client and the competent person to agree the service level required, prior to the inspection and testing commencing.

INTRODUCTION

This book is intended to complement the requirements for inspection, testing and reporting given in *BS 7671* and the information and advice provided in other authoritative publications such as the NICEIC *Inspection, Testing and Certification* book, and the IEE Guidance Note 3: *Inspection and Testing*.

The book also complements NICEIC's DVD on Domestic Periodic Inspection Testing and Reporting.

The book covers the general requirements relating to the inspection, testing and reporting of electrical installations forming part of TN-C-S, TN-S and TT systems – especially in domestic premises!

Chapters 4 and 5 give information on inspection and testing respectively.

The book does **not** cover the particular requirements relating to the inspection, testing and reporting of:

- special locations and installations, other than rooms containing a bath or shower,
- common areas of blocks of flats,
- distribution to the domestic premises,
- Houses of Multiple Occupation (HM0),
- specialized electrical installations, such as fire alarm and detection systems, or
- portable appliances or fixed current-using equipment.

However, such inspection and testing and reporting may be undertaken as part of the **three star** ★★★ service level, providing the inspector is competent to carry out such inspection, testing and reporting, and follows the recommendations of the appropriate British Standard or Code of Practice.

Guidance on inspection, testing and reporting of fire alarm and detection systems is given in the NICEIC *Guide to Completing Specialized Certificates & Reports* book.

Guidance on inspection, testing and reporting on portable appliances and fixed equipment is given in the NICEIC *Guide to electrical equipment maintenance* and the IEE *Code of Practice for In-service Inspection and Testing of Electrical Equipment.*

This book is **not** intended to instruct untrained and inexperienced persons to undertake the inspection and testing of electrical installations. It assumes that all persons proposing to undertake such work have already acquired the necessary knowledge, understanding and skill, and are properly equipped to undertake such work without putting themselves and others at risk.

1.3   NICEIC domestic periodic inspection reports

This book uses as its main theme the preparation of the following domestic electrical installation reports:

- domestic visual condition report

- domestic electrical installation periodic inspection report

NICEIC domestic electrical installation report forms are coloured:

- red █ for use only by NICEIC Approved Contractors and Conforming Bodies

- purple █ for use only by NICEIC Domestic Installers (/Approved Contractors if indicated on the form)

- green █ for use by those listed above who are working outside their scope of NICEIC registration, or those not registered with NICEIC, in particular those preparing for assessment.

The above colour scheme is used throughout the book to help the reader find information about the particular version of the forms.

INTRODUCTION

Red and purple NICEIC report forms are accountable documents and include a unique serial number. The serial number allows the origin of NICEIC report forms to be traced by NICEIC in the event of a query about its authenticity. For this reason, the forms should **only** be used by the NICEIC-registered firm that purchased them.

IF THE SERIAL NUMBER IS ERASED OR ALTERED IN ANY WAY NICEIC WOULD NOT CONSIDER THE REPORT TO BE VALID.

Unused forms should be kept secure by the Qualified Supervisor.

A record of each report issued should be made on the record sheet provided with the report forms.

Green report forms have **no** serial numbers.

Report forms published by NICEIC are designed to be completed by hand or with the aid of a computer (see item 1.10).

NICEIC forms have an issue number after the form prefix. For example, the first issue of a form would have a 1 after the form prefix and the 2nd issue a 2. Forms may be updated from time to time, so reference should be made to the NICEIC website www.niceic.com to check that the version of the form intended to be used is still valid.

Unused sets of obsolete report forms should be destroyed to prevent their misuse.

Forms that should be used for reporting on the condition of domestic electrical installations are shown in items 1.3.1 and 1.3.2. Detailed guidance on completing these and the associated forms (such as continuation sheets) is covered in Chapters 2 and 3.

1.3.1   Visual condition reports
(DVN 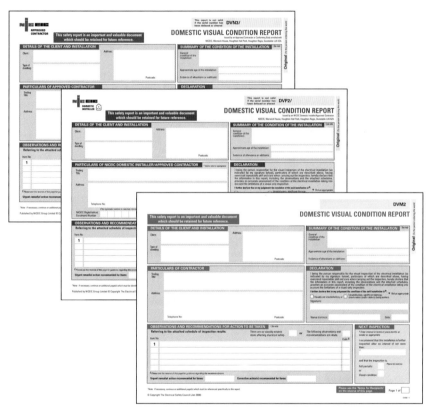, DVP and DVM)

The first pages of reports DVN , DVP and DVM follow respectively.

Full versions of reports DVN , DVP and DVM are available in Annexe B.

INTRODUCTION

1.3.2 Electrical installation periodic inspection reports (DPN 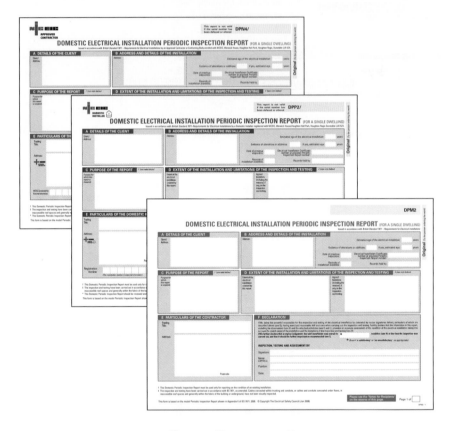, DPP and DPM)

NICEIC domestic electrical installation periodic inspection reports are available.

The first page of reports DPN , DPP and DPM follow respectively.

Full versions of reports DPN , DPP and DPM are available in Annexe C.

The NICEIC guide to
Domestic Periodic Inspection, Testing and Reporting

1.4 Purpose of periodic inspection, testing and reporting

Every electrical installation deteriorates with use and age. It is important for the person responsible for the maintenance of the installation (such as the householder or landlord) to be sure that the safety of the users is not put at risk, and that the installation continues to be in a safe and serviceable condition. Therefore, it is necessary for the installation to be periodically inspected and tested and a report on its condition obtained.

The periodic inspection of an electrical installation may be required for one or more of a variety of reasons, each of which may impose particular requirements or limitations.

The purpose of periodic inspection, testing and reporting on the condition of an electrical installation is to identify damage defects and deterioration that might affect safety, and report on it:

Chapter 62 of *BS 7671 – Requirements for Electrical Installations* gives the requirements for inspection, testing and reporting.

BS 7671: 2008 *Requirements for Electrical Installations, Seventeenth edition*

Reported deficiencies observed during the inspection and testing may then be remedied to enable continued safe use of the installation.

It is in the best interests of both the contractor and the user that inspection, testing, certification and reporting is carried out correctly.

The *Wiring Regulations* date back to 1882. The first edition, called the *Rules and Regulations for the Prevention of Fire Risks Arising from Electric Lighting*, was the first in a long series published by the Institution of Electrical Engineers (IEE) and its predecessor, the Society of Telegraph Engineers and of Electricians. The importance of testing was recognized even in the earliest days, as can be seen from the extract that follows.

INTRODUCTION

Extracts from *Rules and Regulations for the Prevention of Fire Risks Arising from Electric Lighting* published by the Society of Telegraph Engineers and of Electricians, 11 May, 1882.

> *"The difficulties that beset the electrical engineer are chiefly internal and invisible, and they can only be guarded against by 'testing', or probing with electric currents." (Introduction)*
>
> *"NB - The value of frequently testing the wires cannot be too strongly urged. It is an operation, skill in which is easily acquired and applied. The escape of electricity cannot be detected by the sense of smell, as can gas, but it can be detected by apparatus far more certain and delicate. Leakage not only means waste, but in the presence of moisture it means destruction of the conductor and its insulating covering, by electric action." (note to Rule 17)*

The sentiments expressed in those early rules and regulations are as significant today as they were in 1882.

The fundamental reason for periodically inspecting and testing an existing installation is to check it is **safe to remain in service** until the next inspection is due.

Electrical installations need to be inspected and tested at appropriate intervals throughout their lifetime. On each occasion, details of the condition of the installation should be recorded in a **Periodic Inspection Report** for the benefit of the person ordering the inspection, and of the persons subsequently involved in remedial or alteration work, or further inspections.

Periodic Inspection Reports provide an important and valuable record of the condition of an electrical installation at the time of the inspecting and testing.

The reports can help to identify potential electric shock currents and excessive temperatures likely to cause burns fires and other injurious effects.

An example of damage caused by electrical faults and electric shock follows.

> *Government statistics for England and Wales indicate that 20% of all fires in homes are caused by **electrical faults***, *and that on average, these result in about **24 deaths** and **590 non-fatal injuries** each year. On top of this, about **12 deaths** and **750 non-fatal injuries** are caused in homes by **electric shock*** *

**The NICEIC guide to
Domestic Periodic Inspection, Testing and Reporting**

*   Source ODPM (Office of the Deputy Prime Minister), *Fire Statistics, 2004*

** Source ODPM, *Regulatory Impact Assessment for Part P of the Building Regulations for England and Wales, July 2004.*

Note: Contact to the ODPM website is now redirected to **www.communities.gov.uk**

1.5   Legal aspects

Legal publications applicable to inspection, testing and reporting are included in the following list, which is **not** exhaustive.

Legislation applicable to inspection, testing and reporting

- *Building Acts and Regulations*

- *Consumer protection Acts and Regulations*

- *The Control of Asbestos Regulations 2006* (see item 1.7.3)

- *The Electricity at Work Regulations 1989* (see item 1.5.1)

- *The Electricity Safety, Quality and Continuity Regulations 2002*

- *The Health and safety at Work etc. Act 1974*

- *The Landlord and Tenant Act 1985*

- *Management of Health and Safety at Work Regulations 1999* (see item 1.7.4)

- *Personal Protective Equipment Regulations 2002*

- *The Provision and Use of Work Equipment Regulations 1998*

- *Guide to the Reporting of Injuries, Diseases and Dangerous Occurrences Regulations 1995*

- *The Work at Height Regulations 2005* (see item 1.7.5).

INTRODUCTION

Information on legislation is available on the following websites:

Consumer protection	
The Department of Trading Standards	**www.tradingstandards.gov.uk**
Building Acts and Regulations	
Governments:	
- England and Wales	**www.communities.gov.uk**
- Northern Ireland	**www.dfpni.gov.uk**
- Scotland	**www.sbsa.gov.uk**
General	
The Office of Public Sector Information (OPSI)	**www.opsi.gov.uk**
Health and safety	
England, Wales and Scotland The Health and Safety Executive (HSE)	**www.hse.gov.uk**
Northern Ireland The Health and Safety Executive Northern Ireland (HSENI)	**www.hseni.gov.uk**

Information on the *Electricity at Work Regulations* is given in item 1.5.1.

1.5.1   The Electricity at Work Regulations

All persons carrying out inspection and testing of electrical installations, whether as an employee or self-employed person, must comply with the relevant requirements of the *Electricity at Work Regulations*. They apply to all persons carrying out any work activity falling within the scope of the Regulations. They therefore apply to inspection and testing (as well as to other aspects of electrical work) even when being carried out in locations not normally considered being places of work, such as domestic premises.

The NICEIC guide to
Domestic Periodic Inspection, Testing and Reporting

The *Electricity at Work Regulations* does not specifically require electrical installation certificates or reports to be issued and retained. However, such documents may provide the only effective evidence for the contractor or the person(s) responsible for the safety of an electrical installation should either or both be prosecuted under the provisions of those statutory regulations.

Persons undertaking inspection and testing should pay particular attention to Regulation 14, 'working on or near live conductors', and to the associated guidance provided in the *Memorandum of guidance on the Electricity at Work Regulations*[1].

HSE Memorandum of guidance on the Electricity at Work Regulations

Electrical contractors that issue inaccurate or misleading reports are liable to criminal prosecution by Trading Standards Officers under the *Trade Descriptions Act 1968* or other relevant legislation. There have also been successful claims for damages in the civil courts by persons who have relied upon the content of an electrical installation periodic inspection report, such as for house purchase.

Correctly compiled certificates and reports:

- are a record of your involvement and responsibility

- demonstrate that you have carried out the necessary inspection and testing

- can be significant in providing you, if necessary, with a defence under Regulation 29 of the Electricity at Work Regulations.

---

[1] **NOTE:** In Northern Ireland, the *Electricity at Work Regulations (Northern Ireland)* 1991 applies, and there is a corresponding *Memorandum of Guidance* issued by the Health and Safety Executive for Northern Ireland. The Regulations and the Memorandum of Guidance are similar to those applicable in other parts of the UK.

INTRODUCTION

1.6   The inspector and competence

Throughout this book, the term 'inspector' is used to describe a person responsible for inspecting and testing an electrical installation. All persons carrying out the inspection and testing of electrical installations must be competent to do so, unless under the direct supervision of a competent person.

Persons who consider that they are **not** fully competent to undertake the inspection and testing of electrical installations without direct supervision should, as a first step, complete an appropriate course and assessment provided by a reputable training organization, such as NICEIC Training.

NICEIC considers that, to be competent to undertake the inspection and testing of an electrical installation, persons must as a minimum:

- have sufficient knowledge and experience of electrical installation matters to avoid danger to themselves and to others

- be familiar with, and understand, the requirements of *BS 7671*, including those relating to inspection, testing, and certification and reporting

- have a sound knowledge of the particular type of installation to be inspected and tested

- have sufficient information about the function and construction of the installation to allow them to proceed in safety.

NICEIC experience indicates that persons undertaking periodic inspection reporting need to have above-average knowledge and experience of electrical installation matters to enable them to safely and accurately assess the condition of an existing electrical installation, especially when they do not have access to the design information relating to that installation.

If the inspector is competent and takes all the necessary safety precautions, including following the correct procedure, the process of inspection and testing should not create danger to persons or livestock, or cause damage to property.

The NICEIC guide to
Domestic Periodic Inspection, Testing and Reporting

1.7 Safe working procedures

It is essential to follow safe working procedures when carrying any electrical installation work including inspection and testing.

A safe system of work must be used for the isolation of live parts and the measurement of voltage, current and impedance to reduce the risk of electric shock, fire, explosion or mechanical movement that might cause injury or even death.

Working procedures include isolation (see items 1.7.1), measurement of voltage, current or impedance (see item 1.7.2), taking care for potential hazards such as asbestos (see item 1.7.3), carrying out risk assessments (see item 1.7.4) and working at heights (see item 1.7.5). The inspector should take special care when working alone (see item 1.7.6).

1.7.1 Isolation

Guidance on safe isolation procedures for low voltage installations has been produced by The Electrical Safety Council in conjunction with the Health and Safety Executive (HSE) and other organizations. Its purpose is to provide practical guidance for employers and the self-employed on safe isolation procedures to be followed when working on low voltage electrical installations.

The above guide, which should be followed, may be downloaded from The Electricity Safety Council's website **www.electricalsafetycouncil.org.uk**.

The above guide also includes NICEIC *Pocket Guide 5 – Guide to isolation procedure*, which is reproduced as follows, for ease of reference:

INTRODUCTION

NICEIC *Pocket Guide 5*

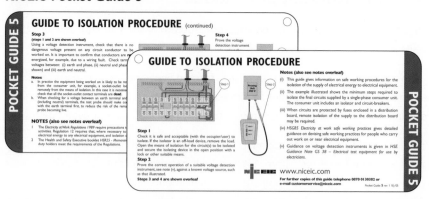

Pocket Guide 5 gives information on safe working procedures for the isolation of the supply of electrical energy to electrical equipment. Some of the key information from the guide follows.

The example illustrated shows the minimum steps required to isolate the final circuits supplied by a single-phase consumer unit. The consumer unit includes an isolator and circuit-breakers.

When circuits are protected by fuses enclosed in a distribution board, remote isolation of the supply to the distribution board may be required.

The Isolation Procedure

Step 1

Check it is safe and acceptable (with the occupier/user) to isolate. If the isolator is an off-load device, remove the load. Open the means of isolation for the circuit(s) to be isolated and secure the isolating device in the open position with a lock or other suitable means.

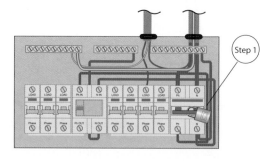

The NICEIC guide to
Domestic Periodic Inspection, Testing and Reporting

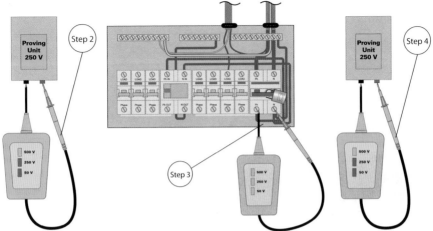

Step 2

Prove the correct operation of a suitable voltage detection instrument, against a known voltage source, such as that illustrated. Guidance on voltage detection instruments is given in *HSE Guidance Note GS 38 – Electrical test equipment for use by electricians*.

Step 3

Using a voltage detection instrument, check that there is no dangerous voltage present on any circuit conductor to be worked on. It is important to confirm that conductors are **not** energized, for example, due to a wiring fault. Check terminal voltages between: (i) earth and line, (ii) neutral and line (as shown) and (iii) earth and neutral.

Step 4

Prove the voltage detection instrument again against the known source to check that it was functioning correctly when the circuit(s) were tested for the presence of voltage.

Notes

1. In practice the equipment being worked on is likely to be remote from the consumer unit, for example, a socket-outlet located remotely from the means of isolation. In this case it is necessary to check that all the socket-outlet contact terminals are **dead**.

2. When checking for a voltage between an earth terminal and live (including neutral) terminals, the test probe should make contact with the earth terminal first, to reduce the risk of the remaining probe becoming live.

INTRODUCTION

The *Electricity at Work Regulations 1989* require precautions to be taken against the risk of death or personal injury from electricity in work activities. Regulation 12 requires that, where necessary to prevent **danger**: a suitable means is available for cutting off the supply of electrical energy to any electrical equipment, and isolation of any electrical equipment.

The Health and Safety Executive booklet *HSR25 - Memorandum of guidance on the Electricity at Work Regulations 1989* is intended to help duty holders meet the requirements of the Regulations.

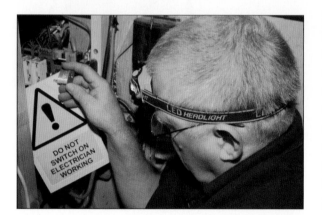

Example of main switch isolated, locked-off and warning label fitted, to enable continuity tests to be carried out on the circuit protective conductors and protective bonding conductors (see item 5.10)

Note: In the circumstances shown in the above photograph precautions **must** be taken to prevent unauthorized access to live parts within the consumer unit, such as by the inspector being in attendance or locking the cupboard housing the consumer unit. In other circumstances for locking off, the consumer unit cover must be fitted, where practicable, or adequate precautions taken to prevent unauthorized access.

When isolating the main source of energy it is also essential to isolate any secondary sources of energy (such as microgeneration).

1.7.2   Measurement of voltage, current or impedance

When measuring voltage, current or impedance appropriate precautions need to be taken to prevent accidents, such as:

- ensuring that test instruments and their test leads and probes are suitable and properly used (see item 1.8),

The NICEIC guide to
Domestic Periodic Inspection, Testing and Reporting

- that the equipment to be worked upon is safe for the intended tests, and
- that the working environment does not present additional dangers.

Particular care must be taken when measuring voltage, prospective fault current and earth fault loop impedance, as the tests are conducted when the installation is energized (live).

Information on testing is given in section 5.

1.7.3   Asbestos

Older installations may have equipment or building materials containing asbestos.

Building materials and equipment containing asbestos were widely used from 1930 to around 1980; particularly from the 1960s onwards. So houses and flats built or refurbished at this time may contain asbestos materials.

Some of areas in a home or electrical equipment where asbestos might be found include:
- garage and shed roofs
- linings for walls, ceilings and doors
- insulation panels in some storage heaters
- bath panels
- central heating flues
- loose asbestos packing between floors and in partition walls
- floor tiles
- semi-enclosed fuses
- contactors.

Most people are exposed to low amounts of asbestos present in the atmosphere. Asbestos fibres and dust are potentially **very dangerous if inhaled** in higher concentrations over a period of time, when they can cause serious lung diseases including cancer. The symptoms of these diseases often do not appear for between 20 -30 years after exposure to asbestos.

INTRODUCTION

Where equipment or building materials contain asbestos:

- care should be taken not to disturb such items, or

- breathe in any asbestos dust (if such materials are accidentally disturbed), and

- notify the occupier/person responsible for safety of the installation and include appropriate details on the report and recommend they SEEK help if required.

Further information on asbestos can be found on the HSE website **www.hse.gov.uk** or by contacting the local council.

1.7.4   Risk assessment

Regulation 3 (1) of the *Management of Health and Safety at Work Regulations 1999* requires:

> *Every Employer shall make a suitable and sufficient assessment of:*
>
> *(a) the risks to the health and safety of his employees to which they are exposed whilst they are at work; and*
>
> *(b) the risks to the health and safety of persons not in his employment arising out of or in connection with the conduct by him of his undertaking.*

The inspector should therefore carry out a **risk assessment**, by careful examination of what, could cause harm to people and taking precautions to prevent such harm.

**The NICEIC guide to
Domestic Periodic Inspection, Testing and Reporting**

The HSE recommend five steps to risk assessment.

Step 1 – Identify the hazards

Step 2 – Decide who might be harmed and how

Step 3 – Evaluate the risks and decide on precautions

Step 4 – Record your findings and implement them

Step 5 – Review your assessment and update if necessary.

Guidance on the above steps is given in the HSE *Five steps to risk assessment* leaflet, which can be found on **www.hse.gov.uk**.

The inspector may produce an electrical installation domestic periodic inspection and testing **generic risk assessment**, which can be updated as appropriate.

1.7.5 Working from heights

HSE statistics show that falls from height remain the most common kind of accident causing fatal injuries, **46 people died** from **a fall** from height at work in 2005/06. In the same year the number of people who suffered **major injury** as a result of **a fall** was **3351**.

The Work at Height Regulations 2005 apply to all work at height where there is a risk of a fall liable to cause personal injury. The Regulations place duties on employers, the self-employed, and any person who controls the work of others (eg facilities managers or building owners who may contract others to work at height) to the extent they control the work.

A place is 'at height' if (unless these Regulations are followed) a person could be injured falling from it, even if it is at or below ground level.

INTRODUCTION

The Regulations require duty holders to ensure:

1	all work at height is properly planned and organised
2	all work at height takes account of weather conditions that could endanger health and safety
3	those involved in work at height are trained and competent
4	the place where work at height is done is safe
5	equipment for work at height is appropriately inspected
6	the risks from fragile surfaces are properly controlled; and
7	the risks from falling objects are properly controlled.

The Regulations also require **planning** so that:

- **no** work is done at height if it is safe and reasonably practicable to do it other than at height

- the work is appropriately supervised, and carried out in as safe a way as is reasonably practicable

- emergencies and rescue take account of the **risk assessment** carried out under regulation 3 of the *Management of Health and Safety at Work Regulations* (see item 1.7.4).

An HSE Employers' *Guide the safe use of ladders and stepladders*, states;

A third of all reported fall-from-height incidents involve ladders and stepladders, on average this accounts for 14 deaths and 1200 major injuries to workers each year.

The NICEIC guide to
Domestic Periodic Inspection, Testing and Reporting

Many of these injuries are caused by inappropriate or incorrect use of the equipment. The HSE guidance is to help employers:

1	know when to use a ladder
2	decide how to go about selecting the right sort of ladder for the particular job
3	understand how to use it
4	know how to look after it; and
5	take sensible safety precautions.

The above HSE guide and other guidance on working at heights are given at **www.hse.gov.uk**.

It is preferable to avoid working at height where possible. For example, testing the external earth fault loop impedance (Z_e), see item 5.8, in a consumer unit (where access is required by the use of steps) should preferably be carried out while standing on the floor, rather than up the steps.

1.7.6 Lone working

Lone workers face particular problems. Some of the issues which need special attention when planning safe working arrangements are as follows:

1 Can the risks of the job be adequately controlled by one person?

2 Lone workers should not be at more risk than other employees. This may require extra risk control measures. Precautions should take account of normal work and foreseeable emergencies, for example fire, equipment failure, illness and accidents.

INTRODUCTION

3 Employers should identify situations where people work alone and ask questions such as:

a Does the workplace present a special risk to the lone worker?

b Is there a safe way in and a way out for one person? Can any temporary access equipment which is necessary, such as portable ladders, be safely handled by one person?

c Can all the testing be safely carried out by one person?

d Consider whether the work involves lifting objects too large for one person.

e Is there a risk of violence?

Checks should be made that a lone worker has returned to their base or home on completion of the inspection.

Information on working alone is given in HSE leaflet *IDNG 73 (rev) Working alone in safety: Controlling the risks of solitary work*, which is available free on the HSE website **www.hse.gov.uk**.

1.8 Test equipment and associated test leads and probes

HSE Guidance Note GS 38 – *Electrical test equipment for use by electricians* gives advice to competent persons on the selection and use of test equipment for circuits with rated voltages not exceeding 650 V.

The NICEIC guide to
Domestic Periodic Inspection, Testing and Reporting

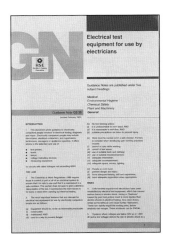

HSE guidance note GS 38 – *Electrical equipment for use by electricians*

Those involved in electrical inspection and testing should familiarise themselves with the guidance given in HSE Guidance Note GS38. Aspects that should be checked with regard to test equipment and their associated test leads and probes include the following (refer to GS38 for full information).

The inspector should check that the equipment:

1   meets the appropriate safety and performance requirements set out in standards, such as;

    a   *BS EN 61243-3: Live working – Voltage detectors – Two-pole low-voltage type*, or

    b   *BS EN 61010: requirements for electrical equipment for measurement, control and laboratory use*, or

    c   *BS EN 61557: Electrical safety in low voltage distribution systems up to 1000 V a.c. and 1500 V d.c.*

2   is of a suitable rating for the anticipated voltage to be tested, or the voltage that might unexpectedly be energised during testing

3   shows no signs of damage or deterioration

4   is maintained for safe use

5   is used only in the environment(s) for which it has been designed.

INTRODUCTION

Test instrument leads and probes

Guidance on test instrument leads and probes is given in 'NICEIC Pocket Guide 12 – *Test instrument leads*', which is reproduced as follows, for ease of reference:

POCKET GUIDE 12

TEST INSTRUMENT LEADS

(1) This guide includes recommendations on various British Standards Institution (BSI) guidance and Health and Safety Executive (HSE) guidance relating to test instrument leads. Such guidance should be followed to reduce the risk of electric shock or explosion and consequent serious injury or death when using electrical test equipment, and to meet the requirements of the *Electricity at Work Regulations 1989*.

(2) As well as injury or death caused directly by electric shock or explosion, injury can occur when a person reacts to an electric shock, for example by falling from a height or touching another hazard.

(3) It is important that **fused** test instrument leads are used where there is a potential risk of a fault current passing through the test instrument leads that could cause damage to the instrument or the installation, and/or cause injury to the user of the instrument. Such a potential risk might be caused by:

- a multimeter that has a voltage and current selector switch which is accidentally set to measure 'current', when in fact a 'voltage' from a high energy source (such as a 230 V circuit) is being measured (this type of instrument is **not** recommended for proving that a circuit is dead), or
- a faulty test lamp or voltage indicator.

(4) Appendix 1 of the HSE *Memorandum of guidance on the Electricity at Work Regulations 1989* lists HSE Guidance Note GS38 – *Electrical test equipment for use by electricians as a publication being particularly relevant to regulations 10 (connections), 14 (work on or near live conductors) and 16 (persons to be competent to prevent danger and injury).

(5) HSE Guidance Note GS38 is also referenced in paragraph 50 of HSE guidance note HSG 85 – *Electricity at work, safe working practices* as a guidance publication covering low voltage test equipment, such as 2-pole detectors, proprietary test lamps, or voltmeters with insulated probes. Furthermore, paragraph 50 of guidance note HSG 85 states:

*The use of multimeters, which can be set to the wrong function, is **not** recommended for proving dead. All instruments used for checking...*

POCKET GUIDE 12

TEST INSTRUMENT LEADS

BS EN 61557: *Electrical safety in low voltage distribution systems up to 1000V a.c. and 1500 V d.c.* fused leads **may not** be necessary. However, the design of the test probes and leads should meet the recommendations of GS 38 in other respects, such as having an exposed metal tips not exceeding 4 mm in length (whilst BS EN 61243-3 and BS EN 61010 allow exposed tip lengths up to 19 mm).

(8) When using any test leads and instruments, the instructions of the manufacturer(s) should be carefully followed and the test equipment regularly inspected for safe continued use.

(9) Contractors and their employees are reminded of their legal obligations relating to the safe use of test instruments, including those under the *Electricity at Work Regulations 1989* and the *Provision and Use of Work Equipment Regulations 1998*. In this context, contractors should carry out risk assessments to protect their employees, customers and bystanders from injury. Contractors should have appropriate test leads designed for use with each of their test instruments.

HSE GS38 examples of design safety requirements

Test leads

Should:
- be adequately insulated
- be coloured so that one lead can be easily distinguished from the other
- be flexible and of sufficient capacity and duty
- be sheathed to protect against mechanical damage
- be of adequate length for use
- not have accessible exposed conductors, other than the probe tips, or have live conductors accessible to a person's finger if a lead becomes detached from a probe, indicator or instrument when in use.

Test probes

Should:
- have finger barriers or be shaped to guard against inadvertent hand contact with live conductors
- be insulated to leave an exposed metal tip not exceeding 4 mm measured across any surface of the tip. Where practicable it is strongly recommended that this is reduced to 2 mm or less, or that spring retractable screen probes are used
- have suitable high breaking capacity (hbc) fuse with a low current rating (usually not exceeding 500 mA) and/or a current-limiting resistor
- have appropriate types of tip for allowing access to the contact where detection is being made.

Typical voltage test lamp (with fused leads)

www.niceic.com

For further copies of this guide
telephone 0870 0130382 or e-mail customerservice@niceic.com
Pocket Guide 12 1/07

NICEIC Pocket Guide 12

TEST INSTRUMENT LEADS

(1) This guide includes recommendations on various British Standards Institution (BSI) guidance and Health and Safety Executive (HSE) guidance relating to test instrument leads. Such guidance should be followed to reduce the risk of electric shock or explosion and consequent serious injury or death when using electrical test equipment, and to meet the requirements of the *Electricity at Work Regulations 1989*.

(2) As well as injury or death caused directly by electric shock or explosion, injury can occur when a person reacts to an electric shock, for example by falling from a height or touching another hazard.

(3) It is important that **fused** test instrument leads are used where there is a potential risk of a fault current passing through the test instrument leads that could cause damage to the instrument or the installation, and/or cause injury to the user of the instrument.

**The NICEIC guide to
Domestic Periodic Inspection, Testing and Reporting**

Such a potential risk might be caused by:

- a multimeter that has a voltage and current selector switch which is accidentally set to measure 'current', when in fact a 'voltage' from a high energy source (such as a 230 V circuit) is being measured (this type of instrument is **not** recommended for proving that a circuit is dead), or

- a faulty test lamp or voltage indicator.

(4) Appendix 1 of the HSE *Memorandum of guidance on the Electricity at Work Regulations 1989* lists HSE Guidance Note GS38 – *Electrical test equipment for use by electricians* as a publication being particularly relevant to regulations 10 (connections), 14 (work on or near live conductors) and 16 (persons to be competent to prevent danger and injury).

(5) HSE Guidance Note GS38 is also referenced in paragraph 50 of HSE guidance note HSG 85 – *Electricity at work, safe working practices* as a guidance publication covering low voltage test equipment, such as 2-pole detectors, propriety test lamps, or voltmeters with insulated probes. Furthermore, paragraph 50 of guidance note HSG 85 states:

*'The use of multimeters, which can be set to the wrong function, is **not** recommended for proving dead. All instruments used for checking circuits should be maintained and inspected frequently'.*

(6) HSE Guidance Note GS38 covers, amongst other things:

- accident causes, such as inadequate insulation of test leads and probes

- design safety requirements for test probes, test leads, and test equipment sockets/terminals

- voltage detection instruments.

Typical 2-pole voltage tester (without fused leads)

INTRODUCTION

(7) Where there is **not** a risk of test leads being accidentally short-circuited together AND the fault current in them is limited **not** to exceed their current-carrying capacity, for example by:

- a voltage detector that conforms to *BS EN 61243-3: Live working – Voltage detectors – Two-pole low-voltage type,* or
- a test instrument that conforms to *BS EN 61010: Safety requirements for electrical equipment for measurement, control and laboratory use* or *BS EN 61557: Electrical safety in low voltage distribution systems up to 1000 V a.c. and 1500 V d.c.,* fused leads may **not** be necessary.

However, the design of the test probes and leads should meet the recommendations of GS 38 in other respects, such as having an exposed metal tips not exceeding 4 mm in length (whilst *BS EN 61243-3* and *BS EN 61010* allow exposed tip lengths up to 19 mm).

(8) When using any test leads and instruments, the instructions of the manufacturer(s) should be carefully followed and the test equipment regularly inspected for safe continued use.

(9) Contractors and their employees are reminded of their legal obligations relating to the safe use of test instruments, including those under the *Electricity at Work Regulations 1989* and the *Provision and Use of Work Equipment Regulations 1998*. In this context, contractors should carry out risk assessments to protect their employees, customers and bystanders from injury. Contractors should have appropriate test leads designed for use with each of their test instruments.

HSE GS38 examples of design safety requirements

Test leads should:

- be adequately insulated
- be coloured so that one lead can be easily distinguished from the other
- be flexible and of sufficient capacity and duty
- be sheathed to protect against mechanical damage
- be of adequate length for use
- not have accessible exposed conductors, other than the probe tips, or have live conductors accessible to a person's finger if a lead becomes detached from a probe, indicator or instrument when in use.

**The NICEIC guide to
Domestic Periodic Inspection, Testing and Reporting**

Test probes should:

- have finger barriers or be shaped to guard against inadvertent hand contact with live conductors

- be insulated to leave an exposed metal tip not exceeding 4 mm measured across any surface of the tip. Where practicable it is strongly recommended that this is reduced to 2 mm or less, or that spring retractable screen probes are used

- have suitable high breaking capacity (hbc) fuses with a low current rating (usually not exceeding 500 mA) and/or a current-limiting resistor

- have appropriate types of tip for allowing access to the contact where detection is being made.

Typical voltage test lamp (with fused leads)

1.9   Assessment of inspection and test results

The inspector should consider and assess the test results (see item 3.11) and compare the results with the relevant criteria to determine whether they comply with all the relevant requirements of *BS 7671*.

For example, if an excessive earth fault loop impedance or phase to neutral fault loop impedance is discovered during the course of a periodic inspection of an existing installation (see item 5.15), the measured (excessive) value should be recorded, together with an appropriate observation and recommendation code for remedial action, on the Domestic Electrical Installation Periodic Inspection Report (see item 2.22).

INTRODUCTION

1.10 Computer-assisted preparation of NICEIC Periodic Inspection Reports

The principal report forms published by NICEIC are designed to be completed by hand or by a computer printer.

Whilst the use of personal computers to assist with the compilation of reports, perhaps in conjunction with data-logging test instruments, is **not** a substitute for a competent person having the necessary knowledge, skill and experience, such use may improve the clarity and presentation of the completed reports.

Some software packages also provide an element of validation or checking of the inspection and test results, identifying obvious errors, omissions and other problems in the data for consideration by a competent person, before the details are printed on to the report. Such software packages, correctly used, can be expected to help ensure the completeness and accuracy of reports. However, the use of software packages may **not** guarantee that reports contain no errors or omissions.

As a Domestic Electrical Installation Periodic Inspection Report is intended to provide an objective assessment of the condition of an existing installation, software for such reports, where available, should be designed to draw the attention of the compiler to any test results which do not meet the requirements of the current issue of *BS 7671*. The software should then permit those test results to be printed on to the report form to provide an accurate record. The compiler of the report is nevertheless expected to include an appropriate observation and recommendation code for remedial action for each such item of non-compliance.

Irrespective of whether or not a Periodic Inspection Report is completed with the aid of software, it remains the responsibility of the compiler of the report to ensure that the information provided in the report is factual and accurately records the condition of the electrical installation to which the report relates, having regard to the stated extent and limitations of the report.

The NICEIC guide to Domestic Periodic Inspection, Testing and Reporting

1.11 Pre-inspection preparation agreement with the client

Before carrying out period inspection, testing and reporting the contractor should agree the following with the client:

1	service levels
2	extent
3	limitations
4	availability of working lamps
5	removal of plugs from socket-outlets
6	clear access to equipment, for example:
	a bonding or earthing clamps
	b the consumer unit
	c accessories.
7	availability of previous records giving the history of the installation, such as Test Certificates and Periodic Inspection Reports
8	control of children and pets
9	arrangement for resetting clocks and timers in electrical equipment
10	access availability to voids, such as the loft
11	access to out-buildings supplied from the installation, such as sheds and garages
12	access to garden lighting, power and water features
13	removal of trips hazards
14	timing of tests and constraints on switching off the supply
15	report condition but not repair, except by agreement of the client
16	agreement to take photographs of defects for the report
17	arrangements for a return visit to carry out live testing, for example, to measure the external earth fault loop impedance (Z_e), if the supply to the installation is unavailable on the initial day of testing. Such as when a power failure occurs or a key meter runs out of credit.

INTRODUCTION

1.12   Sequence of Inspection and testing

In general the sequence of periodic inspection and testing is as follows:

1   **Visual inspection**, without dismantling of equipment, to identify any potential danger, such as absence of main bonding

2   **Identify existing circuits** (see item 1.13), which may involve functional testing of protective devices (see item 5.17) and/or the use of **appropriate** circuit identification test equipment (see Chapter 5)

3   **Isolating all sources of supply** (see item 1.7.1)

4   **Visual inspection**, with limited dismantling of equipment

5   **Testing with the supply dead** (see item 5.4)

6   **Reinstating all sources of supply** (see item 1.7.1)

7   **Testing with the supply live** (see item 5.4).

1.13 Identifying existing protective devices

Where existing protective devices for final circuits are **NOT**-identified by labels or other means, temporary identification numbers (for referencing the devices in the report) may be fitted by the inspector (see adjacent), with agreement of the client. Identifying the protective devices and their position in the consumer unit also helps the inspector to correctly position the devices, following removal for testing.

The NICEIC guide to
Domestic Periodic Inspection, Testing and Reporting

Protective device identification numbers should generally start at 1 adjacent to the main switch and increase in sequence moving horizontally from the main switch. For example, where the main switch (MS) is:

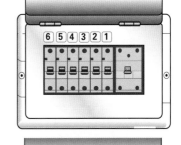

- **RIGHT** of the devices (1 to 6), the arrangement would be:

  6   5   4   3   2   1   MS

- **LEFT** of the devices the arrangement would be:

  MS 1   2   3   4   5   6

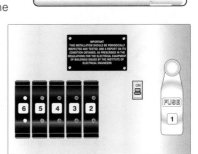

- **BETWEEN** the devices, the device to the **right** of the main switch is generally identified by 1, and the devices to the **left** of the main switch by the number above the highest number on the right of the main switch. **For example:** if there are 5 protective devices to the **left** and 1 to the **right** of the main switch, the arrangement would be:

  6   5   4   3   2   MS   1

Note: the above temporary identification arrangement is used only for reporting and testing purposes and absence of labelling needs to be recorded in the 'Observations and recommendations for actions to be taken' section of the report.

NICEIC PUBLICATIONS

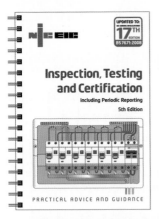

To order any publications, certificates or reports

internet **niceicdirect.com**

call **0870 0130458**

fax **01582 539712**

e-mail **sales@niceic.com**

For full list of certificates and reports visit the NICEIC website

www.niceicgroup.com

The NICEIC guide to
Domestic Periodic Inspection, Testing and Reporting

PERIODIC INSPECTION REPORTS

CHAPTER **2**

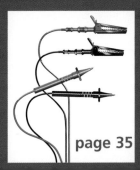

CHAPTER **2**

PERIODIC INSPECTION REPORTS

2.1 General

This Chapter addresses the purpose of a Domestic Periodic Inspection Report (see item 2.2), competence and safety (see item 2.3) and intervals between periodic inspection, testing and reporting (see item 2.4).

BS 7671 report requirements are given in item 2.5 followed by observations and recommendation codes in items 2.6 and 2.7 respectively.

Detailed information on compiling Domestic Visual Condition reports and Domestic Electrical Installation Periodic Inspection Reports are given in items 2.8 to 2.14 and 2.15 to 2.25 respectively. Examples of installations have been included to demonstrate the use of these report forms. Furthermore, the Domestic Electrical Installation report example is based on the installation included in the NICEIC DVD on Periodic Inspection, Testing and Reporting.

Information on report continuation sheets is given in item 2.26.

If a dangerous condition is found in an installation that needs to be brought to the attention of the householder or the landlord in writing an Electrical Danger Notification form may be used, as explained in item 2.27.

Unless the circumstances make it unavoidable (for example, if an installer has ceased trading prior to certifying an installation), a Periodic Inspection Report should **not** be issued by one contractor as a substitute for an Electrical Installation Certificate, Domestic Electrical Installation Certificate or Minor Electrical Installation Works Certificate, for work carried out by another contractor.

A Periodic Inspection Report does **not** provide a declaration by the designer or installer that the aspects of the work for which they were responsible comply with *BS 7671*. Furthermore, cables that are designed to be concealed cannot be inspected when construction is complete.

A client (such as a building control department of a local authority) may request a contractor to produce a Periodic Inspection Report for work designed and installed by others. In such circumstances the contractor should make the client aware of the extent and limitations of the report, in order to unwittingly avoid assuming responsibility for aspects of the work of which the contractor had no knowledge or control. It should also be made clear that the report can only provide some measure of assurance that the work complies with the requirements of *BS 7671* (or not, as the case may be) within the extent and agreed limitations of the inspection and testing.

2.2 Purpose of a Domestic Periodic Inspection Report

The purpose of a Periodic Inspection Report is to formally record the assessment of the condition of an electrical installation. The report needs to accurately record the inspection and tests carried out, which detect so far as is reasonably practicable, any factors impairing the safety of an electrical installation.

The aspects to be covered, as stated in Regulation 621.2, include **all** of the following:

- safety of persons and livestock (such as horses, donkeys or goats that may be kept in outbuilding of certain domestic premises) against the effects of electric shock and burns, in accordance with Regulation 131.3

- protection against damage to property by fire and heat arising from an installation defect

- confirmation that the installation is not damaged or deteriorated so as to impair safety

- identification of non-compliances with *BS 7671* or installation defects which may give rise to danger.

The requirements of *BS 7671* relating to Periodic Inspection Reports are given in item 2.5.

If during the inspection, the inspector considers that the installation is dangerous and cannot be immediately made safe a 'Domestic Electrical Danger Notification Form' **must** be issued as described in item 2.27.

PERIODIC INSPECTION REPORTS

2.3 Competence and safety

Attention is drawn to the need for all persons involved in inspection, testing and reporting to be competent, and to follow safe working procedures (see item 1.7).

In particular, NICEIC experience indicates that persons undertaking periodic inspection reporting need to have above-average knowledge and experience of electrical installation matters to enable them to safely and accurately assess the condition of an existing electrical installation, especially when they do not have access to the design information relating to that installation.

To carry out the inspection and testing safely, sufficient installation record information (see item 2.5) will need to be obtained from the person responsible for the installation (generally the householder or landlord).

2.4 Intervals between periodic inspection, testing and reporting

The interval to the next periodic inspection, testing and reporting will depend on a number of considerations, including some or all of the factors indicated below, depending on the particular circumstances:

- age of the installation (it may be reasonable to expect the intervals to become progressively shorter as the installation ages)
- type of domestic premises
- environmental conditions (ie external influences)
- normal life expectancy of the installation
- level of misuse of the installation (eg vandalism)
- changed usage of the domestic premises (and the installation)
- the extent of any wear and tear, damage or other deterioration of the installation
- details of previous inspection, testing and reporting.

Determination of the interval to the next periodic inspection, testing and reporting will always be a matter of engineering judgement to be exercised by the inspector. However, in general:

- The recommended maximum interval between initial verification and the first periodic inspection, testing and reporting for a domestic property general installation is 10 years.

- If a property includes a special installation or location additional to a bathroom or shower room, such as a swimming pool, the interval may need to be reduced. For example, the recommended interval to the next inspection, testing and reporting for a swimming pool is **1 year**. However, the interval would only apply to the parts of the installation associated with the swimming pool.

- The intervals stated above may need to be adjusted to meet particular circumstances, for example periodic inspection, testing and reporting may be carried out either when:

    an existing property is being prepared to be let or sold

    - a previously occupied property is being purchased

    - an installation is believed to be unsafe.

- Intervals between subsequent periodic inspection, testing (where included) and reporting will again vary depending on the circumstances, such as those given in the following table. However, the ultimate decision must always be the responsibility of the inspector carrying out the inspection/testing and reporting.

PERIODIC INSPECTION REPORTS

Examples of intervals between subsequent periodic inspection/testing and reporting (see previous paragraph) that an inspector may recommend

Example	Installation circumstances at time of inspecting, testing and reporting	Interval (Years) that an inspector may recommend to next inspection/testing
1	The **Domestic Visual Condition Report** shows that the installation is adequate. However, as **testing** has not been carried out for 6 years. An inspector may recommend that **inspection and testing** is carried out next time	4 (or change of occupancy)
2	The **Periodic Domestic Electrical Installation Report** shows that the installation has several defects with recommendation Codes 1 and 2 requiring attention. Apart from the defects the installation is adequate. However, the insulation resistance between live conductors and earth for the installation is 6 megohms. An inspector may recommend that **inspection and testing** is carried out next time	3 (or change of occupancy)
3	The **Periodic Domestic Electrical Installation Report** shows that the installation is adequate. The fully furnished property will be let for **one year.** The insulation resistance between live conductors and earth for the installation is 200 megohms. An inspector may recommend that **inspection** but **not** necessarily **testing** is carried out next time	1 (or change of occupancy)
4	The **Periodic Domestic Electrical Installation Report** shows that the installation has several defects with a recommendation Code 2 requiring attention. Apart from the defects the installation is in a satisfactory condition. The insulation resistance between live conductors and earth for the installation is 100 megohms. All accessories have been renewed this year. An inspector may recommend that **inspection and testing** is carried out next time	5/7 (or change of occupancy)

Note: the above table is only for guidance, and the interval given by an inspector to the next inspection/testing may vary depending on the specific known condition of the installation and the inspector's previous experiences.

The NICEIC guide to
Domestic Periodic Inspection, Testing and Reporting

2.5   Requirements

BS 7671 requires that a Periodic Inspection Report is issued following the in-service periodic inspection and testing of an electrical installation. The report is required to include:

- details of the extent of the installation and of any limitations of the inspection and testing, together with

- a record of the inspection and the results of testing.

A separate report is required for each installation examined. The report provides a formal declaration that, within agreed and stated limitations, the details recorded, including the observations and recommendations and the completed schedules of inspection and test results, give an accurate assessment of the condition of the electrical installation at the time it was inspected.

Wherever possible, before undertaking periodic inspection and testing, it is important for the person undertaking the work of inspection to have sight of the records associated with the installation. Such records should include:

- an Electrical Installation Certificate (formerly the Electrical Installation Completion Certificate) or Domestic Electrical Installation Certificate, issued when the installation was originally completed, and

- any subsequent Minor Electrical Installation Works Certificates and Periodic Inspection Reports.

However, it is likely that these records will not exist. If this is the case, a degree of exploratory work may be necessary so that inspection and testing can be carried out safely and effectively. A survey may be necessary to identify switchgear, controlgear, and the circuits that they control.

A report (based on the form prescribed by *BS 7671*) should be issued to the person ordering the inspection and test, whether or not the inspector is registered with NICEIC, and whether or not a written report has been specifically requested by the client.

PERIODIC INSPECTION REPORTS

NICEIC strongly prefers NICEIC Approved Contractors and Domestic Installers to issue NICEIC red ▮ or purple ▮ report forms respectively, as this provides a measure of safety assurance and confidence to the recipients.

Non-approved contractors are **not** authorized to issue NICEIC Periodic Inspection Report forms, but similar green ▮ report forms, based on the model form given in *BS 7671*, are available from NICEIC (see item 1.3 for information on form colours and their uses).

The Periodic Inspection Report is, as its title indicates, a report and **not** a certificate. It relates to an assessment of the in-service condition of an electrical installation against the requirements of the issue of *BS 7671* current at the time of the inspection, irrespective of the age of the installation. The criteria for assessing the compliance of each part of an older installation with *BS 7671* are, therefore, the same as for new installation work. The report is for the benefit of the person ordering the work, occupants and of persons subsequently involved in additional or remedial work, or further inspections.

2.6   Observations

Each recorded observation should describe a specific defect or omission in the electrical installation. The observation should detail what the situation is, and **not** what is considered necessary to put it right. For example, 'excessive damage to the enclosure of the consumer unit' would be appropriate, whereas 'consumer unit to be replaced' would not.

Remember that observations are intended to be a factual report on the condition of an installation, **not** a proposal for remedial work.

Only observations that can be supported by one or more regulations in the current issue of *BS 7671* should be recorded. The particular regulation number(s) need **not** be entered on the report (unless specifically required by the client), but should serve to remind the inspector that it is **only compliance with *BS 7671*** that is to be

The NICEIC guide to
Domestic Periodic Inspection, Testing and Reporting

considered. Observations based solely on personal preference or 'custom and practice' should not be included.

Each observation should be written in a manner that will be understood by the client. Comments should be clear and unambiguous, and the use of technical terms should be avoided.

Each observation shall be given a recommendation Code as explained in item 2.7.

2.7 Recommendation Codes

Each observation in a Periodic Inspection Report must be given an appropriate recommendation Code 1, 2, 3 or 4 as summarized in the following table.

Recommendation Code	Meaning
1	**Requires urgent attention**
2	**Requires improvement**
3	**Requires further investigation**
4	**Does not comply with *BS 7671* (as amended); this does not imply that the electrical installation inspected is unsafe.**

Some examples of the application of each of the codes are given later.

Only one of the above recommendation codes should be attributed to each observation. If more than one recommendation could be applied to an observation, only the most onerous recommendation should be made (Code 1 being the most onerous).

PERIODIC INSPECTION REPORTS

Where a real and immediate danger is observed, recommendation Code 1 must be used.

Where appropriate the inspector may issue a completed 'Domestic Electrical Danger Notification form' (see item 2.27) to the person ordering the work, such as the householder or landlord.

Where one or more observations are given a Recommendation Code 1 or 2, the overall assessment of the installation should be stated to be **unsatisfactory** in the Periodic Inspection Report.

It would be unusual to attribute a Code 3 (requires further investigation) to an observation made during the periodic inspection of a domestic installation. Where a Code 3 is justified, and if there are no Code 1 or Code 2 recommendations, the competent person needs to exercise judgement as to whether the overall assessment of the condition of the installation should be indicated as 'satisfactory' or 'unsatisfactory'.

Code 1 (Requires urgent attention) – Indicates that the observed deficiency requires urgent remedial action to bring the standard up to a level that complies with *BS 7671*. Examples of items that NICEIC considers would usually warrant a Code 1 recommendation include:

1   Exposed live parts that are accessible to touch, such as where:

    a   a fuse carrier or circuit-breaker is omitted from a consumer unit and a blanking piece is not fitted in its place

    b   terminations or connections have no (or damaged) barriers or enclosures, such as those belonging to a consumer unit

    c   an accessory is damaged

    d   live conductors have no (or damaged) insulation.

2   Conductive parts that have become live as the result of a fault

3   Absence of an effective means of earthing for the installation

The NICEIC guide to
Domestic Periodic Inspection, Testing and Reporting

4   The main RCD or voltage-operated earth-leakage circuit-breaker on a TT system fails to operate when tested with an instrument or integral test button

5   Evidence of excessive heat (such as charring) from electrical equipment causing damage to the installation or its surroundings

6   Incorrect polarity, or protective device in neutral conductor only

7   Circuits with ineffective overcurrent protection (due, for example, to oversized fuse wire in rewireable fuses)

8   Absence of RCD protection for socket-outlets in bathrooms or shower rooms other than SELV or shaver socket-outlets

9   Socket-outlets other than SELV or shaver socket-outlets located within 0.6 m horizontally from the boundary of zone 1 in a location containing a bath or shower

10   Absence of earthing at a socket-outlet.

Code 2 (Requires improvement) – Indicates that the observed deficiency requires action to remove potential danger, as soon as possible to bring the standard up to a level that complies with *BS 7671*. Examples of items that NICEIC considers would warrant a Code 2 recommendation include:

1   A 30/32 A ring final circuit discontinuous or cross-connected with another circuit

2   A public utility water pipe being used as the means of earthing for the installation

3   A gas or oil pipe being used as the means of earthing for the installation

4   Absence of circuit protective conductors for a lighting circuit supplying one or more items of Class I equipment[1]

---

[1] See The Electrical Safety Council Best Practice Guide to replacing a consumer unit in domestic premises where lighting circuits have no protective conductor.

5 Absence of main equipotential bonding (except to a lightning protection system conductor, where a Recommendation Code 3 may be appropriate)

6 Absence of fault protection by RCD (protection against indirect contact) where required, such as for a socket-outlet circuit in an installation forming part of a TT system

7 A 'borrowed neutral', for example where a single final circuit neutral is shared by two final circuits (such as an upstairs lighting circuit and a separately protected downstairs lighting circuit)

8 Absence of a warning notice indicating the presence of a second source of electricity, such as a microgenerator

9 Fire risk from incorrectly installed electrical equipment including incorrectly installed recessed downlighters

10 Undersized main bonding conductors, where the conductor is less than 6 mm^2 or where there is evidence of thermal damage

11 Unenclosed connections at luminaires not enclosed (Such a defect can contribute to a fire, particularly where extra-low voltage filament lamps are used)

12 Immersion heater does not comply with *BS EN 60335-2-73* (that is, it does not have a built in cut-out that will operate if the stored water temperature reaches 98 °C if the thermostat fails), and the cold water storage tank is plastic

13 Unsatisfactory functional operation of equipment where this may result in danger

14 Socket-outlets other than SELV or shaver socket-outlets located between 0.6 m and 3 m horizontally from the boundary of zone 1 in a location containing a bath or shower.

15 Absence of RCD protection for portable or mobile equipment that may reasonably be expected to be used outdoors.

16 Earth fault loop impedance value greater than that required for operation of the protective device within the time prescribed in the version of *BS 7671/IEE Wiring Regulations* current at the time of installation.

17 Insulation of live conductors deteriorated to such an extent that the insulating material readily breaks away from the conductors

18 Neither local supplementary bonding (where necessary) nor RCD protection is present in a bathroom or shower room. Note: where the presence of supplementary bonding cannot be confirmed by inspection, it may be verified by a continuity test

19 Any one circuit has an insulation resistance of less than 20 kilohms.

Code 3 (Requires further investigation) – Indicates that unusually the inspector was unable to come to a conclusion about this aspect of the installation, or that the observation was outside the agreed purpose, extent or limitations of the inspection, but has come to the inspector's attention during the inspection and testing. For example, it might not have been possible to trace a particular circuit. Such a recommendation would usually be associated with an observation on an aspect of the installation that was not foreseen when the purpose and extent of the inspection, and any limitations upon it, were agreed with the client.

It should be remembered that the purpose of periodic inspection is **not** to carry out a fault-finding exercise, but to assess and report on the **condition** of the installation within the agreed extent and limitations of the inspection.

Examples of items that NICEIC considers would warrant a Code 3 recommendation include:

1 Unable to trace final circuits

2 Unable to access equipment or connections needing to be inspected that are known to exist but have been boxed in such as by panels or boards that cannot be easily removed without causing damage to decorations.

PERIODIC INSPECTION REPORTS

3   Insulation resistance of less than 1 megohm between live conductors connected together and Earth, when measured at the consumer unit with all final circuits connected. If any one circuit has an insulation resistance of less than 20 kilohms, a Code 2 recommendation should be given.

4   Absence of a main equipotential bonding connection to a lightning protection system conductor, where it is not known by the inspector if it is required to protect against lightning side flashes[1] (Absence of other main equipotential bonding connections would usually warrant a recommendation Code 2.)

Code 4 (Does not comply with *BS 7671* as amended) – Indicates items that have identified as **not** complying with the requirements of the current issue of *BS 7671*, but that the users of the installation are **not** in any danger as a result.

The persons ordering the report should be advised that the code is not intended to imply that the installation is unsafe, but that careful consideration should be given to the benefits of improving those aspects of the installation. Examples of items that NICEIC considers would warrant a Code 4 recommendation include.

1   Switch lines not identified as line conductors at terminations (for example, a conductor having blue insulation is not sleeved brown in switches or lighting points)

2   Circuit protective conductors or final circuit conductors in a consumer unit not arranged or marked so that they can be identified for inspection, testing or alteration of the installation

3   Undersized main bonding conductors (subject to a minimum size of 6 mm², if there is no evidence of thermal damage

---

[1] Lightning protection bonding may be required by the lightning protection system designer/installer, to protect against lighting side flashes between the lightning protection system and the electrical installation. Such bonding should only be carried out by (or under the instruction of) a specialist lightning protection system designer/installer.

The NICEIC guide to
Domestic Periodic Inspection, Testing and Reporting

4 Absence of circuit protective conductors in circuits having only Class II (or all insulated) luminaires and switches[2]

5 Protective conductor of a lighting circuit not (or incorrectly) terminated at the final circuit connection point to a Class II (or insulated) item of equipment, such as at a switch mounting box or luminaire

6 Absence of 'Safety Electrical Connection – Do Not Remove' notice

7 Absence of a notice indicating that the installation has wiring colours to two versions of *BS 7671*

8 Absence of RCD periodic test notice

9 Absence of circuit identification details

10 Sheath of an insulated and sheathed non-armoured cable not taken inside the enclosure of an accessory, such as at a socket-outlet or lighting switch

11 Bare protective conductor of an insulated and sheathed cable not sleeved with insulation, colour coded to indicate its function

12 Installation not divided into an adequate number of circuits to minimize inconvenience for safe operation, fault clearance, inspection, testing and maintenance

13 Fixed equipment does not have a means of switching off for mechanical maintenance, where such maintenance involves a risk of burns or injury from mechanical movement

14 Absence of supplementary bonding to installed Class II equipment where required (such as in a bathroom or shower room, in case the equipment is replaced with Class I equipment in the future).

---

[2] See The Electrical Safety Council Best Practice Guide to replacing a consumer unit in domestic premises where lighting circuits have no protective conductor

15 Reliance on a voltage-operated earth-leakage circuit-breaker for fault protection (protection against indirect contact)

16 Absence of RCD protection for cables installed at a depth of less than 50 mm from a surface of a wall or partition where the cables do not incorporate an earthed metallic covering, are not enclosed in earthed metalwork, or are not mechanically protected against penetration by nails and the like

17 Absence of RCD protection for cables concealed, at whatever depth, in a wall or partition the internal construction of which includes metallic parts (other than metallic fixings such as nails, screws and the like) where the cables do not incorporate an earthed metallic covering, are not enclosed in earthed metalwork, or are not mechanically protected to avoid damage to them during construction of the wall or during their installation

18 Absence of RCD protection for socket-outlet circuits that are unlikely to supply portable equipment for use outdoors, or that are in a bathroom

19 Absence of supplementary bonding where required, such as in a bathroom or shower room, where all the following three conditions are not satisfied:

a all final circuits of the location comply with the requirements for automatic disconnection, and

b all final circuits of the location have additional protection by means of a 30 mA RCD, and

c all extraneous-conductive-parts of the location are effectively connected to the protective equipotential bonding (main earthing terminal).

CHAPTER **2**

Other issues

The following items are worthy of a note on the periodic inspection report, but should not be given a Recommendation Code:

- The absence of a fire detection and alarm system

- Where appropriate, the absence of an emergency lighting system (for example in a communal area).

The following items are commonly included in periodic inspection reports as requiring remedial action, but are not departures from the current issue *BS 7671*, and should therefore not be recorded:

1 Absence of earthing and/or bonding of metallic sinks and baths (unless they are extraneous-conductive-parts in their own right)

2 The use of rewireable fuses (where they provide adequate circuit protection)

3 The use of circuit-breakers to *BS 3871*

4 Absence of bonding connections to boiler pipework (where the pipework is not an extraneous-conductive-part in its own right)

5 Any other observation not directly related to electrical safety and hence to the continued suitability of the installation for continued service.

It should be noted that the above examples of the application of recommendation Codes 1, 2, 3 and 4 are not exhaustive.

It is entirely a matter for the competent person conducting the inspection to decide on the recommendation code to be given to an observation. The person's own judgement as a competent person should not be unduly influenced by the client. Remember that the person(s) signing the report are fully responsible for its content.

Further explanation of recommendation Codes is given on the reverse of the appropriate reports in Annexes B and C for the benefit of recipients. An example follows on guidance for recipients on recommendation codes, which has been reproduced from the domestic visual condition report DVN for ease of reference.

PERIODIC INSPECTION REPORTS

GUIDANCE FOR RECIPIENTS ON THE RECOMMENDATION CODES

Only one Recommendation Code should have been given for each recorded observation.

Recommendation Code 1

Where an observation has been given a Recommendation Code 1 (requires urgent attention), the safety of those using the installation may be at risk.

The person responsible for the maintenance of the installation is advised to take action without delay to remedy the observed deficiency in the installation, or to take other appropriate action (such as switching off and isolating the affected part(s) of the installation) to remove the potential danger. The NICEIC Approved Contractor issuing this report will be able to provide further advice.

NICEIC make available 'dangerous condition' notification forms to enable inspectors to record, and then to communicate to the person ordering the report, any dangerous condition discovered.

Recommendation Code 2

Recommendation Code 2 (requires improvement) indicates that, whilst the safety of those using the installation may not be at immediate risk, remedial action should be taken as soon as possible to improve the safety of the installation. The NICEIC Approved Contractor issuing this report will be able to provide further advice.

Items which have been attributed Recommendation Code 2 should be remedied as soon as possible.

Recommendation Code 3

Where an observation has been given a Recommendation Code 3 (requires further investigation), the inspection has revealed an apparent deficiency which could not, due to the extent or limitations of this inspection, be fully identified. Items which have been attributed Recommendation Code 3 should be investigated by a competent person as soon as possible.

The NICEIC guide to
Domestic Periodic Inspection, Testing and Reporting

The person responsible for the maintenance of the installation is advised to arrange for the NICEIC Approved Contractor issuing this report (or other competent person) to undertake further inspection and/or testing of the installation to determine the nature and extent of the apparent deficiency.

Recommendation Code 4

Recommendation Code 4 [does not comply with BS 7671 (as amended)] will have been given to observed non-compliance(s) with the current safety standard which do not warrant one of the other Recommendation Codes. It is not intended to imply that the electrical installation inspected is unsafe, but careful consideration should be given to the benefits of improving these aspects of the installation. The NICEIC Approved Contractor issuing this report will be able to provide further advice.

It is important to note that the recommendation given at *Next Inspection* of this report for the maximum interval until the next inspection is conditional upon all items which have been given a Recommendation Code 1 and Code 2 being remedied without delay and as soon as possible respectively.
It would not be reasonable to indicate a 'visually not unsatisfactory' assessment if any observation in the report had been given a Code 1 or Code 2 recommendation.

Information on Recommendation Codes

Information on Recommendation Codes is given in *Best Practice Guide 4: Periodic Inspection Reporting - Recommendation Codes for domestic and similar electrical installations*, published free by the The Electrical Safety Council, on their website **www.esc.org.uk**

PERIODIC INSPECTION REPORTS

COMPILING DOMESTIC VISUAL CONDITION REPORTS

2.8 Compiling Visual Condition Reports – General

The purpose of a visual-only inspection of a dwelling is to determine, so far as is reasonably practicable, whether an electrical installation has suffered any visible damage or deterioration or has any visually-evident defects which affect, or may affect, safety.

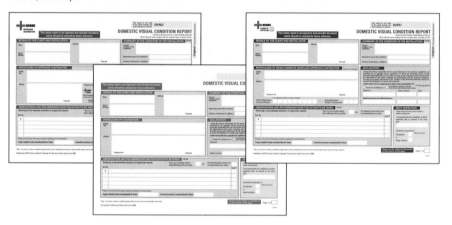

A NICEIC 'Domestic Visual Condition Report' is intended to be used only for the purpose of reporting on the **condition** of an existing electrical installation. The report should identify, so far as is reasonably practicable, any damage, deterioration or defects which may give rise to danger. The report cannot confirm that the installation is safe for continued use, as testing is **not** carried out.

NICEIC considers that the practice of 'visual inspection only' is **not** non-compliant with the requirements of the national standard for electrical safety, *BS 7671: Requirements for Electrical Installations* provided that:

1 the visual inspection is carried out in accordance with all the requirements of *BS 7671* that are applicable to visual inspection

**The NICEIC guide to
Domestic Periodic Inspection, Testing and Reporting**

2   the limitations of 'visual inspection only' which are stated in the Notes for Recipients on the reverse of the report form are drawn to the attention to the person ordering the work

3   it is **not** claimed that a 'visual inspection only' can or will fully determine whether an installation is safe for continued use

4   an objective report of the findings of the visual inspection is given to the person ordering the work, whether or not specifically requested by that person

5   it is made clear to the person ordering the work that a visual inspection does **not** include items that can only be checked with test instruments (such as the adequacy of earthing arrangements)

6   any quotation for proposed remedial work is given separately from the visual inspection report

7   full periodic inspection and testing is recommended to the customer if it is suspected that the installation is in an **unsafe** condition, or if it is believed that other significant defects exist, which may be revealed by testing.

The entire electrical installation should be inspected including accessible loft spaces, conservatories, garages, workshops, greenhouses, outbuildings and other appropriate items, such as outside lighting, garden water features or swimming pools, **except** where a limitation is agreed in writing with the customer, and clearly recorded in the report. The client needs to be made aware that any imposed limitations may reduce the accuracy and effectiveness of the reporting.

A certain amount of dismantling is normally necessary even though the inspection is 'visual-only'. For example, after appropriate isolation (see item 1.7.1), the cover of the consumer unit should be removed to permit the checking of electrical equipment, such as the condition and suitability of the cables installed. In addition samples of, equipment such as socket-outlets, light switches and luminaires should be inspected for signs of deterioration, damage, overheating etc.

PERIODIC INSPECTION REPORTS

For a Domestic Visual Condition Report the minimum percentage sample rate, of accessories or points/circuit (removed for internal inspection) is 10%. Rates for other service levels of inspection are given in Annex A.

A NICEIC Domestic Visual Condition Report may be used only where all the following conditions apply:

- the inspection is limited to the installation in a single dwelling (house or individual flat)

- the supply to the installation is single-phase, 50 Hz, and the nominal voltage does not exceed 230 V

- the installation forms part of a TN-S, TN-C-S (PME) or TT system

- fault protection is provided primarily by Automatic Disconnection of Supply (ADS)

- the installation is supplied from one source only.

The report form marked 'Original', including any additional pages, is to be given to the person ordering the inspection.

The red ▮, purple ▮, or green ▮ report form marked 'Duplicate' is to be retained by the NICEIC Approved Contractor, Domestic Installer or other contractor respectively. Furthermore, red ▮ or purple ▮ report forms should be made available by NICEIC Approved Contractors or Domestic Installers respectively, for possible future review by NICEIC.

It is the responsibility of the compiler of the report to ensure that the information provided in the report is factual, and that the declaration of the condition of the electrical installation to which the report relates is fair and reasonable in all the circumstances, given the limitations of visual inspection only.

The total number of pages which make up the report must be inserted in the box provided at the foot of each of the pages on the right-hand side.

Specimen copies of red 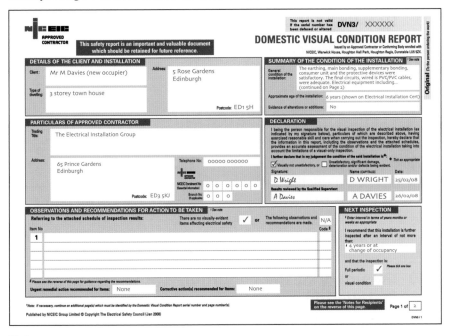, purple and green Domestic Visual Condition Reports, continuation sheets and guidance information are given in Annex B.

Guidance on compiling continuation sheets for the visual condition report DVN and its schedules is given in items 2.26 and 3.12 respectively.

Each section of a DVN Domestic Visual Condition Report should be completed as shown in the guidance given in items 2.9 to 2.14.

Example Page 1 of DVN follows for ease of reference.

Notes:

1   Example entries have been included, in blue for each box for demonstration purposes only.

2   Entries made on reports must relate to the actual installation being reported.

PERIODIC INSPECTION REPORTS

3   Similar guidance to that given for compiling red ■ domestic electrical installation periodic inspection report DVN also applies to the purple ■ and green ■ reports (DVP and DVM) respectively, to supplement:

- the notes for recipients (see Annexes B4 and B7 respectively),and

- the guidance for NICEIC Domestic Installers/Approved Contractors, and electrical contractors (see Annexes B6 and B9 respectively).

2.9   Details of the client and installation

DETAILS OF THE CLIENT AND INSTALLATION	
Client: Mr M Davies (new occupier)	Address: 5 Rose Gardens Edinburgh
Type of dwelling: 3 storey town house	Postcode: ED1 5H

Enter the client's name, address and the type of dwelling being inspected; such as a house, flat or bungalow. The client is the person or organization (such as a housing association) ordering the work. In the case of a lengthy name or address suitable abbreviations may be used if acceptable to the client.

2.10   Summary of the condition of the installation

SUMMARY OF THE CONDITION OF THE INSTALLATION ¹ See note	
General condition of the installation:	The earthing, main bonding, supplementary bonding, consumer unit and the protective devices were satisfactory. The final circuits, wired is PVC/PVC cables, were adequate. Electrical equipment including... (continued on Page 2)
Approximate age of the installation:	6 years (shown on Electrical Installation Cert)
Evidence of alterations or additions:	No

General condition of the installation

Enter a brief description of the condition of the installation. The summary should adequately describe the overall condition of the installation having considered, for example:

- whether the earthing and bonding appears to be adequate
- the condition of the consumer unit and the protective devices
- the type of wiring system and its condition
- the serviceability of equipment including accessories
- the presence of adequate identification (including final circuit details) and notices
- excessive wear and tear, damage or other deterioration that might impact on safety.

Where the visual inspection has identified damage or deterioration to an installation or visually-apparent defects which may significantly affect electrical safety, the condition of that installation must be recorded as **unsatisfactory**.

If the space available on the form for the summary of the inspection is insufficient, additional numbered pages should be provided as necessary. Additional pages should be identified by the unique Domestic Visual Condition Report serial number.

Approximate age of the installation

This may be determined from information relating to the original installation. Otherwise a reasonable estimate should be made by other means, such as the appearance of the installed equipment.

When carrying out work on existing, older installations, some features will be encountered which differ from those found in modern installations.

Electrical installations began to be commonplace in domestic dwellings as early as the 1920s, and over the years there have been considerable changes to the types of wiring materials and other equipment being installed, and in the ways that electrical installations are structured. From the electrical safety point of view, these changes have had two main causes: advances in technology, and amendments to the Wiring Regulations published by the Institution of Electrical Engineers (issued as British Standard *BS 7671* since 1992).

Examples of changes in requirements of the Wiring Regulations follow:

1   In many installations put in up to the 1950s, the circuits have a fuse in the neutral conductor as well as in the line conductor. This is a potentially dangerous practice for a.c. installations, and ceased to be permitted by the Wiring Regulations in about 1955. In the event of a short-circuit, there is a 50% chance that the fuse in the neutral conductor will operate. When this happens, the line conductor is not automatically disconnected from the faulty circuit

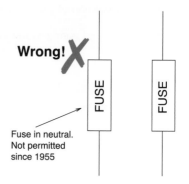

Fuse in neutral. Not permitted since 1955

Fuses in neutral conductor have not been permitted since 1955.

as would now normally be expected, thereby leaving a danger for the unwary.

2   The installation of socket-outlets other than the current standard 13 A square-pinned type was common prior to the early 1950s. These outlets accept non-fused plugs (some with an earth pin and some without), generally having round pins. These older types of socket-outlet designed for non-fused plugs must not be connected to a ring circuit. Such an arrangement can be dangerous. In addition, socket-outlets that will accept unearthed (2-pin) plugs must not be used to supply equipment needing to be earthed. It is strongly recommended that such outlets be taken out of service.

The NICEIC guide to Domestic Periodic Inspection, Testing and Reporting

3   Lighting circuits installed before 1966, and not including any metalwork needing to be earthed, often do not include a circuit protective conductor. Consequently, any new or replacement light fittings, switches or other components must be of a type not requiring earthing, eg non-metallic varieties, unless new circuit protective (earthing) conductors are provided. Otherwise, there will be a potential danger of electric shock under earth fault conditions. All lighting circuits installed since 1966 (with the exception of certain extra-low voltage circuits) have been required to include a circuit protective conductor.

4   Prior to 1966 the Wiring Regulations contained no requirements for main equipotential bonding. Since then, the installation of main equipotential bonding conductors has been required to water installation pipes, gas installation pipes, oil supply pipes, and certain other 'earthy' metalwork that may be present on the premises

5   The Wiring Regulations used to accept the single colour green for the identification of protective conductors. However, since 1977 a green-yellow coding has been required for all protective conductors.

6   During the 1980s new Regulations were introduced, requiring the minimum size of main protective bonding conductors to be larger than previously called for, particularly where there is a PME (protective multiple earthing) electricity supply. For most dwellings the minimum size now permitted to be installed is 10 mm^2 (see item 4.6.8).

7   Prior to 1981 there were virtually no requirements in the Wiring Regulations for supplementary bonding conductors. Since then, the installation of supplementary bonding conductors has been required in installations and locations of increased electric shock risk, such as bathrooms and shower rooms (see item 4.6.12), where appropriate.

8   Voltage-operated type of earth-leakage circuit-breakers ceased to be recognized in 1981. It can be distinguished by its two separate earthing terminals – one for an earthing connection to the load and one for an earthing connection to a means of earthing (often a driven rod). The major drawback with this type of device is that a parallel earth path can render it disabled.

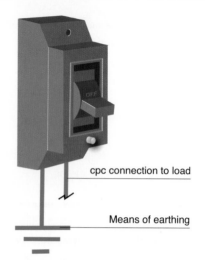

cpc connection to load

Means of earthing

Voltage operated ELCB

9   A person receiving an electric shock when using portable electrical equipment outdoors can be at great risk of death or serious injury. The risk is significantly reduced if the socket-outlet supplying the equipment is provided with sensitive RCD protection (fitted either at the socket-outlet itself or at the consumer unit). However, prior to 1981 the Wiring Regulations did not require such protection. Nowadays, sensitive RCD protection (RCD with a rated residual operating current of 30 mA or less) is required for earth fault protection (see item 4.6.10). The initial requirement, in 1981, was for this protection to be provided to at least one such socket-outlet. However, this was found to be inadequate, and Regulation 411.3.3 requires additional protection by an RCD in accordance with Regulation 415.1 for socket-outlets with a rated current not exceeding 20 A.

10 Until the latter part of the 1980s the Wiring Regulations did not contain any specific requirements for the positioning of cables concealed in walls and partitions in prescribed zones (to reduce the risk of striking a cable), which is now required by Regulation 522.6.6 (iv) in *BS 7671* (see item 4.9.5) Therefore installations prior to 1980 cables are particularly likely to be found outside of the zones. A cable detector may be used to detect concealed cables.

Evidence of alterations or additions

Enter 'Yes' or 'No' in the box, if there is clear evidence as to whether or not alterations or additions have been made to the installation since the previous inspection (or from new, if no subsequent information is available).

2.11   Particulars of Approved Contractor

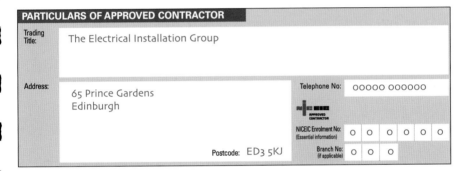

Enter trading title, address, postcode and telephone number, together with the NICEIC Enrolment Number and Branch Number (if applicable).

On a purple ▮ Domestic Visual Condition Report enter the NICEIC Registration Number, since the Enrolment Number is **not** applicable.

On a green ▮ Domestic Visual Condition Report the Registration or Enrolment numbers are **not** applicable.

PERIODIC INSPECTION REPORTS

2.12 Declaration

DECLARATION

I being the person responsible for the visual inspection of the electrical installation (as indicated by my signature below), particulars of which are described above, having exercised reasonable skill and care when carrying out the inspection, hereby declare that the information in this report, including the observations and the attached schedules, provides an accurate assessment of the condition of the electrical installation taking into account the limitations of a visual-only inspection.

I further declare that in my judgement the condition of the said installation is✤:

✤ *Tick as appropriate*

☑ Visually **not** unsatisfactory, or ☐ Unsatisfactory, significant damage, deterioration and/or defects being evident.

Signature:	Name (CAPITALS):	Date:
D Wright	D WRIGHT	25/02/08

Results reviewed by the Qualified Supervisor:

A Davies	A DAVIES	26/02/08

Tick one of the two boxes, namely:

☐ 'Visually **not** unsatisfactory', or

☐ 'Unsatisfactory, significant damage, deterioration and/or defects being evident.'

The declaration must be consistent with the observations and recommendations made.

Where the second box 'Unsatisfactory, significant damage, deterioration, defects being evident' is ticked a list of corrective action(s) necessary to maintain the installation in a safe working order should be given in the observations and recommendations for action to be taken box.

A list of observations and recommendations for urgent remedial work and corrective action(s) necessary to restore the installation to a **not** unsatisfactory (satisfactory) condition should be given. However, given the limitations of a visual inspection, these recommendations may be incomplete, and in such a case, a recommendation should be given that full periodic inspection and testing be performed to determine the full extent of the remedial action required.

The declaration should be signed by the person who carried out the inspection, and then by a person who is competent to review the contents of the report, to check that it has been correctly compiled. Names should also be printed (in capital letters) and dates of signing entered in the appropriate boxes.

This 2nd signature also applies to a purple 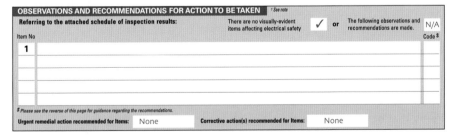 Domestic Visual Condition Report but it is **not** applicable to a green ▌ Domestic Visual Condition Report.

Where the Qualified Supervisor has personally conducted the inspection and has compiled the report, that person should sign in both places.

In an organization where substantial quantities of inspection reports need to be signed on a regular basis, it may be acceptable for the reviewer to delegate the countersigning of the inspection reports to a person of equivalent competence and responsibility, and to verify on a sampling basis that reports are being correctly compiled. However, in such cases the responsibility for all issued reports remains with the Qualified Supervisor.

2.13 Observations and recommendations for action to be taken

OBSERVATIONS AND RECOMMENDATIONS FOR ACTION TO BE TAKEN † *See note*					
Referring to the attached schedule of inspection results:		There are no visually-evident items affecting electrical safety	✓ or	The following observations and recommendations are made.	N/A
Item No					Code $
1					
$ *Please see the reverse of this page for guidance regarding the recommendations.*					
Urgent remedial action recommended for Items: None			Corrective action(s) recommended for Items: None		

Enter any observations and their recommendation codes (see items 2.6 and 2.7 respectively) relating to the installation. These should take due account of the results of the visual inspection, based on the requirements of the issue of *BS 7671* current at the time of the inspection.

PERIODIC INSPECTION REPORTS

Enter in one of the two small boxes at the top of this section, a tick (✓) to indicate that 'there are no visually-evident items affecting electrical safety' or, alternatively, 'the following observations and recommendations are made'. The box which does not contain a tick (✓) should be completed by recording '**N/A**', meaning 'Not Applicable'.

Where recommendation Codes 1, 2 or 3 have **not** been attributed to any of the items or observations, a tick (✓) should be inserted in the box at the top of the section identified by the words 'there are no visually-evident items adversely affecting safety'. In these circumstances, the two boxes at the bottom of the section should each be completed by inserting the word '**None**'.

If it is determined by inspection that any item requires 'urgent attention', 'improvement' or 'further investigation', the box near the top of section, identified by the words 'The following observations and recommendation are made', should be completed by inserting a tick (✓).

In cases where observations and recommendations are appropriate, these are to be itemized and given a numerical reference under the left-hand column headed 'Item No'. The observation(s) must be provided in the wide centre column in an accurate, succinct and easily-understandable manner. Each observation must be attributed with a recommendation Code 1, 2, 3 or 4, which is to be recorded in the right-hand column.

Where a positive entry has been given in the data-entry box identified by the words 'The following observations and recommendation are made', the data-entry boxes at the bottom of the section are also required to be completed as follows.

Items that have:

- attracted a recommendation Code 1, which indicates that urgent remedial work is required, must be prioritized by inserting the Item number(s) into the box identified with the words 'Urgent remedial work recommended for Items:'

- been given recommendation Code 2 or 3, indicating 'requires improvement' and 'requires further investigation', respectively, must be entered into the data-entry box identified with the words 'Corrective actions(s) recommended for Items:'.

Where a recommendation **Code 1 (requires urgent attention)** is given, the client is to be advised immediately, in writing, that urgent work is necessary to remedy the deficiency to satisfy the duties imposed on the inspector by the *Electricity at Work Regulations 1989*.

If the space on the form is insufficient, additional numbered pages should be provided as necessary. Additional pages should be identified by the unique Domestic Visual Condition Report Serial Number.

2.14 Next inspection

NEXT INSPECTION

§ *Enter interval in terms of years months or weeks as appropriate*

I recommend that this installation is further inspected after an interval of not more than:

§ 4 years or at change of occupancy

and that the inspection is:

Full periodic ✓ *Please tick one box*

or

visual condition

Enter the appropriate time interval before re-inspection of the installation becomes due (see item 2.4).

PERIODIC INSPECTION REPORTS

The recommended interval to the next inspection assumes that:

- all items that have attracted a recommendation Code 1 in the section 'Observations and recommendations for actions to be taken' will be remedied **without delay**, and

- all items which have attracted a recommendation Code 2 or 3 will be remedied **as soon as practicable**.

The type of the next inspection, that is, 'full periodic' or 'visual condition' is to be ticked as appropriate (see item 2.4). This will depend on the condition of the installation, and the recommended interval to the next inspection.

COMPILING DOMESTIC ELECTRICAL INSTALLATION PERIODIC INSPECTION REPORTS

2.15 Compiling Domestic Electrical Installation Periodic Inspection Reports – General

A NICEIC Domestic Electrical Installation Periodic Inspection Report is intended to be used only for the purpose of reporting on the condition of an existing electrical installation in a domestic property. The report should identify, so far as is reasonably practicable and having regard to the extent and limitations recorded in section D (see item 2.19), any damage, deterioration, defects, dangerous conditions and any non-compliances with the requirements of the current issue of *BS 7671* which may give rise to danger.

It should be noted that the greater the limitations applying to a report, the less its value to the recipient.

The Domestic Electrical Installation Periodic Inspection Report may be used only where all the following conditions apply:

1 the inspection and testing work relates to a **single dwelling** (house or individual flat)

The NICEIC guide to Domestic Periodic Inspection, Testing and Reporting

CHAPTER 2

2   the installation forms part of a TT, TN-S or TN-C-S (PME) system

3   fault protection is provided primarily by Automatic Disconnection of Supply (ADS).

The report form marked 'Original', including any additional pages, is to be given to the person ordering the inspection, as required by Regulation 634.1.

The red ▮, purple ▮, or green ▮ report form marked 'Duplicate' is to be retained by the NICEIC Approved Contractor, Domestic Installer or other contractor respectively. Furthermore, red ▮ or purple ▮ report forms should be made available by NICEIC Approved Contractors or Domestic Installers respectively, for possible future review by NICEIC.

The total number of pages which make up the report must be inserted in the box provided at the foot of each of the pages on the right-hand side.

Specimen copies of electrical installation periodic inspection reports, schedules, continuation sheets, and guidance for NICEIC Approved Contractors, Conforming Bodies, Domestic Installers, and electrical contractors are given in Annex C.

Reference should be made to items 2.26 and item 3.12 for compiling continuation sheets and schedule sections of the electrical installation periodic inspection reports respectively.

Items 2.16 to 2.25 give guidance for compiling the purple ▮ domestic electrical installation periodic inspection report DPP (see Annex, C4), to supplement the:

- notes for recipients on DPP, and

- guidance for Domestic Installers (see Annex, C5).

PERIODIC INSPECTION REPORTS

Example Page 1 of DPP follows for ease of reference.

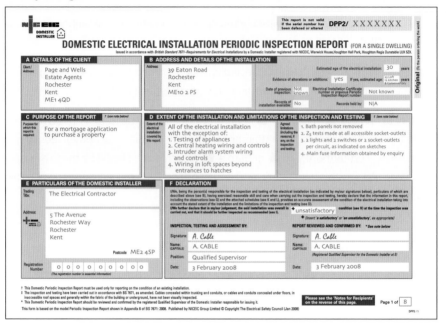

Notes:

1   Example entries have been included, in blue for each box for demonstration purposes only.

2   Entries made on reports must relate to the actual installation being reported.

3   Similar guidance to that given for compiling domestic electrical installation periodic inspection report DPP also applies to the red and green reports (DPN and DPM) respectively, to supplement:

   •   the notes for recipients (see Annexes C1 and C6 respectively), and

   •   the guidance for Approved Contractors and Conforming Bodies, and electrical contractors (see Annexes C3 and C8 respectively).

The NICEIC guide to
Domestic Periodic Inspection, Testing and Reporting

2.16 Details of client

A DETAILS OF THE CLIENT

| Client /
Address: | Page and Wells
Estate Agents
Rochester
Kent
ME1 4QD |

Enter the client's name and address. The client is the person or organization (eg housing association) ordering the work. In the case of a lengthy name or address suitable abbreviations may be used if acceptable to the client.

2.17 Address and details of the installation

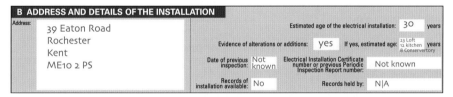

B ADDRESS AND DETAILS OF THE INSTALLATION

Address:	39 Eaton Road Rochester Kent ME10 2 PS		
		Estimated age of the electrical installation:	30 years
		Evidence of alterations or additions: **yes** If yes, estimated age:	23 Loft 12 kitchen years 8 Conservertory
	Date of previous inspection: Not known	Electrical Installation Certificate number or previous Periodic Inspection Report number:	Not known
	Records of installation available: No	Records held by:	N|A

Address of installation

Enter the address of the installation (which might differ from the clients address described in item 2.16).

Estimated age of the installation

Enter the estimated age of the installation in years. This may be determined from available information relating to the original installation. Otherwise a reasonable estimate should be made by other means, such as the appearance of the installed equipment. See item 2.10 for information on estimated age of the installation.

PERIODIC INSPECTION REPORTS

Evidence of alterations or additions

If there is clear evidence as to whether or not alterations or additions have been made to the installation since the previous inspection (or from new, if no subsequent information is available), this should be indicated by stating 'Yes' or 'No' in the box as appropriate. If there is clear evidence of alterations or additions either visually or by reference to subsequent certificates, its actual or estimated age in years should be given in the space available. Otherwise write 'N/A' (meaning 'Not Applicable').

Date of previous inspection

It may be possible to ascertain the date of the previous inspection from a Periodic Inspection Report or the original Electrical Installation Certificate or equivalent. Alternatively, the 'Periodic Inspection Notice' fixed at the origin of the installation (to comply with Regulation 514.12.1) should provide an indication of the date of previous inspection. If the information cannot be ascertained, then 'not known' should be entered.

Electrical Installation Certificate number or previous Periodic Inspection Report number.

Where the inspector has details of the original Electrical Installation Certificate or Domestic Electrical Installation Certificate, or a subsequent Periodic Inspection Report for the particular installation, the serial number of the latest document should be recorded in the space provided. If the information cannot be ascertained, then 'not known' should be entered.

Records of installation available

This refers to the availability of records of original certification, previous periodic inspection(s) and/or other relevant records, such as operating instructions for equipment. Indicate 'yes' or 'no', as appropriate.

The NICEIC guide to
Domestic Periodic Inspection, Testing and Reporting

Records held by

If the previous indication was 'yes', give the name of the person, company or organization that is holding the records of the previous inspection(s). If the previous indication was 'no', write 'N/A'.

2.18 Purpose of the report

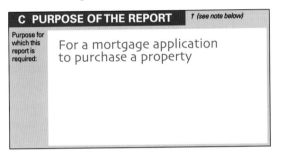

It is important, for all concerned, to enter a clear statement of the purpose of the report. A report may be required, for example, in connection with a proposed property sale or purchase. Alternatively, a report may be required on the condition of an installation following a fire or flood. A report may be required at the end of the period recommended in the original Electrical Installation Certificate or Domestic Electrical Installation Certificate, or a previous Periodic Inspection Report, or as an assessment of the condition of an installation in relation to current standards.

2.19 Extent of the installation and limitations of the inspection and testing

D EXTENT OF THE INSTALLATION AND LIMITATIONS OF THE INSPECTION AND TESTING ‡ *(see note below)*

| Extent of the electrical installation covered by this report: | All of the electrical installation with the exception of:
1. Testing of appliances
2. Central heating wiring and controls
3. Intruder alarm system wiring and controls
4. Wiring in loft spaces beyond entrances to hatches | Agreed limitations (including the reasons), if any, on the inspection and testing: | 1. Bath panels not removed
2. Z_s tests made at all accessible socket-outlets
3. 2 lights and 2 switches or 2 socket-outlets per circuit, as indicated on sketches
4. Main fuse information obtained by enquiry |

PERIODIC INSPECTION REPORTS

Extent of electrical installation covered by this report

Before commencing an inspection, it is essential to agree with the client the exact extent of the installation to be inspected. It might be necessary to make a cursory inspection of the installation and available inspection records before discussing with the client the scope of the detailed inspection required, and the available options.

The agreed extent of the installation covered by the inspection should be fully recorded in this part of Section D. The extent of the installation covered by the report might be the whole of the installation in the premises, or it might be only a part of that installation. The part could, for example, be a particular area (such as the second floor only) or particular circuits (such as all lighting circuits). The extent could also be indicated by exclusions from the whole electrical installation, such as the central heating system wiring or the fire alarm system. The wording will need to be tailored exactly to each inspection requirement and, in some instances, a continuation sheet (appropriately numbered, and identified) may be necessary.

Agreed limitations, if any, on the inspection and testing

The limitations imposed on the inspection and testing should also be explained to, and agreed with, the client before work commences. Section D of the Periodic Inspection Report form includes standard text which states:

> *'Cables concealed within trunking and conduits, or cables and conduits concealed under floors, in inaccessible roof spaces and generally within the fabric of the building or underground, have not been visually inspected.'*

Any other necessary limitations should also be agreed before commencing (or exceptionally during) the inspection and all should be clearly recorded on the report.

A periodic inspection must include a thorough visual inspection of all the electrical equipment that comprises the extent of the installation described in the previous section, and which is not concealed or inaccessible. However, in most cases, it will be appropriate to apply a sampling process to the detailed inspection of the internal

**The NICEIC guide to
Domestic Periodic Inspection, Testing and Reporting**

condition of equipment, the condition of joints and terminations etc. It may also be appropriate to apply a sampling process to the inspection and testing of the installation.

If sampling is intended, this should be made clear to the client, and the initial degree of sampling for both the inspection and the testing elements should be agreed before the work commences. Recommendations for the minimum degree of sampling (service levels) for both inspection and testing are shown in Annex A. Should the actual degree of sampling carried out be different from that agreed initially (because, for example, increased sampling was necessary due to deficiencies being found during the initial sampling), the actual degree should be recorded on the report.

Details of the sampling technique and identification of the equipment selected for inspection and testing on a sampling basis should also be fully identified, on an additional page if necessary.

The contractor should **not** set unnecessary limitations on the inspection. The aim should be to produce a report that is both fair to the client and reasonable for the contractor. It should be remembered that the greater the limitations applying to a report, the less its value.

Liabilities arising from inadequate description

It should be appreciated that failure to clearly describe and record the extent of the installation and the agreed limitations of the inspection and testing could involve the contractor in unforeseen liabilities at a later date. For example, if a contractor failed to clearly record that any luminaires mounted at high level, such as on a landing, had been excluded from a periodic inspection report, the contractor might be held responsible if an electrical fault in that part of the installation later resulted in danger or damage. Information on insurance is given in item 2.30.

If there is insufficient space in Section D to provide full details of the extent of the work to which the inspection report refers, the details should be provided on an additional page attached to the report, and reference to the additional page should be included in the relevant part(s) of the box.

2.20 Particulars of the Domestic Installer

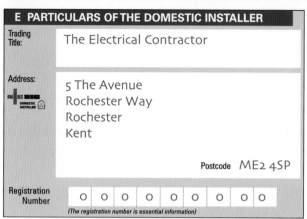

E	PARTICULARS OF THE DOMESTIC INSTALLER

Trading Title: The Electrical Contractor

Address:
5 The Avenue
Rochester Way
Rochester
Kent

Postcode ME2 4SP

Registration Number: O O O O O O O O O

(The registration number is essential information)

Enter trading title, address, and postcode for purple ▮, red ▮ and green ▮ forms. Additionally, for purple ▮ forms Domestic Installers need to enter their NICEIC Registration Number or for red ▮ forms Approved Contactors need to enter their NICEIC Enrolment Number and Branch Number (if applicable).

2.21 Declaration

F DECLARATION

I/We, being the person(s) responsible for the inspection and testing of the electrical installation (as indicated by my/our signatures below), particulars of which are described above (see B), having exercised reasonable skill and care when carrying out the inspection and testing, hereby declare that the information in this report, including the observations (see G) and the attached schedules (see K and L), provides an accurate assessment of the condition of the electrical installation taking into account the stated extent of the installation and the limitations of the inspection and testing (see D).

I/We further declare that in my/our judgement, the said installation was overall in ✦ unsatisfactory condition (see H) at the time the inspection was carried out, and that it should be further inspected as recommended (see I).

✦ *(Insert 'a satisfactory' or 'an unsatisfactory', as appropriate)*

INSPECTION, TESTING AND ASSESSMENT BY:	REPORT REVIEWED AND CONFIRMED BY: *See note below*
Signature: *A. Cable*	**Signature:** *A. Cable*
Name: (CAPITALS) A. CABLE	**Name: (CAPITALS)** A. CABLE
Position: Qualified Supervisor	*(Registered Qualified Supervisor for the Domestic Installer at E)*
Date: 3 February 2008	**Date:** 3 February 2008

A declaration of the overall condition of the installation must be given by the inspector, repeating the overall assessment given in Section H which should summarize the observations and recommendations made in Section G. The inspection, testing and assessment by the inspector must be reviewed and confirmed by the registered NICEIC Qualified Supervisor. The signatures are to be those of the competent person undertaking the inspection of the installation and of the Qualified Supervisor of NICEIC Domestic Installer, who should review each report. Where the Qualified Supervisor carries out the inspection personally, the Qualified Supervisor should sign in both places.

Example Page 2 of DPP follows for ease of reference.

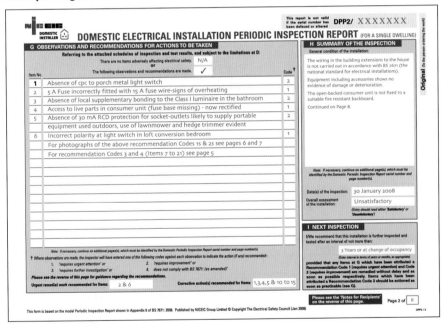

2.22 Observations and recommendations for actions to be taken

G OBSERVATIONS AND RECOMMENDATIONS FOR ACTIONS TO BE TAKEN	

Referring to the attached schedules of inspection and test results, and subject to the limitations at D:

	There are no items adversely affecting electrical safety.	N/A

or

	The following observations and recommendations are made.	✓

Item No		Code †
1	Absence of cpc to porch metal light switch	2
2	5 A Fuse incorrectly fitted with 15 A fuse wire-signs of overheating	1
3	Absence of local supplementary bonding to the Class I luminaire in the bathroom	2
4	Access to live parts in consumer unit (fuse base missing) - now rectified	1
5	Absence of 30 mA RCD protection for socket-outlets likely to supply portable equipment used outdoors, use of lawnmower and hedge trimmer evident	2
6	Incorrect polarity at light switch in loft conversion bedroom	1
	For photographs of the above recommendation Codes 1s & 2s see pages 6 and 7	
	For recommendation Codes 3 and 4 (Items 7 to 21) see page 5	

Note: If necessary, continue on additional pages(s), which must be identified by the Domestic Periodic Inspection Report serial number and page number(s).

† *Where observations are made, the inspector will have entered one of the following codes against each observation to indicate the action (if any) recommended:-*

1. 'requires urgent attention' or	2. 'requires improvement' or
3. 'requires further investigation' or	4. does not comply with BS 7671: (as amended)'

Please see the reverse of this page for guidance regarding the recommendations.

Urgent remedial work recommended for Items:	2 & 6	Corrective action(s) recommended for Items:	1,3,4,5 & 10 to 15

Enter any observations and their recommendation codes (see items 2.6 and 2.7 respectively) relating to the installation. These should take due account of the results of the inspection and testing, and be based on the requirements of the issue of *BS 7671* current at the time of the inspection (not the requirements of an earlier standard current at the time the installation was constructed).

Enter in one of the two small boxes at the top of this section, a tick (✓) to indicate that *'There are no items affecting electrical safety'* or, alternatively, *'The following observations and recommendations are made'*. The box which does not contain a tick (✓) should be completed by recording **'N/A'**, meaning 'Not Applicable'.

Where recommendation Codes 1, 2 or 3 have **not** been attributed to any of the items or observations, a tick (✓) should be inserted in the box at the top of the section identified by the words *'There are no items adversely affecting safety'*. In these circumstances, the two boxes at the bottom of the section should each be completed by inserting the word '**None**'.

If it is determined by inspection and testing that one or more items require 'urgent attention', 'improvement' or 'further investigation', the box near the top of section, identified by the words *'The following observations and recommendation are made'*, should be completed by inserting a tick (✓).

In cases where observations and recommendations are appropriate, these are to be itemised and given a numerical reference under the left-hand column headed *'Item No'*. The observation(s) must be provided in the wide centre column in an accurate, succinct and easily-understandable manner. Each observation must be attributed with a recommendation Code 1, 2, 3 or 4, which is to be recorded in the right-hand column.

Where a positive entry has been given in the data-entry box identified by the words *'The following observations and recommendation are made'*, the data-entry boxes at the bottom of the section are also required to be completed as follows.

Items that have:

- attracted a recommendation Code 1, which indicates that urgent remedial work is required, must be prioritized by inserting the Item number(s) into the box identified with the words *'Urgent remedial work recommended for Items:'*

- been given recommendation Code 2 or 3, indicating 'requires improvement' and 'requires further investigation', respectively, must be entered into the data-entry box identified with the words *'Corrective actions(s) recommended for Items:'*.

Where a recommendation Code 1 (requires urgent attention) is given, the client is to be advised immediately, in writing, that urgent work is necessary to remedy the deficiency to satisfy the duties imposed on the contractor by the *Electricity at Work Regulations 1989.*

PERIODIC INSPECTION REPORTS

If the space on the form is insufficient, additional numbered pages are to be provided as necessary. For NICEIC Domestic Periodic Inspection Reports, additional pages should be identified by the unique Domestic Periodic Inspection Report number.

Photographs of examples of observation warranting a recommendation Code 1 or 2 are shown in item 2.28.

2.23 Summary of the inspection

H SUMMARY OF THE INSPECTION

General condition of the installation:

The wiring in the building extensions to the house is not carried out in accordance with BS 7671 (the national standard for electrical installations).

Equipment including accessories shows no evidence of damage or deterioration.

The open-backed consumer unit is not fixed to a suitable fire resistant backboard.

Continued on Page 8.

Note: If necessary, continue on additional page(s), which must be identified by the Domestic Periodic Inspection Report serial number and page number(s).

Date(s) of the inspection:	30 January 2008
Overall assessment of the installation:	Unsatisfactory

(Entry should read either 'Satisfactory' or 'Unsatisfactory')

The summary should adequately describe the overall condition of the installation, taking into account the specific observations made. It is essential to provide a clear summary of the condition of the installation having considered, for example, the:

- adequacy of the earthing and bonding

- suitability of the consumer unit (or main switch and distribution board)

- type(s) of wiring system, and its condition

  The NICEIC guide to Domestic Periodic Inspection, Testing and Reporting

CHAPTER **2**

- serviceability of equipment, including accessories

- presence of adequate identification and notices

- extent of any wear and tear, damage or other deterioration

- changes in use of the premises which have led to, or might lead to, deficiencies in the installation. Such as a single occupation large house converted to multiple apartments were the maximum demand of the installation now exceeds the current rating of the original supply.

Minimal descriptions such as 'poor', and superficial statements such as 'Recommend a rewire' are considered unacceptable by NICEIC as they do not indicate the true condition of the installation.

It will, however, often be necessary or appropriate to explain the implications of a Domestic Electrical Periodic Inspection Report in a covering letter, for the benefit of recipients who require additional advice and guidance about their installation. For example, where an installation has deteriorated or been damaged to such an extent that its safe serviceable life can reasonably be considered to be at an end, a recommendation for renewal should be made in a covering letter, giving adequate supporting reasons. Reference to the covering letter should be made in the report.

The date (or dates if the inspection and testing were undertaken over a number of days) should be entered in the left-hand box at the bottom of this section. This is intended to be the date(s) when the inspection and testing was actually carried out, rather than when the report was issued.

At the bottom right-hand side of Chapter G of the report, a box is provided for the overall assessment of the condition of the installation to be given. After due consideration, the overall assessment should be given as either 'satisfactory' or 'unsatisfactory'. It would not be reasonable to indicate a 'satisfactory' assessment if any observation in the report had been given a 'Code 1 or Code 2' recommendation.

Where the space provided for the description of the general condition of the installation is inadequate for the purpose and it is necessary to continue the description on an additional page or pages, the continuation should be shown (see entry in Section H of the example report above). Each additional page must be identified by the report serial number and appropriate page number.

2.24 Next inspection

I NEXT INSPECTION

I/We recommend that this installation is further inspected and tested after an interval of not more than:

> 3 Years or at change of occupancy

(Enter interval in terms of years or months, as appropriate)

provided that any items at G which have been attributed a Recommendation Code 1 (*requires urgent attention*) and Code 2 (*requires improvement*) are remedied without delay and as soon as possible respectively. Items which have been attributed a Recommendation Code 3 should be actioned as soon as practicable (see G).

Enter time interval before re-inspection of the installation becomes due. Information on intervals between inspections, testing and reporting is given in items 2.4 and 2.14.

CHAPTER **2**

Example Page 3 of DPP follows for ease of reference.

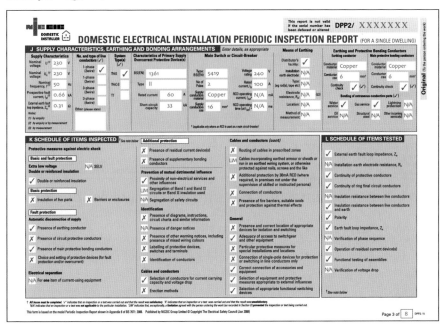

Information on completing schedule section J follows.

Note: Information on completing sections K and L is given in items 3.8 and 3.9 respectively.

PERIODIC INSPECTION REPORTS

2.25 Supply characteristics, earthing and bonding arrangements

J SUPPLY CHARACTERISTICS, EARTHING AND BONDING ARRANGEMENTS									Enter details, as appropriate	
Supply Characteristics		**No. and type of live conductors (✓)**	**System Type(s) (✓)**	**Characteristics of Primary Supply Overcurrent Protective Device(s)**		**Main Switch or Circuit-Breaker**				
Nominal voltage: $U^{(1)}$	230 V	1-phase (2wire) ✓				Type: BS(EN)	5419	Voltage rating	240	V
Nominal voltage: $U_0^{(1)}$	230 V	1-phase (3wire)	TN-S ✓	BS(EN)	1361	No of Poles	2	Rated current, I_n	100	A
Nominal frequency, $f^{(1)}$	50 Hz	3-phase (3wire)	TN-C-S	Type	II	Supply conductors material	Copper	RCD operating current, $I_{\Delta n}$	N/A	mA
Prospective fault current, $I_{pf}^{(2)}$	0.66 kA	3-phase (4wire)	TT	Rated current	60 A	Supply conductors csa	16 mm²	RCD operating time (at $I_{\Delta n}$) *	N/A	ms
External earth fault loop impedance, $Z_e^{(3)}$	0.31 Ω	Other (please state)		Short-circuit capacity	33 kA					
Notes: (1) by enquiry (2) by enquiry or by measurement (3) by measurement						* (applicable only where an RCD is used as a main circuit-breaker)				

2.25.1 Supply Characteristics and No. of live conductors

Nominal voltage, *U* (line-to-neutral), in volts.

This parameter can generally be determined only by enquiry. For public supplies in the UK it is nominally/invariably 230 V for single-phase supplies. Do not record measured values, however accurate.

Nominal frequency, *f* (in Hertz).

This parameter can generally be determined only by enquiry, but for public supplies in the UK the nominal frequency is 50 Hz.

Prospective fault current, I_{pf} (in kA).

This is the maximum fault current likely to occur in the installation, on which value the design and selection of equipment have been based. The magnitude of the prospective fault current may be obtained by 'measurement', or 'by enquiry'. Detailed guidance on the measurement of prospective fault current is given in Chapter 5. Alternatively, the inspector may obtain a value of prospective fault current by enquiring at the appropriate department of the electricity distributor. However, the value usually given by the distributor is 16 kA, which is likely to be unrealistically high.

External earth fault loop impedance Z_e (in Ω).

As with the prospective fault current, guidance relating to the measurement of the external earth fault loop impedance (Z_e) is given in Chapter 5.

NICEIC considers that for domestic premises the determination of this parameter by calculation or enquiry is **not** appropriate for an existing installation, and these options are therefore not catered for on the form.

No. and type of live conductors

Tick the appropriate 'phase (wire)' box to show the number of live supply conductors.

Enter any other arrangements in the 'Other' box, for example if there is a secondary source of supply from a microgenerator.

2.25.2 System type(s)

In the United Kingdom, it is likely that the type of system will be either TT, TN-S or TN-C-S. TN-C and IT systems would be unlikely (if ever) to be used in domestic premises in the UK, and are therefore not covered in this guide. The common types of system can be briefly described by means of their particular earthing arrangements (assuming that the supply is derived from an electricity distributor at low voltage):

- **TT** – Earthing provided by the consumer's own installation earth electrode – no earthing facility is made available to the consumer by the distributor, or if such a facility is made available, it is not used.

- **TN-S** – Earthing facility provided by the distributor for the consumer's use - provision usually by means of a connection to the supply cable sheath or a separate protective conductor in the form of a split-concentric cable or overhead conductor.

- **TN-C-S** – Earthing facility provided by the distributor, connected to the incoming supply neutral to give a Protective Multiple Earth (PME) supply, where the supply neutral and protective conductors are in the form of a Combined Neutral and Earth (CNE) conductor.

System types

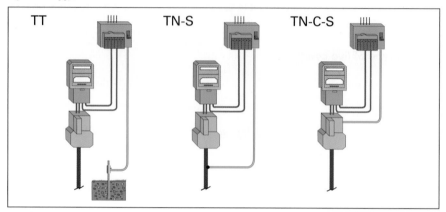

Within certain types of domestic premises, more than one system earthing arrangement may have been installed. For example, an installation in a large property may as a whole form part of a TN-C-S system, with the majority of the installation earthed to the PME earthing facility. For electrical design reasons, however, particular parts of the installation, such as a remote garage or a swimming pool area, may form part of a TT system. Where an installation has more than one system earthing arrangement, each arrangement needs to be recorded on the certificate.

2.25.3 Characteristics of primary supply overcurrent protective device(s)

The information to be recorded here is the British Standard (or other appropriate Standard) product specification in terms of BS (EN) number, together with the type, the nominal current rating (I_n), and the short-circuit capacity of the device, typically the cut-out fuse. Where available, this information should be obtained from the installation certificate or previous periodic inspection report and confirmed by inspection of the markings on the electricity distributor's cut-out fuse. However, if no clear indication is given on the overcurrent device, confirmation of its type and rating should be sought from the electricity distributor.

Where more than one source is available to supply the installation (for example, a microgeneration system) an additional page should be included in the report giving the relevant information of the other source.

2.25.4 Main switch or circuit-breaker

It needs to be confirmed that the equipment and its rating is suitable for the installation by visual inspection before completing the entries on the form. Where available, previous records, such as electrical installation certificates or periodic inspection reports, may be useful for reference purposes, providing the information is current.

Type BS (EN)

Where available previous records may be useful for reference purposes, providing the information is current. The types of main switch and circuit- breaker commonly used in consumer units should have the relevant British Standard or BS EN number clearly marked.

If after checking both the record information and the equipment **no** BS number or any other meaningful identification of the type of the device can be found, the lack of this essential information should be investigated by other means, such as by contacting the manufacturer of the equipment. Do **not** leave the box blank.

Voltage rating

The voltage rating is normally indicated on the main switch or circuit-breaker.

Number of poles

In the majority of domestic installations the main switch or circuit-breaker will be single-phase. A single pole main switch or circuit-breaker (for a single-phase

PERIODIC INSPECTION REPORTS

installation) is **not** appropriate. The number of poles needs to be 2 for a single-phase main switch or circuit-breaker, and may be 3 or 4 for a three-phase device.

Current rating (I_n)

The current rating is normally clearly indicated on the main switch or circuit-breaker.

Supply conductors: material

The supply conductor material is generally the conductor material of the 'tails' from the electricity distributor's meter to the consumer's installation main switch, usually copper.

Supply conductors: csa

This is the cross-sectional area (csa) of the supply conductors (for example, 25 mm^2).

Where the main switch is a residual current device

The BS (EN) number, voltage rating, number of poles and current rating should be determined by examining both the device and any available appropriate record information. The rating referred to in this case is the rated current (I_n) of the device, and **not** its rated residual operating current ($I_{\Delta n}$).

RCD rated residual operating current ($I_{\Delta n}$)

This should be determined from the marking on the RCD and any available appropriate record information. $I_{\Delta n}$ will usually be given in mA (for example '30 mA'), but in some instances it may be stated in amperes (for example '0.03 A'). An RCD may operate (trip) at a current just a little more than half its rated residual operating current. Where an RCD is used as a main switch, it should generally **not** have a low rated residual operating current (i.e. below 100 mA), in order to minimise unwanted tripping.

If a downstream RCD is connected on the load side of the RCD (that is used as a main switch), the RCD used as the main switch should be provided with a time-

The NICEIC guide to
Domestic Periodic Inspection, Testing and Reporting

delay. This is to prevent the RCD that is used as the main switch tripping in the event of an earth fault on the load side of the downstream RCD, which should disconnect the supply to the fault.

RCD operating time (at $I_{\Delta n}$)

Guidance on this test, which requires the use of an RCD test instrument, is given in Chapter 5.

Record in the box the operating time, in milliseconds, when subjected to a test current equal to the operating current, $I_{\Delta n}$.

2.25.5 Means of Earthing

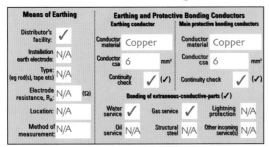

Means of Earthing		Earthing and Protective Bonding Conductors			
		Earthing conductor		Main protective bonding conductors	
Distributor's facility:	✓	Conductor material	Copper	Conductor material	Copper
Installation earth electrode:	N/A	Conductor csa	6 mm²	Conductor csa	6 mm²
Type: (eg rod(s), tape etc)	N/A	Continuity check	✓ (✓)	Continuity check	✓ (✓)
Electrode resistance, R_A:	N/A (Ω)	Bonding of extraneous-conductive-parts (✓)			
Location:	N/A	Water service ✓	Gas service ✓	Lightning protection	N/A
Method of measurement:	N/A	Oil service N/A	Structural steel N/A	Other incoming service(s)	N/A

Where fault protection is provided by Automatic Disconnection of Supply, there is a need to provide a connection for all exposed-conductive-parts and extraneous-conductive-parts to the means of earthing via the main earthing terminal (MET). The information required here is for the purpose of identifying the particular means of earthing used, in terms of a distributor's facility and/or an installation earth electrode.

Do **not** leave any boxes empty.

Distributor's facility

If the distributor has provided a means of earthing tick (✓) the check box. If there is none write 'None'.

If the system is a TT system write (N/A) in the check box.

PERIODIC INSPECTION REPORTS

Installation earth electrode

Every TT system must have an installation earth electrode. The presence of an installation earth electrode should be confirmed by ticking the check box or if one is not present write 'None'.

If the system is not TT and there is no earth electrode, write (N/A).

Type

If the installation has an earth electrode, give a brief description of its type (usually one or more earth rods for domestic premises). The types of earth electrode recognized by *BS 7671* are listed in Regulation 542.2.1. Metal pipework forming part of a gas, water or any other service network must **not** be used as an earth electrode.

If the system is not TT and there is no earth electrode, write 'N/A' in the check box.

The earth electrode resistance, R_A

R_A must be measured (see method of measurement shown below) and the value recorded, in ohms, in the space provided.

If the system is not TT and there is no earth electrode, write 'N/A' in the check box.

Location

Sufficient details must be given under 'location' so that persons unfamiliar with the installation and building layout will be able to locate the electrode for subsequent periodic inspection and testing purposes.

If the system is not TT and there is no earth electrode, write 'N/A' in the check box.

Method of measurement

The method used to measure the earth electrode resistance to earth must also be recorded. Two test methods are generally used to measure R_A:

- using a proprietary earth electrode test instrument. Indicate its use by inserting 'P' in the check box, or

- using an earth fault loop impedance test instrument. Indicate its use by inserting 'L' in the check box.

Where suitable and sufficient ground area is available for measurement purposes, a proprietary earth electrode test instrument may be used. Where hard surfaces or lack of space make the use of this method impracticable, the use of an earth fault loop impedance test instrument is appropriate. Guidance on both of these test methods is given in Chapter 5.

If the system is not TT and there is no earth electrode, write 'N/A' in the check box

2.25.6 Earthing and protective bonding conductors

Earthing conductor

The earthing conductor is the protective conductor that connects the main earthing terminal of the installation to the means of earthing. The conductor material and cross-sectional area of the earthing conductor must be stated here, followed by a tick (✓) to confirm that its continuity has been checked. This indication confirms that the inspector has tested the earthing conductor, and/or inspected it throughout its length and checked its connections, and that the result is satisfactory. A cross (✗) should be entered if it is unsatisfactory.

Information on presence and cross-sectional area of earthing conductor and its continuity testing is given in items 4.6.6 and 5.10.5 respectively.

Main protective bonding conductors

The conductor material and cross-sectional area of the main protective bonding conductors must be stated here, followed by a tick (✓) to confirm that their continuity has been checked. This indication confirms that the inspector has tested the continuity of the bonding conductors and/or inspected them throughout their length and checked their connections, and that the results are satisfactory. A cross (✗) should be entered if it is unsatisfactory.

Information on presence and cross-sectional area of main bonding conductors and their continuity testing is given in items 4.6.8 and 5.10.7 respectively.

PERIODIC INSPECTION REPORTS

Bonding of extraneous-conductive-parts

Provision is made to record the extraneous-conductive-parts to which main bonding to the main earthing terminal of the installation has been effected, such as the incoming water and gas services. A tick (✓) in the appropriate box confirms that the inspector has tested the conductor and/or inspected it throughout its length and checked the connections, and that the results are satisfactory. A cross (✗) should be entered if it is unsatisfactory. 'N/A' should be entered in boxes that are not applicable, such as where an item does not exist (such as a lightning protection scheme, which would normally be the case for domestic premises) or is not an extraneous-conductive-part (such as where the incoming water service and connected water installation pipes are non-metallic). If the service is non-metallic, '(N/M)' should be entered after 'N/A'.

2.26 Report continuation sheets

Where there is inadequate space on the form continuation sheets will need to be used as appropriate.

Purpose-made report continuation sheets are generally available for Domestic Visual Condition reports (see Annex B) or Domestic Electrical Period Inspection Reports (see Annex C). Where purpose made sheets are not available other sheets containing continued information to the form being continued are acceptable.

Continuation sheets need to be appropriately identified and include report page numbers. Continuation sheets for red or purple reports also need to include the report serial number.

**The NICEIC guide to
Domestic Periodic Inspection, Testing and Reporting**

2.27 **Domestic Electrical Danger Notification forms**

2.27.1 The Electrical Danger Notification – General

Electrical danger notification forms are available **only** in:

- red 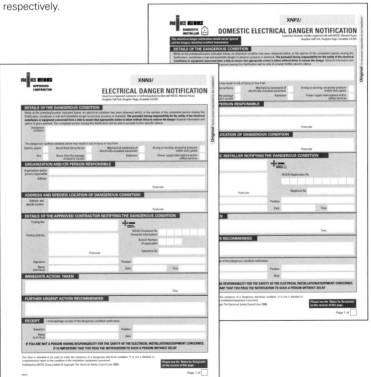 XNN for Approved Contractors and Conforming Bodies, as shown below (also see Annex D1), or

- purple XNP for Domestic Installers, as shown below (also see Annex D3.

Note: Guidance on notification forms XNN and XNP is given in Annexes D2 and D4 respectively.

2.27.2 Requirements

All persons carrying out inspections and testing of electrical installations must comply with the requirement of *Electricity at Work Regulations (EWR) 1989* (see item 1.5.1).

The purpose of the Electrical Danger Notification form is to allow an NICEIC Approved Contractor or Domestic Installer to:

- advise in writing a person ordering the work (such as the householder or the landlord) the nature of a dangerous condition discovered in an installation being inspected, and

- provide a record of the immediate action taken to remove or minimize the danger, thereby assisting the inspector comply with the *Electricity at Work Regulations*, and

- provide a record of the advice given to remedy the deficiency as a matter of urgency.

The Notification form marked 'original' should be issued to the person ordering the work.

The Electrical Danger Notification is not intended to be used to notify danger arising from equipment not forming part of a fixed electrical installation, such as portable and transportable electrical appliances. The removal of danger arising from such equipment should not warrant the formal notification procedure.

Similarly, the Electrical Danger Notification is not to be used to notify danger arising from non-electrical hazards, such as the presence of asbestos (see item 1.7.3). However, the Approved Contractor and Domestic Installer has a duty of care under the *Health and Safety at Work etc Act 1974* to report such hazards immediately to the person ordering the work; this should be done verbally or in writing to the person ordering the work.

CHAPTER **2**

The Notification should identify only damage, deterioration, defects, dangerous conditions and any non-compliances with the requirements of the current issue of *BS 7671 Requirements for Electrical Installations* which give rise to real and immediate danger. It is considered that real and immediate danger would arise from conditions such as:

- live parts exposed to touch

- connections or equipment showing evidence of arcing or overheating that pose an immediate risk of fire

- safety devices removed or bypassed

- overheating cables

- inadequate switching arrangements for emergency or mechanical maintenance purposes

- incorrectly selected, damaged or poorly maintained equipment in potentially explosive atmospheres (hazardous areas).

It should be noted that not all conditions that would warrant a Code 1 recommendation ('requires urgent attention') in a Periodic Inspection Report necessarily constitute immediate danger, and therefore the issue of an Electrical Danger Notification.

Where a real and immediate danger exists, with the agreement of a person ordering the work, appropriate action should be taken to remove or minimize the danger immediately (such as switching off and isolating the affected part(s) of the installation).

Approved Contractors and Domestic Installers have **no** legal right to isolate or disconnect any part of an electrical installation without the owner's permission. However, if permission cannot be obtained to remove the danger immediately, Approved Contractors and Domestic Installers should act without delay to minimize the danger so far as is reasonably practicable, such as by providing temporary barriers or enclosures for exposed live parts and/or posting danger notices etc.

PERIODIC INSPECTION REPORTS

The Electrical Danger Notification form consists of a single-page. However, if the space on the form is insufficient, additional numbered pages should be provided as necessary.

2.27.3 Compilation of the form

This item and items 2.27.4 to 2.27.10 give guidance on completing an electrical danger notification red ▶ form XNN.

Example consumer unit showing evidence of arcing or overheating, possibly due to a loose termination, exposing live parts

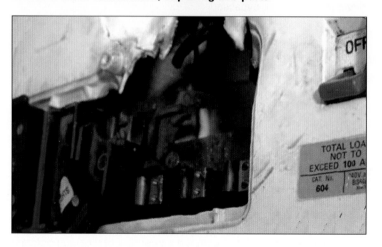

2.27.4 Details of the dangerous condition

DETAILS OF THE DANGEROUS CONDITION

While at the premises/location indicated below, an electrical condition has been observed which, in the opinion of the competent person issuing this Notification, constitutes a real and immediate danger to persons, property or livestock. **The person(s) having responsibility for the safety of the electrical installation or equipment concerned have a duty to ensure that appropriate action is taken without delay to remove the danger.** General information and advice is given overleaf. The competent person issuing this Notification will be able to provide further specific advice.

Dangerous condition	Consumer unit shows evidence of arcing or overheating. In particular the consumer unit does <u>not</u> meet the requirements relating to protection for safety given in Part 4 of BS 7671.

The dangerous condition detailed above may result in risk of injury or loss from

| Electric shock | ✓ | Burns from hot surfaces | ✓ | Mechanical movement of electrically-actuated equipment | | Arcing or burning, excessive pressure and/or toxic gases | ✓ |
| Fire | ✓ | Burns from the passage of electric current | ✓ | Explosion | ✓ | Power supply interruptions and/or safety services | |

The NICEIC guide to Domestic Periodic Inspection, Testing and Reporting

Notes:

1 Example entries have been included, in blue for each box for demonstration purposes only.

2 Entries made on forms must relate to the actual installation conditions.

3 Similar guidance (to that given for compiling electrical danger notification form XNN) also applies to the purple ▮ form XNP.

Dangerous condition

This section of the Notification should explain clearly the details of the dangerous condition where there is a real and immediate danger. Reference should be made to the relevant applicable Regulations in the national standard for electrical safety, *BS 7671 Requirements for Electrical Installations*.

The dangerous condition detailed above may result in risk of injury or loss from

The dangerous condition may result in risk of injury or loss from the following items, which should be ticked (✔).in the appropriate boxes of this section:

- electric shock
- fire
- burns from hot surfaces
- burns from the passage of electric current
- mechanical movement of electrically-actuated equipment, in so far as such injury is intended to be prevented by electrical emergency switching or mechanical maintenance of non-electrical parts of such equipment
- explosion
- arcing or burning, excessive pressure and/or toxic gases
- power supply interruptions and/or safety services.

PERIODIC INSPECTION REPORTS

2.27.5 Organization and/or person responsible

ORGANIZATION AND/OR PERSON RESPONSIBLE	
Organization and/or person responsible	The Property Landlord
Address	Landlord House 25 Bridge Street Croydon Postcode CR7 9BA

The details to be provided are the name and address of the person or organization having responsibility for the safety of the electrical installation (the person ordering the work). The details may or may **not** be the same as those listed in the 'Receipt' section of the Notification.

For example, where the person ordering the work (such as a landlord) does not live in the domestic premises where the dangerous condition exists, the details entered should be those of that person.

2.27.6 Address and specific location of dangerous condition

ADDRESS AND SPECIFIC LOCATION OF DANGEROUS CONDITION	
Address and specific location	67 Highlands Road Croydon Postcode CR9 9FE

The address to be provided is the complete postal address, including the postcode, of the installation where the dangerous condition exists.

2.27.7 Details of the Inspector notifying the dangerous condition

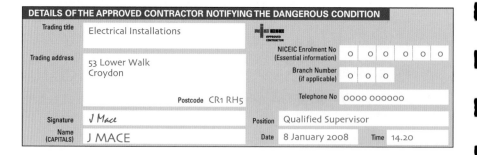

The NICEIC guide to
Domestic Periodic Inspection, Testing and Reporting

Completion of the 'Details of the Approved Contractor notifying the dangerous condition' will identify to the recipient the Approved Contractor or Domestic Installer (purple ▉ form XNP) responsible for identifying the real and immediate danger as described in the Notification. The contractor's trading title, address, postcode and telephone number must be given, together with the Approved Contractor's NICEIC Enrolment Number and Branch Number, where appropriate, or Domestic Installer's (purple ▉ form XNP) NICEIC Registration Number.

The signature, name and position are to be that of the competent person notifying the dangerous condition, and the date and time are to be entered at the time of signature.

2.27.8 Immediate action taken

IMMEDIATE ACTION TAKEN

Supply to consumer unit isolated at the distributor's cut-out. (The person ordering the work did not want the consumer unit to be replaced until competitive quotations have been obtained.)
Time 14.05

Details of the immediate action taken to remove the dangerous condition, such as isolating the supply to the consumer unit at the distributor's cut-out, should be fully recorded, including the time that such remedial action was taken.

2.27.9 Further urgent action recommended

FURTHER URGENT ACTION RECOMMENDED

Investigate cause of consumer unit failure and replace it with a suitable unit. Rectify any other defects, such as replacing damaged or inadequate equipment (for example, cables or accessories). Test and inspect the installation during and at completion of the remedial installation work.

The details provided in the previous section 'Immediate action taken', were those actions required to remove the real and immediate danger. However, due to the nature of the dangerous condition, the Approved Contractor may wish to recommend to the person ordering the work further urgent action that in his/her opinion is advisable to ensure that the electrical installation is restored to a safe condition for continued service. For example, the Approved Contractor may consider it appropriate/necessary to recommend that a full Periodic Inspection and Test of the installation or part(s) are carried out to determine the full extent of any deficiencies.

PERIODIC INSPECTION REPORTS

2.27.10 Receipt

RECEIPT	I acknowledge receipt of this dangerous condition notification.		
Signature	*A Jones*	Position	Occupier
Name (CAPITALS)	A JONES	Date	3 March 2007

IF YOU ARE NOT A PERSON HAVING RESPONSIBILITY FOR THE SAFETY OF THE ELECTRICAL INSTALLATION/EQUIPMENT CONCERNED, IT IS IMPORTANT THAT YOU PASS THE NOTIFICATION TO SUCH A PERSON WITHOUT DELAY

The 'Receipt' section enables the recipient to acknowledge receipt of the Notification, and, if not responsible for the safety of the electrical installation (the person ordering the work) to pass the Notification to that person.

The signature, name and position are to be that of the recipient of the dangerous condition notification, and the date is to be entered at the time of signature.

2.28 Photographs for reports

Photographs can help support a report.

Digital cameras are readily available and it is relatively easy to take photographs and attach prints of them to the report. Each additional page needs to be appropriately identified and include a report page number. Furthermore, for a red or purple report the report serial number needs to be included.

Examples of the photographs for some of the recommendation Codes 1 and 2 shown in Section G, of the DPP report example (item 2.22) follow.

1   **Absence of cpc to porch metal light switch and non-compliant enclosure**

The NICEIC guide to Domestic Periodic Inspection, Testing and Reporting

2   15 A fuse wire (not shown), incorrectly, fitted to the 5 A fuse (shown), signs of overheating visible (at the top of the fuse carrier and on the insulation of the three conductors)

 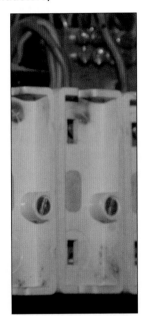

3   Access to live parts in a consumer unit (fuse base missing)

PERIODIC INSPECTION REPORTS

2.29 Sketches for reports

Sketches, such as floor plans, included with a report can help locate equipment inspected for future reference. An example of a sketch used in the DPP model report described in items 2.15 to 2.25 follows.

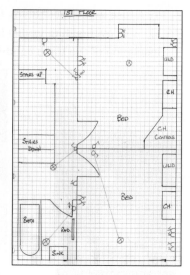

2.30 Insurance

While the contractor should have **public liability insurance**, such insurance does not generally cover a claim that may be taken by a client against the contractor. For example, if the contractor fails to clearly describe and record the extent of the installation and the agreed limitations of the inspection and testing in a report (see item 2.19 for an example of liabilities that may arise from an inadequate description being given in a report), which results in a loss to the client. However, **professional indemnity insurance** taken out by the contractor may give the contactor some protection in such circumstances.

Further information on professional indemnity cover (to protect you against your legal liability to compensate third parties should they sustain any injury, loss or damage due to professional negligence on your part) can be obtained from NICEIC Insurance Services.

SCHEDULES

3.1   Requirements

Compiling Domestic Visual Condition Reports

3.2   Origin of installation

    3.2.1   System types

    3.2.2   Primary supply overcurrent protective device

    3.2.3   Means of earthing and earthing system

    3.2.4   Bonding of extraneous-conductive-parts

3.3   Consumer unit

    3.3.1   Main switch type and overcurrent protective devices

    3.3.2   Schedule of circuit details

    3.3.3   Labels

    3.3.4   Overall condition

3.4   Final circuits

    3.4.1   Condition

    3.4.2   Observations

3.5   Wiring system

    3.5.1   Type

    3.5.2   Condition

3.6   Location containing a bath or shower - additional protection

3.7   Operational tests

Compiling Domestic Electrical Installation Periodic Inspection Reports

3.8   Schedule of items inspected

    3.8.1   Methods of protection against electric shock

    3.8.2   Prevention of mutual detrimental influence

    3.8.3   Identification

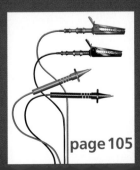

An NICEIC publication © Electrical Safety Council (JAN 2008)

page 105

SCHEDULES

3.1 Requirements

This chapter gives guidance on compiling the schedules of the 'Domestic Visual Condition Reports – DVN ▐ , DVP ▐ , and DVM ▐ ,' and the 'Domestic Electrical Installation Periodic Inspection Reports – DPN ▐ , DPP ▐ and DPM ▐ '.

An introduction to the above reports and information on compiling sections of them is given in Chapters 1 and 2 respectively.

BS 7671 requires that a record of inspections performed and the results of the testing are issued with a Periodic Inspection Report (PIR), Regulation 634.1 refers. The inspection should include, at least, the checking of the items listed in Regulation Group 611, and the test schedule should record the results of the appropriate tests detailed in Regulations 612.2 to 612.14.

The requirement of *BS 7671* for the recording of inspection and test results relates to final circuits, and distribution circuits (or 'sub-mains' as they used to be called) where they form part of the installation.

The Domestic Visual Condition Reports – DVN, DVP, and DVM, include the following sections (see items 3.2 to 3.7):

- Origin of installation

- Consumer unit

- Final circuits

- Wiring system

- Location containing a bath or shower – additional protection

- Operational tests.

The NICEIC guide to
Domestic Periodic Inspection, Testing and Reporting

The Domestic Electrical Installation Periodic Inspection Reports – DPN, DPP and DPM include the following sections (see items 3.8 to 3.11):

- Schedule of items inspected

- Schedule of items tested

- Circuit details

- Test results.

COMPILING DOMESTIC VISUAL CONDITION REPORTS

On the schedules of the 'Domestic Visual Condition Reports' – DVN, DVP and DVM, all unshaded boxes should be completed either by insertion of the relevant details or by entering:

- a tick (✓), indicating that the outcome of a particular inspection was **not unsatisfactory**, as far as can be ascertained from a visual-only inspection,

- a cross (✗), indicating that the outcome of a particular inspection was **unsatisfactory**, or

- **'N/A'**, indicating that an inspection was **'Not Applicable'** to the particular installation.

Note: that for every cross (✗) meaning **'unsatisfactory'**, an observation should be made in the 'Observations and recommendations for actions to be taken' section of the report.

Each section of a DVN ▌, Domestic Visual Condition Report should be completed as shown in the guidance given in items 3.2 to 3.7.

SCHEDULES

Example Page 2 of DVN follows for ease of reference.

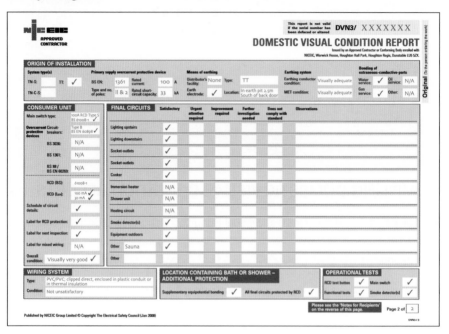

Notes:

1 Example entries have been included, in blue for each box for demonstration purposes only.

2 Entries made on reports must relate to the actual installation being reported upon.

3 Similar guidance to that given for compiling Domestic Visual Condition Report DVN also applies to the purple and green reports (DVP and DVM) respectively, to supplement:

- the notes for recipients (see Annexes B4 and B7 respectively), and

- the guidance for NICEIC Domestic Installers/Approved Contractors, and electrical contractors (see Annexes B6 and B9 respectively).

The NICEIC guide to
Domestic Periodic Inspection, Testing and Reporting

3.2   Origin of installation

ORIGIN OF INSTALLATION					
System type(s)		**Primary supply overcurrent protective device**			
TN-S:	TT: ✓	BS EN: 1361	Rated current:	100	A
TN-C-S:		Type and no. of poles: II & 2	Rated short-circuit capacity:	33	kA

3.2.1   System types

Enter 'System type(s)' (see item 2.25.2).

3.2.2   Primary supply overcurrent protective device

Enter 'BS EN number' and 'Rated current' (see item 2.25.3). Followed by, 'Type and no of poles' and 'Rated short-circuit capacity' (see items 25.4 and 25.3 respectively).

3.2.3   Means of earthing and earthing system

Means of earthing			Earthing system	
Distributor's facility: None	Type:	TT	Earthing conductor condition:	Visually adequate
Earth electrode: ✓	Location:	In earth pit 2.5m South of back door	MET condition:	Visually adequate

Distributor's facility

If the distributor has provided a means of earthing enter a tick (✓) in the check box if it is **not unsatisfactory** or a cross (✗) if it is **unsatisfactory**. If there is none, write '**None**'. For example, a distributor's facility that has an unsuitable earth clamp connected to the lead sheath of the service cable is **unsatisfactory**.

Type

Enter the type of system earthing arrangement, such as TT (see item 2.25.2).

Earthing conductor condition

Enter details of the condition of the earthing conductor, such as visually adequate.

SCHEDULES

Earth electrode

For an earth electrode use a tick (✔) in the check box if it is **not unsatisfactory**, a cross (✗) if it is **unsatisfactory**, or **N/A** if it is not applicable.

Location

Sufficient details must be given under 'location' so that persons unfamiliar with the installation and building layout will be able to locate the electrode for periodic inspection and testing purposes.

If the system is not TT and there is no earth electrode, enter 'N/A' in the check box.

Main Earthing Terminal (MET) condition

Enter details of the condition of the main earthing terminal (MET), such as visually adequate.

3.2.4 Bonding of extraneous-conductive-parts

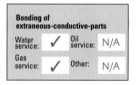

Enter details of the extraneous-conductive-parts that are bonded (on the installation pipework side) to the main earthing terminal of the installation, such as the incoming water or gas service.

For extraneous-conductive-parts that are main bonded, against each appropriate check box, use a tick (✔) if it is **not unsatisfactory**, a cross (✗) if it is **unsatisfactory**, or **'N/A'** if it is **not** applicable (such as where the service is not an extraneous-conductive-part). If the distributor's service installation pipework and the consumer's installation pipework are not extraneous-conductive-parts, and they are **non-metallic**, enter '(N/M)' after **'N/A'**.

The NICEIC guide to
Domestic Periodic Inspection, Testing and Reporting

3.3   Consumer unit

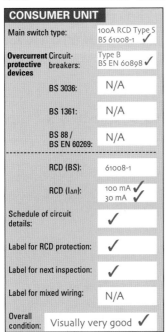

CONSUMER UNIT	
Main switch type:	100A RCD Type S BS 61008-1 ✓
Overcurrent protective devices Circuit-breakers:	Type B BS EN 60898 ✓
BS 3036:	N/A
BS 1361:	N/A
BS 88 / BS EN 60269:	N/A
RCD (BS):	61008-1
RCD (IΔn):	100 mA ✓ 30 mA ✓
Schedule of circuit details:	✓
Label for RCD protection:	✓
Label for next inspection:	✓
Label for mixed wiring:	N/A
Overall condition:	Visually very good ✓

3.3.1   Main switch type and overcurrent protective devices

Enter the main switch current rating, type and the standard that it is manufactured to, such as 100 A RCD Type S, *BS 61008-1* respectively, in the 'Main switch type' box. Use a tick (✓) if it is **not unsatisfactory** or a cross (✗) if it is **unsatisfactory**. Information on entering data about main switches is given in item 2.25.4.

Enter the circuit-breaker details, such as manufacturing standard and type as appropriate (for example *BS EN 60898* Type B respectively), in the 'Circuit-breakers' box.

For each overcurrent protective device, use a tick (✓) if it is **not unsatisfactory**, a cross (✗) if it is **unsatisfactory**, or **N/A** if it is not applicable. Information on

SCHEDULES

inspection of protective devices is given in item 4.6.10. Enter the BS, and the residual operating current ($I_{\Delta n}$) of any RCD installed, in thousandths of amperes (mA).

Describe the overall condition of the consumer unit and use a tick (✓) if it is **not unsatisfactory**, a cross (✗) if it is **unsatisfactory**.

3.3.2   Schedule of circuit details

For 'Schedule of circuit details' (see item 4.8.1) use a tick (✓) in the check box if it is **not unsatisfactory**, a cross (✗) if it is **unsatisfactory**.

3.3.3   Labels

The labels boxes cover:

- RCD protection

- Next inspection

- Mixed wiring, that is, colours according to different versions of *BS 7671*.

For each label check box, enter a tick (✓) if the label is **not unsatisfactory**, a cross (✗) if it is **unsatisfactory**, or **N/A** if it is not applicable.

(Item 4.8.2 gives inspection information on labels).

3.3.4   Overall condition

Enter a clear description of the overall condition of the consumer unit. For example, the consumer unit visually is in very good condition, or the consumer unit is **unsatisfactory** (such as where the enclosure is broken or incorrect final circuit protective devices are installed).

3.4 Final circuits

FINAL CIRCUITS	Satisfactory	Urgent attention required	Improvement required	Further investigation needed	Does not comply with standard	Observations
Lighting upstairs	✓					
Lighting downstairs	✓					
Socket-outlets	✓					
Socket-outlets	✓					
Cooker	✓					
Immersion heater	N/A					
Shower unit	N/A					
Heating circuit	N/A					
Smoke detector(s)	✓					
Equipment outdoors	✓					
Other Sauna	✓					
Other						

3.4.1 Condition

Record the overall condition of each listed final circuit by marking (as shown below) **one** of the check boxes (shown above) with a tick (✓) to indicate it is **not unsatisfactory** (satisfactory), or a cross (✗) to indicate it is **unsatisfactory**.

- Satisfactory – mark box with a tick (✓).
- Urgent attention required (recommendation Code 1)
  – mark box with a cross (✗).
- Improvement required (recommendation Code 2), as soon as possible
  – mark box with a cross (✗).
- Further investigation needed (recommendation Code 3), to determine if it is safe or unsafe for continued use – mark box with a cross (✗).
- Does not comply with the requirements of the current edition of BS 7671 (recommendation Code 4), but it may not be unsafe for continued use – mark with a cross (✗).

See item 2.7 for information on recommendation Codes.

N/A should be entered in the appropriate '**Satisfactory**' check box of any final circuit listed that does **not** form part of the inspection.

SCHEDULES

Where appropriate, the 'Other' box should be used. If more items need be added to the list one or more continuation pages may be necessary. Such continuation pages need to be referenced, cross-referenced and numbered as part of the report (see item 3.12).

3.4.2 Observations

An explanation will be required in the corresponding 'Observations' entry box for any final circuit item condition check box that is crossed (✗). (Information on observations is given in item 2.6.) Any observations will also need to be recorded in the 'Observations and recommendations for actions to be taken' section of the report (see item 2.13).

3.5   Wiring system

WIRING SYSTEM	
Type:	PVC/PVC; clipped direct, enclosed in plastic conduit or in thermal insulation
Condition:	Not unsatisfactory

3.5.1 Type

Enter brief details of the type of wiring, such as PVC/PVC ((poly vinyl chloride) now referred to as thermoplastic), VRI (vulcanized rubber insulated) or lead sheathed cables. Cables may, for example, be clipped direct, enclosed in conduit and/or in thermal insulation.

3.5.2 Condition

Enter brief details of the visible condition of the wiring. For example, wiring with exposed conductors (due to cut or crushed insulation) would be **unsatisfactory**.

Touch and smell might also be used to help to determine the condition of cables. For example, a cable that has brittle insulation that cracks when touched or has a burnt smell (showing signs of overheating) would be **unsatisfactory**.

The NICEIC guide to
Domestic Periodic Inspection, Testing and Reporting

3.6 Location containing a bath or shower - additional protection

LOCATION CONTAINING BATH OR SHOWER – ADDITIONAL PROTECTION			
Supplementary equipotential bonding	✓	All final circuits protected by RCD	✓

In 'Location containing bath or shower additional protection' section a visual check for supplementary equipotential bonding is made, enter a tick (✓) if it is **not unsatisfactory**, a cross (✗) if it is **unsatisfactory**. Where all final circuits in the location are provided with 'additional protection' by means of a 30 mA RCD a tick (✓) should be placed in 'All final circuits protected by RCD' box.

Examples, where supplementary bonding is required and would be **unsatisfactory** if a bonding conductor is:

- absent,

- connected to a metallic pipe using an unsuitable bonding clamp, or

- its cross-sectional area is undersized.

3.7 Operational tests

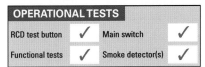

OPERATIONAL TESTS			
RCD test button	✓	Main switch	✓
Functional tests	✓	Smoke detector(s)	✓

In each 'operational tests' check box, enter a tick (✓) if it is **not unsatisfactory**, a cross (✗) if it is **unsatisfactory**, or **N/A** if it is not applicable.

Information on the above tests is given as follows:

- RCD test button – item 5.16

- Main switch[1] – item 5.17

---

[1] When the main switch is switched OFF, check that the line and neutral load side conductors are isolated (see item 1.7.1).

SCHEDULES

- Functional tests – item 5.17

- Smoke detector(s), and other items forming part of a fire detection and alarm system– item 5.17

COMPILING DOMESTIC ELECTRICAL INSTALLATION PERIODIC INSPECTION REPORTS

On the schedules of the 'Domestic Electrical Installation Periodic Reports' – DPN ▮, DPP ▮ and DPM ▮, all unshaded boxes should, in general, be completed either by insertion of the relevant details or by entering:

- A tick (✓) meaning a particular inspection or test was carried out and the result is **satisfactory**,

- A cross (✗) meaning a particular inspection or test was carried out and the result is **unsatisfactory**,

- '**N/A**', indicates that an inspection or test was '**Not Applicable**' to the particular installation,

- '**LIM**' indicates that, exceptionally, a **limitation** agreed with the person ordering the work prevented the inspection or test being carried out. The reasons/technical justification should be clearly explained and recorded in Section D of the report (see item 2.19).

To avoid doubt, **no** unshaded box should be left blank.

Note: that for every cross (✗) meaning '**unsatisfactory**', an observation should be made in the 'Observations and recommendations for actions to be taken' section of the report.

Schedule section K onwards of a DPP▮, Domestic Electrical Installation Periodic Inspection Report should be completed as shown in the guidance given in items 3.8 to 3.11. Information on completing section J is given in item 2.25.

**The NICEIC guide to
Domestic Periodic Inspection, Testing and Reporting**

Example Pages **3 & 4** of DPP follow for ease of reference.

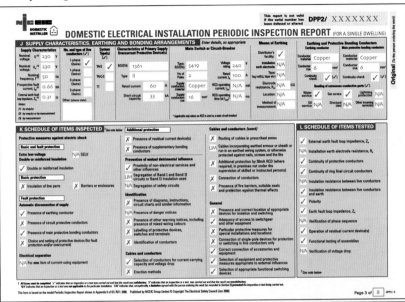

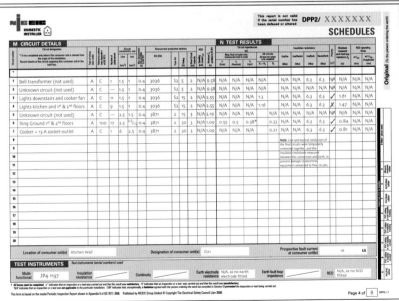

SCHEDULES

Notes:

1. Example entries have been included, in blue for each box for demonstration purposes only.

2. Entries made on reports must relate to the actual installation being reported on.

3. Similar guidance to that given for compiling Domestic Electrical Installation Periodic Inspection Report DPP  also applies to the red  and green  reports (DPN and DPM) respectively, to supplement:

   - the notes for recipients (see Annexes C1 and C6 respectively), and

   - the guidance for Approved Contractors and Conforming Bodies, and electrical contractors (see Annexes C3 and C8 respectively).

The NICEIC guide to
Domestic Periodic Inspection, Testing and Reporting

3.8   Schedule of items inspected

For each item enter a tick (✓) in the check box if it is **satisfactory**, a cross (✗) if it is **unsatisfactory**, **N/A** if it is not applicable or a **LIM**' if it is a **limitation**.

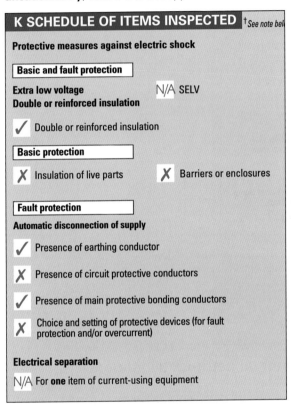

3.8.1 Methods of protection against electric shock

Information about methods of protection against electric shock is given in item 4.6. Absence of appropriate protective measures for 'basic' and 'fault protection', and 'additional protection' (where appropriate), such as **no** RCD protection for socket-outlets likely to be used to plug in outdoor hand held portable equipment, is **unsatisfactory**.

SCHEDULES

Additional protection

✗ Presence of residual current device(s)

✗ Presence of supplementary bonding conductors

Prevention of mutual detrimental influence

✓ Proximity of non-electrical services and other influences

LIM Segregation of Band I and Band II circuits or Band II insulation used

N/A Segregation of safety circuits

Identification

✗ Presence of diagrams, instructions, circuit charts and similar information

N/A Presence of danger notices

✗ Presence of other warning notices, including presence of mixed wiring colours

✗ Labelling of protective devices, switches and terminals

✗ Identification of conductors

Cables and conductors

✓ Selection of conductors for current carrying capacity and voltage drop

✗ Erection methods

3.8.2 Prevention of mutual detrimental influence

Information about prevention of mutual detrimental influence is given in item 4.7. Absence of prevention of mutual detrimental influence, such as **no** separation between a cable and a hot water pipe, is **unsatisfactory**.

3.8.3 Identification

Information on identification is given in item 4.8. Absence of appropriate identification, such as a circuit chart, is **unsatisfactory**.

**The NICEIC guide to
Domestic Periodic Inspection, Testing and Reporting**

Cables and conductors *(cont)*

✗ Routing of cables in prescribed zones

LIM Cables incorporating earthed armour or sheath or run in an earthed wiring system, or otherwise protected against nails, screws and the like

✗ Additional protection by 30mA RCD (where required, in premises not under the supervision of skilled or instructed persons)

✗ Connection of conductors

✗ Presence of fire barriers, suitable seals and protection against thermal effects

General

✗ Presence and correct location of appropriate devices for isolation and switching

✓ Adequacy of access to switchgear and other equipment

✗ Particular protective measures for special installations and locations

✗ Connection of single-pole devices for protection or switching in line conductors only

✓ Correct connection of accessories and equipment

✓ Selection of equipment and protective measures appropriate to external influences

✓ Selection of appropriate functional switching devices

3.8.4 Cables and conductors

Where it is possible to identify cables routed outside permitted zones, or where the wiring system does not incorporate an earthed metallic covering (or not is enclosed in earthed conduit, trunking/ducting or not mechanically protected against damage sufficient to prevent penetration of the cable by nails, screws and the like) it should be reported as being **unsatisfactory**. **Damaged** cables or unsuitable connections should also be reported as being **unsatisfactory**. Information about the selection, additional protection by RCD, and installation of cables and conductors is given in item 4.9.

SCHEDULES

3.8.5 General

Information about the following general listed items is given in the items shown in brackets.

- Presence and correct location of appropriate devices for isolation and switching (item 4.10).

- Adequacy of access to switchgear and other equipment (item 4.11).

- Particular protective measures for special installations and locations (item 4.12).

- Connection of single-pole devices for protection or switching in phase conductors only (item 4.13.1).

- Correct connection of accessories and equipment (items 4.13.2 & 4.13.3).

- Selection of equipment and protective measures appropriate to external influences (item 4.14).

- Selection of appropriate functional switching devices (item 4.10.4).

Example recommendation Codes, for items that are unsatisfactory, are given in item 2.7.

3.9   Schedule of items tested

For each item enter a tick (✓) in the check box if it is **satisfactory**, a cross (✗) if it is **unsatisfactory**, **N/A** if it is not applicable or a **LIM'** if it is a **limitation**.

L SCHEDULE OF ITEMS TESTED	
✓	External earth fault loop impedance, Z_e
N/A	Installation earth electrode resistance, R_A
✓	Continuity of protective conductors
✓	Continuity of ring final circuit conductors

The NICEIC guide to
Domestic Periodic Inspection, Testing and Reporting

Information about 'External earth fault loop impedance, Z_e' and 'Installation earth electrode resistance', R_A is given in items 5.8 and 5.9 respectively.

Information on 'Continuity of protective conductors' and 'Continuity of ring final circuit conductors' is given in item 5.10.

N/A	Insulation resistance between live conductors
✓	Insulation resistance between live conductors and earth
✓	Polarity
✓	Earth fault loop impedance, Z_s
N/A	Verification of phase sequence
✓	Operation of residual current device(s)
✓	Functional testing of assemblies
N/A	Verification of voltage drop

Information on the following listed items is given in the items shown in brackets:

- Insulation resistance between live conductors (item 5.11.1)
- Insulation resistance between live conductors and earth (item 5.11.2)
- Polarity (item 5.14)
- Earth fault loop impedance, Z_s (item 5.15)
- Verification of phase sequence (item 5.14)
- Operation of residual current device(s) (item 5.16)
- Functional testing of assemblies (item 5.17)
- Verification of Voltage drop (item 4.9.1).

SCHEDULES

3.10 Circuit details

Details of each final circuit should be entered in the body of the schedule; one row being used for each final circuit.

M CIRCUIT DETAILS														
Circuit number	Circuit designation * To be completed only where this consumer unit is remote from the origin of the installation. Record details of the circuit supplying this consumer unit in the bold box.	Type of wiring (see code)	Reference method (see Appendix 4 of BS 7671)	Number of points served	Circuit conductors: csa		Max. disconnection time permitted by BS 7671 (s)	Overcurrent protective devices				RCD		Maximum Zₛ permitted by BS 7671 (Ω)
					Live (mm²)	cpc (mm²)		BS (EN)	Type No	Rating (A)	Short Circuit capacity (kA)	Operating current Iₙ (mA)		
*														
1	Bell transformer (not used)	A	C	1	1.5	1	0.4	3036	S2	5	2	N/A		9.58
2	Unknown circuit (not used)	A	C	---	1.5	1	0.4	3036	S2	5	2	N/A		9.58
3	Lights downstairs and cooker fan	A	C	11	1.5	1	0.4	3036	S2	15	2	N/A		2.55
4	Lights kitchen and 1ˢᵗ & 2ⁿᵈ floors	A	C	9	1.5	1	0.4	3036	S2	15	2	N/A		2.55
5	Unknown circuit (not used)	A	C	---	2.5	1.5	0.4	3871	2	15	3	N/A		2.19
6	Ring Ground 1ˢᵗ & 2ⁿᵈ floors	A	100	17	2.5	2.5/1.5	0.4	3871	2	30	3	N/A		1.09
7	Cooker + 13 A socket-outlet	A	C	1	6	2.5	0.4	3871	2	30	3	N/A		1.09
8														
9														
10														

Note: Circuit 6 has a mix of 2.5 mm² and 1.5 mm² cross-section area circuit protective conductors (cpc).

3.10.1 Circuit number

Use the circuit numbers given in schedule M. Information about numbering of final circuits is given in item 1.13.

3.10.2 Circuit designation

If the consumer unit is remote from the origin of the installation, enter the details of the circuit supplying the consumer unit, in the bold box.

Entries should be as descriptive as possible so that they cannot be confused with any other circuits on the consumer unit.

The NICEIC guide to
Domestic Periodic Inspection, Testing and Reporting

3.10.3 Type of wiring

Details of the type of wiring, such as PVC/PVC cables or PVC cables in metallic conduit etc, should be entered. A table at the side of the schedule (see below) lists a set of codes for use in this respect. Where Code O (other) is used, a note must be added in the space provided in the table to identify the specific type of wiring.

CODES FOR TYPE OF WIRING								
A	B	C	D	E	F	G	H	O (Other - please state)
PVC/PVC cables	PVC cables in metallic conduit	PVC cables in non-metallic conduit	PVC cables in metallic trunking	PVC cables in non-metallic trunking	PVC/SWA cables	XLPE/SWA cables	Mineral-insulated cables	

3.10.4 Reference method

The reference method(s), as detailed in Appendix 4 of *BS 7671*, used for installation of the circuit should be recorded here. Reference methods A, C, 100, 101, 102 or 103 for thermoplastic insulated and sheathed flat cables (detailed in Table 4D5 of *BS 7671*) generally apply to installations in domestic premises, although other methods may apply, such as method B, when non-sheathed single-core cables are installed in conduit fixed to a masonary wall (Table 4A2 refers).

3.10.5 Number of points served

Record the number of items of current-using equipment or socket-outlets on the circuit (**Note:** a twin socket-outlet counts as 2 outlets).

3.10.6 Circuit conductors (csa)

Live (mm²)

Enter the cross-sectional area (csa) of the live circuit conductors (line and neutral)

cpc (mm²)

Enter the csa of the circuit protective conductor (cpc) where it is a single-core cable or forms part of a multi-core cable. If the cpc is provided by the steel wire armouring of an armoured cable, the copper sheath of a mineral insulated cable, or by steel conduit or trunking. the cpc should be indicated by an abbreviation of its type, such as 'Arm', 'Con', or 'Trun' respectively, rather than by its cross-sectional area.

SCHEDULES

3.10.7 Maximum disconnection time permitted by *BS 7671*

The maximum permitted disconnection time is determined by the requirements of *BS 7671*, having regarded factors such as the type and location of equipment supplied by the circuit. Table 41.1 of the Standard provides maximum disconnection times for final circuits not exceeding 32A. For example, for a TN system a socket-outlet circuit in domestic premises would generally have a maximum permitted disconnection time of 0.4 seconds. However, a final circuit supplying an item of fixed equipment in excess of 32A, such as a cooker rated at 40 A (where the cooker control unit does not contain a 13 A socket-outlet), would in general have a maximum permitted disconnection time of 5 seconds (Regulation 411.3.2.3).

3.10.8 Overcurrent protective devices

BS (EN)

For each overcurrent protective device enter the appropriate:

- British Standard (BS) number, for example, *BS 3036*, which is a standard for semi-enclosed (rewireable) fuses, or

- BS EN, for example, *BS EN 60898*, which is a standard for circuit-breakers.

Type

Enter the type of the protective device, for example, Type B circuit-breaker.

Rating (A)

Enter the rated current of the protective device, in units of amperes (A).

Short-circuit capacity (kA)

Enter the short-circuit capacity of the device, in units of thousands of amperes (kA).

The NICEIC guide to
Domestic Periodic Inspection, Testing and Reporting

3.10.9 RCD: Operating current, $I_{\Delta n}$ (mA)

Enter the rated residual operating (tripping) current, in thousandths of amperes (mA), of any residual current device that may be in circuit. If an RCD is not installed, then 'N/A' should be entered.

3.10.10   Maximum Z_s permitted by *BS 7671* (Ω)

Enter the maximum permitted values of Z_s by reference to the limiting earth loop impedance values given Chapter 41 of *BS 7671*, **not** to other tabulated 'corrected' values used for comparison with measured values obtained at ambient temperature.

For convenience maximum permitted values of Z_s for common overcurrent devices are shown in Table 3A, based on values given in Chapter 41 of *BS 7671*, for disconnection times of 0.4 seconds and/or 5 seconds (s) respectively.

Maximum permitted values of earth fault loop impedance for non-delayed RCDs to *BS EN 61008* and *BS EN 61009* for final circuits not exceeding 32 A are given in Table 41.5 of *BS 7671* (which is partly reproduced in item 4.6.10).

SCHEDULES

Table 3A

	Fuses						Circuit-breakers to BS 3871 or BS EN 60898 or RCBOs to BS EN 61009				
MAXIMUM LIMITING VALUES OF EARTH LOOP IMPEDANCE (Z_S) IN OHMS FOR COMMON OVERCURRENT PROTECTIVE DEVICES, FOR PROTECTION AGAINST INDIRECT CONTACT OPERATING AT 230 V, BASED ON VALUES GIVEN IN CHAPTER 41 OF BS 7671 (where the conductors are at their normal operating temperature)											
Rated current (A)	BS 88 (gG) Parts 2 and 6		BS 1361 or BS 1362		BS 3036		Type 1	Type 2	Type B	Type 3 and C	Type D
	0.4 s	5 s	0.4 s	5 s	0.4 s	5 s	0.4 s and 5 s				
3	N/A	N/A	16.40	23.20	N/A	N/A	N/A	N/A	15.33	N/A	N/A
5	N/A	N/A	10.45	16.4	9.58	17.7	11.50	6.57	N/A	4.60	2.30
6	8.52	13.5	N/A	N/A	N/A	N/A	9.58	5.47	7.67	3.83	1.92
10	5.11	7.42	N/A	N/A	N/A	N/A	5.75	3.28	4.60	2.30	1.15
13	N/A	N/A	2.42	3.83	N/A	N/A	N/A	N/A	N/A	N/A	N/A
15	N/A	N/A	3.28	5.00	2.55	5.35	3.83	2.19	N/A	1.53	0.76
16	2.70	4.18	N/A	N/A	N/A	N/A	3.59	2.05	2.87	1.44	0.72
20	1.77	2.91	1.70	2.80	1.77	3.83	2.87	1.63	2.30	1.15	0.57
25	1.44	2.30	N/A	N/A	N/A	N/A	2.30	1.31	1.84	0.92	0.46
30	N/A	N/A	1.15	1.84	1.09	2.64	1.91	1.09	N/A	0.76	0.38
32	1.04	1.84	N/A	N/A	N/A	N/A	1.80	1.02	1.44	0.72	0.36
40	0.82	1.35	N/A	N/A	N/A	N/A	1.43	0.82	1.15	0.57	0.29
45	N/A	N/A	0.57	0.96	0.59	1.59	1.27	0.72	1.02	0.51	0.27
50	0.60	1.04	N/A	N/A	N/A	N/A	1.15	0.66	0.92	0.46	0.23
60	N/A	N/A	0.38	0.70	0.41	1.12	N/A	N/A	N/A	N/A	N/A
63	0.46	0.82	N/A	N/A	N/A	N/A	0.91	0.51	0.73	0.36	0.18
80	0.31	0.57	0.28	0.50	N/A	N/A	0.72	0.41	0.57	0.29	0.14
100	0.23	0.42	0.19	0.36	0.19	0.53	0.57	0.32	0.46	0.23	0.11

Data reproduced courtesy of the IET (Previously the IEE)

Not all types of overcurrent protective devices are included in the data given in *BS 7671*. If a device is found in an installation that is **not** included in *BS 7671* the manufacturer of the device should be contacted, to obtain the maximum permitted value of Z_S.

The NICEIC guide to
Domestic Periodic Inspection, Testing and Reporting

3.10.11 Test instruments (serial numbers used)

At the bottom of the schedule, enter the serial number(s) of the test instrument(s) used for measuring continuity, insulation resistance, earth fault loop impedance, RCD disconnection times and earth electrode insulation resistance, as appropriate.

If any instrument does **not** have a serial number, a suitable number should be assigned and permanently marked on the instrument. Where a combined instrument such as an insulation/continuity test instrument is used to carry out more than one type of test, the serial number of that instrument should be repeated in the space corresponding to each of the relevant types of test.

Where a multi-functional test instrument has been used to carry out the required tests, the serial number should be entered in the multi-functional box with a line through the remaining relevant boxes.

Enter N/A if a particular type of test instruments is not applicable (and therefore is not used). For example if no RCD or earth electrode is installed there is no need to use an RCD test instrument or earth electrode resistance test instrument respectively.

3.11 Test results

The section 'N Test Results' for each outgoing circuit must be entered in the body of the schedule, in the same rows and in the same order as the corresponding circuits on section 'M Circuit Details' of the schedule (see item 3.10), to enable the results to be read in conjunction with each other.

The method for carrying out each test in this item is described in Chapter 5. The information to be entered under each column heading is discussed in items 3.11.1 to 3.11.7.

SCHEDULES

N TEST RESULTS

Maximum Z_s permitted by BS 7671 (Ω)	Circuit impedances (Ω) Ring final circuits only (measured end to end) r₁ (Line)	r_n (Neutral)	r₂ (cpc)	All circuits (At least one column to be completed) R₁+R₂	R₂	Insulation resistance Line/Line (MΩ)	Line/Neutral (MΩ)	Line/Earth (MΩ)	Neutral/Earth (MΩ)	Polarity (✓)	Maximum measured earth fault loop impedance, Z_s (Ω)	RCD operating times at $I_{\Delta n}$ (ms)	at 5 $I_{\Delta n}$ (if applicable) (ms)
9.58	N/A	N/A	N/A	N/A		N/A	N/A	6.3	6.3	N/A	N/A	N/A	N/A
9.58	N/A	N/A	N/A	N/A		N/A	N/A	N/A	N/A	N/A	N/A	N/A	N/A
2.55	N/A	N/A	N/A	1.3		N/A	N/A	6.3	6.3	✓	1.61	N/A	N/A
2.55	N/A	N/A	N/A	1.16		N/A	N/A	6.3	6.3	✗	1.47	N/A	N/A
2.19	N/A	N/A	N/A		N/A	N/A	N/A	N/A	N/A	N/A	N/A	N/A	N/A
1.09	0.55	0.5	0.38*	0.33		N/A	N/A	6.3	6.3	✓	0.84	N/A	N/A
1.09	N/A	N/A	N/A		0.21	N/A	N/A	6.3	6.3	✓	0.81	N/A	N/A

Note: Line and neutral conductors of the final circuits were temporarily connected together, and the insulation resistance measured between this connection and Earth, to prevent damage to electronic equipment connected to final circuits.

(Right margin: Original (To the person ord...) / 0 (Other – please state) / H Mineral-insulated cables*)*

unit(s)	CU₁	Prospective fault current at consumer unit(s)	16	kA

Earth electrode resistance	N/A, as no earth electrode fitted	Earth fault loop impedance	———	RCD	N/A, as no RCD fitted

* Note: For circuit 6, the value of 0.38 ohm of the end-to-end ring circuit protective conductor resistance would in general be greater than the value of 0.55 ohm of the line conductor end-to-end ring resistance. However, since parallel gas and water installation metal pipework connected between electrical equipment connected at different points on the ring circuit (producing a parallel path to the cpc), and mixed sized cpc cross-sectional areas were present, the value of the cpc end-to-end ring circuit resistance was less than that of the line conductor end-to-end ring circuit resistance.

3.11.1 Circuit impedance – ring final circuits only (r_1, r_n, and r_2)

For each ring circuit use the procedure given in item 5.10.4 to confirm the continuity of the ring circuit conductors.

Enter the resistance, measured from end to end in units of ohms:

- line conductor ring (r_1),

- neutral conductor ring (r_n), and

- the circuit protective conductor ring (r_2).

For circuits other than ring final circuits, enter 'N/A' meaning 'Not applicable' in each of the three columns (r_1, r_n, and r_2).

3.11.2 Circuit impedance – final circuits ($R_1 + R_2$)

If the '$R_1 + R_2$' test is used (see item 5.10.1) to measure the final circuit line and circuit protective conductor resistance, enter the maximum value of measured resistance, in units of ohms (Ω), in the box. Otherwise leave the box blank.

If this test is not applicable to a circuit, such as where Z_s is measured at an appropriate socket-outlet using an earth fault loop impedance tester (see item 5.15.2), enter 'N/A' in the box.

Note: An entry in at least one of the two columns, ($R_1 + R_2$) or (R_2) is necessary for all circuits including ring final circuits.

3.11.3 Circuit impedance – final circuits (R_2)

If the circuit protective conductor (R_2) resistance is measured using the 'R_2' (wander lead) method (described in item 5.10.2) enter the maximum value of R_2 in the box, in units of ohms (Ω). Otherwise leave the box blank.

If this test is not applicable, such as where '$R_1 + R_2$' is measured and used to calculate Z_s on a circuit without socket-outlets (see item 5.15.1), enter 'N/A'.

SCHEDULES

3.11.4 Insulation resistance

For each final circuit enter the measured values of insulation resistance (see item 5.11), in units of millions of ohms (MΩ), in the following columns:

1   Line/Line (Enter N/A, instead of the measured value, if the preferred method described below is used)

2   Line/Neutral (Enter N/A, instead of the measured value, if the preferred method described below is used)

3   Line/Earth (Enter the insulation resistance value between the temporarily connected Line(s)/Neutral and Earth, if the preferred method described below is used)

4   Neutral/Earth (Enter the insulation resistance value between the temporarily connected Line(s)/Neutral and Earth, if the preferred method described below is used).

The **preferred** method (after isolation of the main switch) of measuring insulation resistance may be made by connecting the insulation resistance test instrument leads between the 'Line(s)/Neutral load terminals of the consumer unit' and 'Earth' (see item 5.11.2).

One insulation resistance test instrument lead may be connected to a temporary connection, made between the 'line(s)' and 'neutral' load terminals, using a short circuiting lead (which, for example, may be made from shrouded crocodile clips connected at each end of a single-core cable).

The other insulation resistance test instrument lead may be connected to 'Earth' (typically at the main earthing terminal), and **not** just to the circuit protective conductor. This is because the insulation resistance between the 'line/neutral circuit conductors' and any metalwork (that may **not** form part of the installation) in contact with 'Earth' gets included in the measured value of resistance.

Using the **preferred** method of measurement helps to prevent over-voltage damage to equipment (such as appliances, heating controls or lighting dimmers) during

The NICEIC guide to
Domestic Periodic Inspection, Testing and Reporting

testing, and minimize disturbing final circuit connections. The measured value of insulation resistance should be entered in the Line/Earth and Neutral/Earth boxes. N/A should be entered in the Line/Neutral box. Furthermore, a note should be added to the schedule, to read something like, 'The line and neutral of the final circuits were connected together, and the insulation resistance measured between this connection and Earth' (see previous example in schedule section N).

If the measured insulation resistance exceeds the maximum range of the test instrument, record the measurement as 'greater than the maximum range' (for example, > 200 MΩ). Do **not** record the value as 'infinity'.

If in **exceptional** circumstances, the **preferred** method is **not** used, that is, insulation resistance is measured between live conductors. Then enter details in schedule section N as follows:

1   for a single-phase circuit, enter the appropriate measured resistance values in the Line/Neutral, Line/Earth and Neutral/Earth respective columns but in the Line /Line column enter 'N/A', or

2   for a 2-phase or 3-phase circuit, enter the **lowest** Line/Line, Line/Neutral and Line/Earth measured resistance values in the appropriate columns, and the Neutral/Earth measured resistance value.

3.11.5 Polarity

Enter a tick (✓) to indicate confirmation of correct polarity, throughout the circuit by testing, or a cross (✗) to indicate incorrect polarity.

In the event of incorrect polarity constituting a real and immediate danger, this would require immediate action before continuing with the inspection and testing (as is the case with any defect which poses a real and immediate danger). It may even warrant the issue of an Electrical Danger Notification form (see item 2.27).

SCHEDULES

3.11.6 Maximum measured earth fault loop impedance, Z_s

Enter the maximum measured value of earth fault loop impedance (Z_s), in units of ohms (Ω), at the point (or accessory) which is electrically most remote from the origin of the circuit.

The electrically most remote position of a point or accessory in a circuit may not be obvious. However, comparing earth continuity (R_2) test measurement values, using the 'R_2' test method (see item 5.10.2), at each point or accessory, may help to establish the most electrically remote position. That is, the position where the maximum value of R_2 is measured.

3.11.7 RCD operating times

In the left hand column, enter the operating (tripping) time, in milliseconds (ms), of any RCD which is in circuit. This test is carried out at a current equal to that of the rated residual operating current ($I_{\Delta n}$) of the RCD.

If an RCD protects a number of circuits, the RCD (on no load) should be tested by connecting the test instrument immediately downstream of the device (for example, at the load side terminals of the RCD), and the test currents and corresponding disconnection times recorded. Alternatively, the tests may be, more conveniently, carried out at a socket-outlet that is protected by the RCD.

The right-hand column is applicable only if the RCD has a rated residual operating current of 30 mA or less, and has been installed to provide 'additional protection'. This second test is carried out at a current of 5 $I_{\Delta n}$. Enter the RCD test operating time (if this test is applicable) or N/A if not applicable.

Information on RCD testing is given in item 5.16.

3.12 Continuation sheets

If there is inadequate space on schedules for entering information, continuation sheets will need to be used as appropriate.

Purpose made available continuation schedule sheets for Domestic Visual Condition Reports or Domestic Electrical Periodic Inspection Reports should be used (see Annexes B or C respectively) as appropriate. If purpose-made continuation sheets are **not** available, other suitable sheets should be used.

Continuation sheets need to be appropriately identified and include report page numbers. Furthermore, red ▌ or purple ▌ continuation sheets also need to include the report serial number.

3.13 Sketches

If necessary (or requested) for reference purposes, test measurement values, such as Z_s, R_1+R_2 or R_2 may be added next to accessories or lighting points shown on sketches (see item 2.29 and the following example).

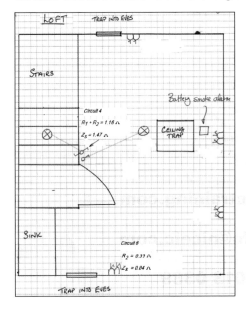

NICEIC TRAINING COURSES

All the courses to meet your training needs

Since its operation in 2004, NICEIC Training has become the UK's leading provider of Electrical Safety Training and Qualification.

We provide courses and qualifications through our nationwide network of centres on all aspects of Commercial, Industrial and Domestic Installations, including;

COMMERCIAL/INDUSTRIAL TRAINING AND QUALIFICATIONS

- Commercial & Industrial Periodic Inspection, Testing & Reporting
- Fire Alarm and Emergency Lighting

DOMESTIC TRAINING AND QUALIFICATIONS

- Domestic Periodic Inspection, Testing and Reporting
- Domestic Installer Scheme Qualification (DISQ)
- Mastering Inspection & Testing
- Completing Certification for Part P Domestic Installations

CITY AND GUILDS QUALIFICATIONS:

- Certificate in the Requirements for Electrical Installations
  (*BS 7671: January 2008*) – 2382-10
- Certificate in the Requirements for Electrical Installations Update
  (*BS 7671: January 2008*) – 2382-20
- Certificate in Fundamental Inspection, Testing and Initial Verification – 2392-10
- Certificate in Inspection, Testing and Certification of Electrical Installations – 2392-20
- Certificate in Design, Erection and Verification of Electrical Installations – 2392-30
- Portable Appliance Testing (PAT) - 2377-01

IN-COMPANY/BESPOKE COURSES:

If you wish to train a number of your own staff or you would like a course tailored to your specific needs, we will be happy to help. NICEIC Training has developed several bespoke courses to clients on-site who also include Local Authorities and Housing Associations.

For further information please visit
www.niceictraining.com.
You can contact us on email
traininginfo@niceic.com
or ring our National Helpline number on
0870 013 0389

**The NICEIC guide to
Domestic Periodic Inspection, Testing and Reporting**

INSPECTION

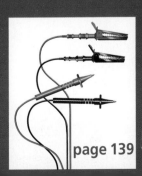

An NICEIC publication © Electrical Safety Council (JAN 2008)

INSPECTION

4.1 General

Before an installation is tested, it is necessary to carry out a careful and thorough inspection using the senses of sight, hearing, smell and touch. Such inspection may reveal deficiencies that are unlikely to be detected by testing, such as incomplete enclosures, damaged accessories and cable sheaths, unsuitable erection and installation methods, overheating, absence of fire barriers, and adverse external influences.

An inspection may follow the sequence embodied in the 'schedule of items inspected' included in the appropriate:

- Domestic Visual Condition Report (see items 3.2 to 3.7), or

- Domestic Electrical Installation Periodic Inspection Report (see items 2.25 and 3.8).

In general, the following items supplement the information contained in the 'schedules of items inspected'.

4.2 Safety

Wherever possible, inspection should be carried out when the installation is **not** energized, in accordance with the *Electricity at Work Regulations* (see item 1.5.1). Where written information about the installation is **not** available, as is likely in most cases, a degree of exploratory work will be necessary to enable the inspection and subsequent testing to be carried out safely.

4.3 Accessible live equipment parts

Accessible live equipment parts may be found during an inspection. For example, an inspector may isolate the circuit-breaker supplying the final circuit of an accessory being inspected, but find an energized (live) exposed conductor at the accessory (when proving if the final circuit is dead). The conductor might be live due to a wiring fault or a defective isolating device. In such a situation an inspector working alone

The NICEIC guide to
Domestic Periodic Inspection, Testing and Reporting

might have to leave the live conductor unattended to isolate the whole installation by means of the main switch. This might be a source of danger to persons or pets in the vicinity of the exposed live conductor.

Such risks (and appropriate protective measures) need to be considered as part of the risk assessment (see item 1.7.4). Furthermore, issues relating to lone working (see item 1.7.6) or the control of persons or pets need to be agreed with the client before (see item 1.11), and if necessary, during the inspection.

Wherever possible, the whole installation should be isolated using the main switch to prevent access to exposed live parts during the inspection.

4.4   In-service inspection of an installation

Since electrical installations deteriorate with age, as well as with wear and tear (see item 2.1), every installation needs to be inspected at appropriate intervals during its service life to check that its condition is such that it is safe to remain in service, and is likely to remain so at least until the next inspection is given in item 2.4.

4.5   Sequence of inspection

The overall sequence of inspection and testing is given in item 1.12.

The detailed sequence of items to be inspected, based generally on the items embodied in the report schedule (see item 4.1), may follow the remaining items of this chapter. However, it may **not** always be appropriate to follow such a sequence of inspection.

4.6   Methods of protection against electric shock

A visual check is required to verify that basic protection and fault protection provisions against electric shock have been implemented to meet the requirements of *BS 7671*.

INSPECTION

4.6.1 Terminology

Basic Protection – means protection against electric shock under fault-free conditions. This term replaces the term **Direct Contact** – which meant coming into contact with parts of electrical equipment intended to be live in normal use. It included touching un-insulated live conductors, and coming into contact with live parts because an enclosure is damaged or otherwise provides an inadequate barrier.

Fault Protection – means protection against electric shock under single fault conditions. This term replaces the term **Indirect Contact** – which meant coming into contact with exposed-conductive-parts of electrical equipment which have become live as the result of an earth fault.

A protective measure, as described in *BS 7671*, must consist of:

- an appropriate combination of a provision for basic protection and an independent provision for fault protection, or

- an enhanced protective provision which provides both basic protection and fault protection.

Additional Protection – is specified as part of a protective measure under certain conditions of external influences and in certain special locations. Such protection may be provided by an RCD or supplementary equipotential bonding, depending on the requirements of the specific Regulations (see item 4.6.12).

In each part of an installation one or more protective measures should have been been applied, taking into account the conditions of external influence. The following protective measures are generally permitted by *BS 7671* and are applicable to an electrical installation in a domestic dwelling.

Automatic Disconnection of Supply (ADS)

Where:

- Basic protection is provided by basic insulation of live parts or by barriers or enclosures, and

- Fault protection is provided by protective earthing, equipotential bonding and automatic disconnection in case of a fault. Circuit protective devices, such as fuses and circuit-breakers, must be coordinated to enable a fault to earth to be disconnected in the required time.

The NICEIC guide to
Domestic Periodic Inspection, Testing and Reporting

Basic protection by basic insulation

Fault protection by protective earthing, equipotential bonding and automatic disconnection of supply

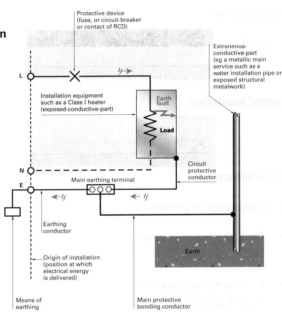

Double or reinforced insulation

Double or reinforced insulation is provided where:

- Basic protection is provided by basic insulation of live parts and fault protection is provided by supplementary insulation, or
- Basic and fault protection are provided by reinforced insulation between lives parts and accessible parts.

An NICEIC publication © Electrical Safety Council (JAN 2008)

INSPECTION

Double or reinforced insulation must not be used as the sole protective measure (i.e. where a whole installation or circuit is intended to consist entirely of equipment with double insulation or reinforced insulation) unless that installation or circuit is under effective supervision in normal use. Therefore, this protective measure should not normally be used as the sole protective measure for an installation or circuit in a domestic dwelling.

Double insulation

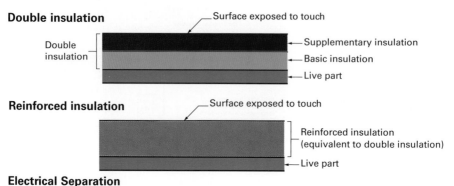

Electrical Separation

Electrical separation is provided where:

- Basic protection is provided by basic insulation of live parts or by barriers or enclosures, and

- Fault protection is provided by simple separation of the separated circuit and from Earth. The voltage of the separated circuit must not exceed 500 V. Live parts of the separated circuit must not be connected at any point to another circuit or to Earth or to a protective conductor.

Extra-low voltage provided by SELV or PELV

Both basic protection and fault protection is deemed to be provided if:

- the nominal voltage is limited to 50 V a.c. or 120 V d.c., and

- the supply is a SELV or PELV source (Regulation 413.4), and

- there is basic insulation between live parts and other SELV and PELV circuits, and protective separation from all circuits other than SELV or PELV.

The NICEIC guide to
Domestic Periodic Inspection, Testing and Reporting

Electrically separated system

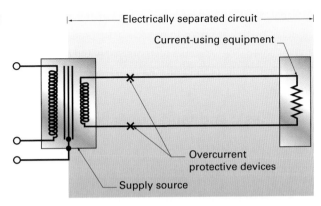

SELV

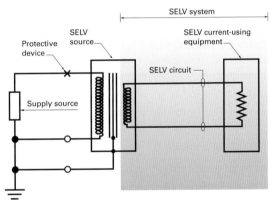

PELV

Note: it is unlikely that the protective measure 'extra-low voltage by PELV' will apply to an electrical installation in a domestic dwelling. Therefore no further information relating to PELV systems is given in this book. Further information on PELV systems can be found in the NICEIC publication *Inspection, Testing and Certification*.

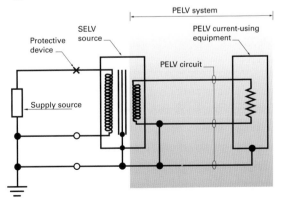

INSPECTION

A visual check is required to verify that the protective measures and provisions intended by the designer to provide basic protection and fault protection have been implemented. The schedule of items inspected considers these under four headings: Basic and fault protection, Basic protection, Fault protection and Additional protection.

4.6.2 Basic and fault protection

The protective measures likely to be found in a domestic installation that can provide basic and fault protection are:

- SELV (Separated Extra-Low Voltage), or

- double or reinforced insulation.

Extra-Low voltage by SELV (Separated Extra-Low Voltage)

Inspection of this protective measure includes checking that the SELV source is suitable. Several types of source for a SELV system are recognized by *BS 7671*, but the most common likely to apply to an installation in domestic premise is a safety isolating transformer complying with a *BS EN 61558-2-6 – Safety of power transformers, power supply units and similar. Particular requirements for safety isolating transformers for general use.* This standard supersedes *BS EN 60742/BS 3535: Part 1*, to which earlier products may comply.

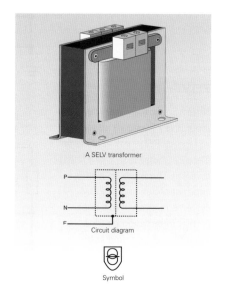

A SELV transformer

Circuit diagram

Symbol

Such a transformer has no connection to Earth on the secondary extra-low voltage winding and is designed to provide an output of no more than 50 V. Such transformers might be used as supply sources for door bells, luminaires or garden water features.

The NICEIC guide to
Domestic Periodic Inspection, Testing and Reporting

Double or reinforced insulation

Class II equipment does not rely on basic insulation only, but has additional safety precautions against electric shock by using double or reinforced insulation. The equipment has no provision for the connection of exposed metalwork to a protective conductor to be connected to the fixed wiring of the installation.

In general, in whole or part installations of domestic premises, only **individual** items of Class II (or equivalent insulation) equipment, such as luminaires or space heaters, are used.

It is to be expected that most equipment providing this protective measure will comprise type-tested items, marked to the appropriate standards. The inspector should 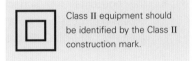 Class II equipment should be identified by the Class II construction mark.

check the markings on such equipment to see that it has double or reinforced insulation (Class II equipment). A check should also be made that Class II protection has not been impaired by the method of installing the equipment.

Whatever the type of equipment providing protection by Class II or equivalent insulation, the inspector should also check that the installation complies with the requirements of Regulations 412.2.1 to 412.2.4 which address the provisions for basic and fault protection by Class II equipment or by equivalent insulation.

4.6.3 Basic protection

Provision of basic protection likely to found in installations in domestic premises are:

- Insulation of live parts, and
- Barriers or enclosures.

Basic insulation of live parts

An inspection of the parts that will be live in service is required to verify that all the necessary insulation is present, has not been damaged during construction or use, and is in a sound and serviceable condition.

INSPECTION

Barriers or enclosures

An understanding of *BS EN 60529: Specification for degrees of protection provided by enclosures (IP code)*, and of the particular requirements of *BS 7671*, is required for the inspection of barriers or enclosures. However, for a domestic installation, the basic requirements are that:

- barriers or enclosures containing live parts must provide a degree of protection against solid objects of at least IP2X or IPXXB, with certain exceptions (Regulation 416.2.1)

- the horizontal top surface of a barrier or enclosure which is readily accessible must provide a degree of protection against solid objects of at least IP4X or IPXXD (Regulation 416.2.2).

Notes:

1 – **IP2X** means that the enclosure is protected against access to hazardous parts with a British Standard test finger having a diameter of 12 mm and 80 mm long, and will not permit the insertion of any object 12.5 mm or more in diameter.

2 – **IP4X** means that at no point on the surface must the insertion of a wire or object greater than 1 mm thick be possible.

3 – **X** indicates that no particular degree of protection against ingress of liquids has been specified. It does not necessarily mean that no such protection is provided.

In general, it should be possible for the inspector to confirm by thorough visual inspection that barriers and enclosures provide the necessary minimum degree of protection against the ingress of solid objects. In particular, it should be verified that all unused entries in enclosures have been closed, and that no blanks are missing from spare ways in consumer units.

The NICEIC guide to
Domestic Periodic Inspection, Testing and Reporting

International Protection (IP) Code

FIRST NUMERAL		SECOND NUMERAL	
a PROTECTION OF PERSONS AGAINST CONTACT WITH HAZARDOUS PARTS INSIDE ENCLOSURE		PROTECTION OF EQUIPMENT AGAINST INGRESS OF WATER	
b PROTECTION OF EQUIPMENT AGAINST INGRESS OF SOLID BODIES AND DUST			
No./ SYMBOL	**DEGREE OF PROTECTION**	**No./ SYMBOL**	**DEGREE OF PROTECTION**
0	a No special protection. b No special protection.	**0**	No special protection.
1	a Protection against accidental or inadvertent contact by a large surface of the body, e.g. hand, but not against deliberate access. b Protection against ingress of large solid objects of 50 mm diameter and greater.	**1**	Protection against drops of water. Drops of water falling on enclosure shall have no harmful effect.
2	a Protection against contact by standard finger (12 mm in diameter and 80mm in length). b Protection against ingress of solid objects of 12.5 mm diameter and greater.	**2**	**Drip Proof:-** Protection against water. Vertically dripping water shall have no harmful effect when the enclosure is tilted at any angle up to 15° from the vertical.
3	a Protection against contact by tools, wires or suchlike of 2.5 mm diameter. b Protection against ingress of solid objects of 2.5 mm diameter and greater.	**3**	**Rain Proof:-** Water falling as rain at any angle up to 60° from vertical shall have no harmful effect.
4	a As 3 above but against contact by wires of 1 mm diameter. b Protection against ingress of small foreign bodies of 1mm diameter and greater.	**4**	**Splash Proof:-** Water splashed from any direction shall have no harmful effect.
5	a As 4 above. b DUSTPROOF:- Protection against harmful deposits of dust. Dust may enter but not in amount sufficient to interfere with satisfactory operation.	**5**	**Jet Proof:-** Water projected by a nozzle from any direction (under stated conditions) shall have no harmful effect.
6	a As 4 above. b DUST-TIGHT No ingress of dust.	**6**	**Watertight Equipment:-** Protection against conditions on ships decks, etc. Water from heavy seas or power jets shall not enter the enclosures under prescribed conditions.
IP CODE NOTES - Degree of protection is stated in form IPXX. - Protection against contact or ingress of water respectively is specified by replacing first or second X by a digit number tabled. For example, IP2X defines an enclosure giving protection against finger contact but without any specific protection against ingress of water or liquid.		**7**	**Protection Against Immersion in Water:-** It shall not be possible for water to enter the enclosure under stated conditions of pressure and time.
		8	**Protection Against Indefinite Immersion in Water Under Specified Pressure:-** It shall not be possible for water to enter the enclosure, to harmful effect.

N.B. - Use this table for General Guidance only - refer to BS EN 60 529: 1992 for full information on degrees of protection provided by enclosures.

INSPECTION

In general, equipment in a location containing a bath or shower is required to have the following degree of protection against ingress of water:

- Zone 0: IPX7 (protected against the effects of temporary immersion in water)

- Zones 1 and 2: IPX4 (protected against splashing water)

- Areas exposed to water jets, for example, as used for cleaning purposes: IPX5 (protected against water jets)

    (Regulation 701.512.2 refers.)

In a location containing a bath or shower, wherever possible, the inspector should refer to the IP reference marked on the equipment, to identify its degree of protection against water.

Additional information is shown on IP codes for ease of reference.

4.6.4 Fault protection

The two provisions likely to be found in a domestic installation that can provide fault protection are:

- Protective earthing, equipotential bonding and automatic disconnection of supply in case of a fault, as explained in item (4.6.5), or

- Electrical Separation (see item 4.6.11).

4.6.5 Protective earthing, equipotential bonding and automatic disconnection of supply

Protective earthing, equipotential bonding and automatic disconnection of supply, previously known as EEBAD, is applied in accordance with the requirements for the type of system earthing used, which for a domestic installation is likely to be either a TN-S, TN-C-S or TT system as explained in item 2.25.2.

Under earth fault conditions, protective earthing, equipotential bonding and automatic disconnection of supply limits the duration of voltages (sometimes called touch voltages) between exposed-conductive-parts, extraneous-conductive-parts and/or Earth (the general mass of Earth) in an installation, by causing the automatic disconnection of the supply to the faulty circuit within the time specified in *BS 7671*. This is achieved by adequate fault current causing the relevant protective device(s) such as a fuse, circuit-breaker or residual current device, to operate. Fault current is equal to the nominal voltage divided by the earth fault loop impedance.

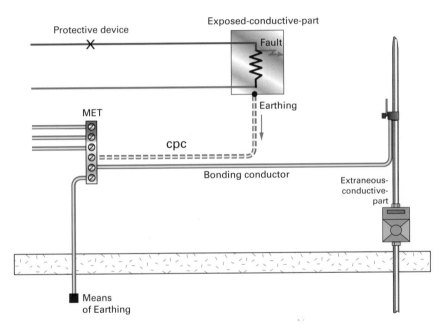

Example of protective device and protective conductors under earth fault conditions

Where protective earthing, equipotential bonding and automatic disconnection of supply is used for fault protection the following checks need to be included in the inspection:

- presence and cross-sectional area of the:

  - earthing conductor, explained in item 4.6.6

  - circuit protective conductors (cpc), explained in item 4.6.7

  - main protective bonding conductors, explained in item 4.6.8

INSPECTION

- choice and setting of protective devices (for fault protection and/or overcurrent), as explained in item 4.6.10

Example of earthing and bonding in a domestic installation

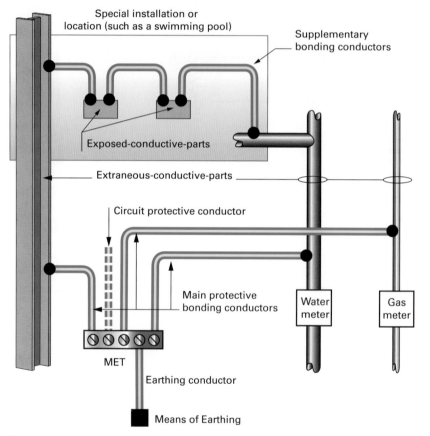

Notes:

1   An electrically-powered radiator is often another exposed-conductive-part found in a location (such as a bathroom) that should be bonded.

2   Isolated metallic items, such as hand rails or window frames do not require bonding, unless they introduce an earth potential (that is. they are exposed-conductive-parts).

The NICEIC guide to
Domestic Periodic Inspection, Testing and Reporting

4.6.6 Presence and cross-sectional area of earthing conductor

The earthing conductor is the protective conductor which connects the Main Earthing Terminal (MET) of the installation to the means of earthing (such as the installation earth electrode for a TT system, as shown in the following illustration). The earthing conductor is a vitally important part of the earth fault loop, and it must be confirmed by inspection that the conductor is present and properly connected.

Example of an earthing conductor in a TT system connected between the MET and the earth electrode

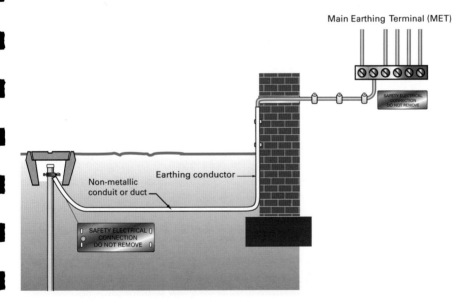

Main Earthing Terminal (MET)

SAFETY ELECTRICAL
CONNECTION
DO NOT REMOVE

Earthing conductor

Non-metallic
conduit or duct

SAFETY ELECTRICAL
CONNECTION
DO NOT REMOVE

The inspection must also confirm that the earthing conductor has a cross-sectional area of at least that required by *BS 7671*. Testing alone is not sufficient to determine that the earthing conductor has been correctly selected and installed.

INSPECTION

The minimum cross-sectional area of the earthing conductor should be in accordance with Table 54.7 of *BS 7671*. Additionally, where the earthing conductor is buried in the ground, its cross-sectional area must be **not** less than that given in Table 54.1 of *BS 7671*. These tables have been reproduced below for ease of reference.

Part Table 54.7 of *BS 7671* – Minimum cross-sectional area of protective conductor in relation to the cross-sectional area of associated line conductor

Cross-sectional area of line conductor (S)	Minimum cross-sectional area of corresponding protective conductor if it is the same material as the line conductor*
(mm²)	(mm²)
S ≤ 16	S
16 < S ≤ 35	16
S > 35	S/2

Table courtesy of the IET

* If the material of the protective conductor is different to the line conductor, multiply the minimum cross-sectional area given in this column by the line conductor value of k (see Table 43.1 of *BS 7671*), and divide the result by the protective conductor value of k (see Tables 54.2 to 6).

Table 54.1 of BS 7671 – Minimum cross-sectional areas of a buried earthing conductor

	Protected against mechanical damage	Not protected against mechanical damage
Protected against corrosion by a sheath	2.5 mm² copper 10 mm² steel	16 mm² copper 16 mm² coated steel
Not protected against corrosion	25 mm² copper 50 mm² steel	

Table courtesy of the IET

If the cross-sectional area of the earthing conductor is less than that indicated in Table 54.7 (or Table 54.1, if applicable), the inspector should carry out a calculation using the adiabatic equation given in Regulation 543.1.3 to confirm its adequacy. A calculation example follows, which is based on the earthing conductor size used in the example report shown in item 2.25.5 and the other conditions of that installation.

Example calculation to determine the minimum cross-sectional area of an earthing conductor

Problem

A TN-S installation (with a single-phase supply) has a single-core copper earthing conductor with a 6 mm² cross-sectional area without mechanical protection. However, the cross-sectional area of the copper line conductor (S) is 16 mm². Therefore, by selection, the 2nd column of Table 54.7 of BS 7671 requires the earthing conductor to have minimum cross-sectional area of 16 mm². How do I calculate the minimum cross-sectional area to see if the existing 6 mm² cross-sectional area of the earthing conductor is adequate?

Solution

Using the formula in Regulation 543.1.3 which follows:

$$S = \frac{\sqrt{I^2 t}}{k}$$

Where:

S   is the **minimum** nominal cross-sectional area of the earthing conductor, in mm²

I   is the earth fault current in amperes (calculated by dividing the nominal voltage, in volts, by the earth fault loop impedance (Z_s), in ohms)

t   is the operating time of the device, in seconds, corresponding to the fault current I amperes

k   is a factor taking into account the conductor material.

INSPECTION

The values for entering into the previous formula are determined as follows:

I – it is known that the installation has a nominal voltage of 230 volts and a Z_s of 0.29 ohms therefore, $I = \dfrac{230}{0.29} = 793.1$ amperes (A). However, Z_s was measured at around 20 °C but the fault current will decrease during the fault period, due to the resistance of the earthing conductor increasing with rising temperature of the conductor under fault conditions. I is divided by a factor of 1.04[1] to compensate for the temperature rise of the conductor during the fault period. The temperature corrected value of $I = \dfrac{793.1}{1.04} = 763$ A.

Note: If a supply is three-phase, the single-phase current (I) is doubled in value.

t – it is known that the installation has a 60 A rated BS 1361 type II fuse. Therefore, from the fuse characteristic in Fig 3.1 of Appendix 3 in BS 7671, it can be seen that a 60 A fuse will operate in 0.18 seconds(s) at a fault current of 763 A. Hence, $t = 0.18$ s. Where the required information about the protective device is not known, this can usually be obtained from the distributor, as explained in item 2.25.3.

k – from Table 54.2 in BS 7671, for a protective copper conductor not incorporated in a cable or not bunched with cables where the assumed initial temperature is 30 °C, the value of k is 143.

Note: *Where a protective copper conductor is incorporated in a cable or bunched with cables where the assumed initial temperature is 70 °C or greater, the value of k is 115 (as Table 54.3 of BS 7671).*

Entering the above values in the formula gives $S = \dfrac{\sqrt{763^2 \times 0.18}}{143}$

$$S = \frac{\sqrt{582169 \times 0.18}}{143} = \frac{324}{143}$$

$S = 2.3$ mm^2

---

[1] The factor of 1.04 is explained in Table E2 in Annex E of this guide.

The NICEIC guide to
Domestic Periodic Inspection, Testing and Reporting

*Regulation 543.1.1 requires a single-core copper earthing conductor without mechanical protection to have a **minimum** cross-sectional area of 4 mm². However, since the cross-sectional area of the installed 6 mm² earthing conductor is greater than both 2.3 mm² and 4 mm², it is adequate in size to comply with both Regulations 543.1.3 and 543.1.1.*

4.6.7 Presence and cross-sectional area of circuit protective conductors (cpc)

A visual inspection must be made to check that circuit protective conductors are correctly selected and installed to comply with Section 543 of *BS 7671*.

Circuit protective conductors may be separate or incorporated in cables, or be formed by metallic cable sheath or armouring. Metallic enclosures such as conduit, trunking and so on may also be used provided that the installation satisfies the requirements of Section 543 of *BS 7671*, in terms of continuity, cross-sectional area and reliability.

In older installations (pre 1966) the inspector may find lighting circuits without circuit protective conductors. An appropriate observation and recommendation code should be included on the report.

Information on unearthed lighting circuits is given in The Electrical Safety Council's *Best Practice Guide to replacing a consumer unit where lighting circuits have no protective conductor.*

4.6.8 Presence and cross-sectional area of main protective bonding conductors

Presence of main protective bonding conductors

Main protective bonding conductors (also known as main bonding conductors) are bonding conductors connecting the main earthing terminal of the installation to extraneous-conductive-parts, which may include:

- water installation pipes
- gas installation pipes

INSPECTION

- other installation pipework and ducting

- central heating and air conditioning systems

- exposed metallic structural parts of buildings

- lightning protection (see section at end of this item).

Presence of main protective bonding conductors

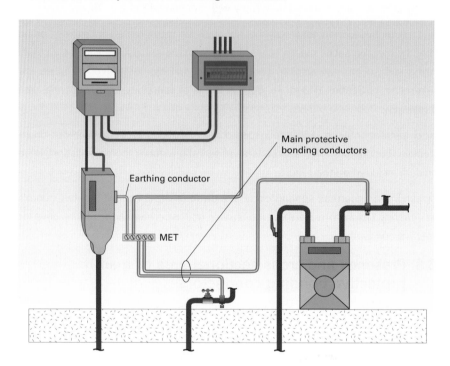

The NICEIC guide to
Domestic Periodic Inspection, Testing and Reporting

Cross-sectional area of main protective bonding conductors

Except where Protective Multiple Earthing (PME) conditions apply, the cross-sectional area of protective bonding conductors must be not less than half the cross-sectional area required by *BS 7671* for the earthing conductor, with a minimum of 6 mm^2. The cross-sectional area need not be more than 25 mm^2 if the bonding conductor is of copper. If the bonding conductor is not copper, its cross-sectional area must be such that its conductance is **not** less than that of the required size of copper conductor.

Cross-sectional area of protective bonding conductors for an installation forming part of a protective multiple earthing (PME) system (a TN-C-S system)

For an installation forming part of a PME system (a TN-C-S system), the cross-sectional area of the protective bonding conductors must be not less than that given in Table 54.8 of *BS 7671* (see below).

Part Table 54.8 of *BS 7671* – Minimum cross-sectional area of the main protective bonding conductor in relation to the neutral of the supply, for a PME system (a TN-C-S system)

Note: Local distributor's network conditions may require a larger conductor

Copper equivalent cross-sectional area of the supply neutral conductor	Main copper equivalent* cross-sectional area of the main protective bonding conductor
35 mm^2 or less	10 mm^2
Over 35 mm^2 up to 50 mm^2	16 mm^2
Over 50 mm^2 up to 95 mm^2	25 mm^2

Table data courtesy of the IET

* The minimum copper equivalent cross-sectional area is given by a copper bonding conductor of the tabulated cross-sectional area or a bonding conductor of another metal affording equivalent conductance.

INSPECTION

The cross-sectional areas of main protective bonding conductors shown in Table 54.8 are the minimum sizes permitted for a PME system (a TN-C-S system). As the note above that table, the electricity distributor may require a larger cross-sectional area in some instances. Therefore, the inspector should seek specific advice from the electricity distributor to confirm if a larger conductor cross-sectional area, to that shown in the table, is required or not.

Where the inspector finds that the main protective bonding conductors have a cross-sectional area of say 6 mm², rather than (say) 10 mm² as required by *BS 7671* or by the distributor, the inspector may, having carefully considered all the circumstances, conclude that the deficiency does not pose a serious risk to the users. For example, where the installation has been modified by an addition or alteration, and where the existing main equipotential bonding satisfies the requirements of *BS 7671* except in terms of cross-sectional area and colour-coding. However, the deficiency must be recorded, together with the reasons why the inspector has concluded that the deficiency does not pose a serious risk to the users and an appropriate recommendation, on the Periodic Inspection Report.

This dispensation is NOT applicable to an existing installation served by a PME supply which was commenced, or in certain cases has been worked upon, by the electricity distributor on or after 1 October 1988. Even where a PME supply was commenced before this date, careful consideration should be given to any decision to rely on existing main protective bonding conductors with cross-sectional areas less than that required by Table 54.8 of *BS 7671*. There is always the possibility that main protective bonding conductors may have to carry network circulating currents continuously or for long periods.

Bonding installation pipes

In the case of an installation pipe, such as a gas or water pipe, the main protective bonding conductor should have been connected as near as practicable to the point at which the particular installation pipe enters the premises.

The main equipotential bonding connection should have been made on the consumer's installation hard metal pipework, on the consumer's installation side of

The NICEIC guide to
Domestic Periodic Inspection, Testing and Reporting

any meter (or insulating section) and before any installation branch pipework. Where practicable, the connection should be within 600 mm of the meter outlet union. Where the meter is external, the main equipotential bonding connection should be at the point(s) of entry of the service into the building (Regulation 544.1.2).

Lightning protection system bonding to the installation main earthing terminal

Lightning protection systems are unlikely to be found on domestic buildings, except perhaps a tall block of flats.

Exceptionally, where a lightning protection system exists, there may **not** be a requirement for bonding it to the main earthing terminal (MET), unless there is a risk of side flashing. Any bonding installed should meet the requirements of *BS EN 62305 – Protection against lightning*. The inspector should check if the lightning protection system is bonded to the installation MET, and if it is **not** bonded enter an appropriate observation and recommendation code in the report.

4.6.9 Adequate arrangements for secondary source(s) of energy

Where a supply to the installation is available from one or more secondary source of energy (as may be the case where a *microgeneration system*[2] has been installed), the inspector should check that adequate arrangements in terms of protection for safety are present, including appropriate provision for isolation, manual and automatic switching, and any necessary interlocking. The particular requirements for generators, including those used as parallel and standby sources, are given in Section 551 of *BS 7671*.

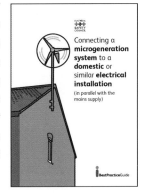

Connecting a **microgeneration system** to a **domestic** or similar **electrical installation** (in parallel with the mains supply)

BestPracticeGuide

---

[2] Information on microgeneration systems is given in The Electrical Safety Council's Best Practice Guide - *Connecting a microgeneration system to a domestic or similar electrical installation*.

INSPECTION

4.6.10 Choice and setting of protective devices (for fault protection and/or overcurrent)

This item is mainly concerned with fuses, circuit-breakers and residual current devices. The inspector should check that the current ratings and characteristics of the devices are suitable for the circuits that the devices protect.

For each fuse and circuit-breaker, a check should be made of not only the rated current but also the type (such as gG for a fuse to *BS 88-2.2* and *BS 88-6*, or Type B for a circuit-breaker to *BS EN 60898*[3]).

> *Check before withdrawing a semi-enclosed (rewireable) fuse that it does NOT have a length of live fuse wire accessible to touch (which has been incorrectly installed)*

A check should be made on rewireable fuses that the fuse link (fuse wire) matches the current rating of the fuse link carrier.

The NICEIC Technical Helpline is often asked if the continued use of rewireable fuses should be reported as a deficiency in a periodic inspection. The answer is no, provided that a rewireable fuse is suitable for the circuit that it protects and is undamaged (for example, free from deposits of burnt metal). However, householders generally prefer circuit-breakers, because they are easier (and safer) to reset compared with replacing the fuse wire in a rewireable fuse.

---

[3] Older installations may contain push-button operated *BS 3871* 'Type B' circuit-breakers, which have different characteristics to a *BS EN 60898* 'Type B' circuit-breaker. More recent installations may contain *BS 3871* Type 1, 2, 3 or 4 circuit breakers. Information on the older push-button operated *BS 3871* Type B circuit-breakers is given in Appendix F.

The NICEIC guide to
Domestic Periodic Inspection, Testing and Reporting

**Choice and setting of protective and monitoring devices –
Examples of devices which should be checked**

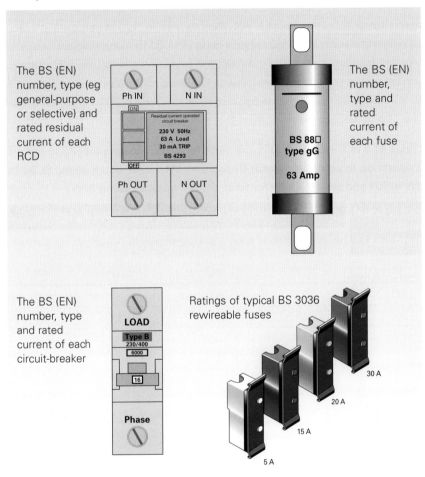

The BS (EN)
number, type (eg
general-purpose
or selective) and
rated residual
current of each
RCD

Ph IN   N IN

ON
Residual current operated circuit breaker
230 V 50Hz
63 A Load
30 mA TRIP
BS 4293
OFF

Ph OUT   N OUT

BS 88□
type gG

63 Amp

The BS (EN)
number,
type and
rated
current of
each fuse

The BS (EN)
number, type
and rated
current of each
circuit-breaker

LOAD
Type B
230/400
6000
16
Phase

Ratings of typical BS 3036
rewireable fuses

30 A
20 A
15 A
5 A

Note: Drawings not to scale.

INSPECTION

Presence of residual current devices (RCDs)

The inspector should verify the presence of any residual current devices (RCDs) necessary for earth fault protection. *BS 7671* requires an RCD to be provided in any circuit where the earth fault loop impedance is too high for earth fault protection to be provided by other means. For example, this is often the case with a TT system. In such cases, the maximum values of earth fault loop impedance given in Table 41.5 of *BS 7671* may be applied for non-delayed RCDs to *BS EN 61008* and *BS EN 61009* for final circuits not exceeding 32 A.

Part Table 41.5 of *BS 7671* – Maximum earth fault loop impedance (Z_s) to ensure RCD operation in accordance with Regulation 411.5.3 for non-delayed RCDs to *BS EN 61008* and *BS EN 61009* for final circuits not exceeding 32 A

Rated residual operating current (mA)	Maximum earth fault loop impedance Z_s (ohms)			
	$50\,V < U_o \leq 120\,V$	$120\,V < U_o \leq 230\,V$	$230\,V < U_o \leq 400\,V$	$U_o > 400\,V$
30	1667*	1667*	1533*	1667*
100	500*	500*	460*	500*
300	167	167	153	167
500	100	100	92	100

Table data courtesy of the IET

*   The resistance of the installation earth electrode should be as low as practicable. A value exceeding 200 ohms may not be stable. For example, in dry or freezing soil conditions (see Regulation 542.2.2)..

It should also be verified that where an RCD is used for earth fault protection in an installation forming part of a TT system it meets the requirement $Z_s\,I_{\Delta n} \leq 50\,V$, given in Regulation 411.5.3. The requirements of this regulation are deemed to be met if the earth fault loop impedance of the circuit protected by the RCD meets the requirements of Table 41.5 (see above).

Note: where an RCD is used to provide earth fault protection the circuit should also incorporate an overcurrent device, which must provide protection against overload and short-circuit current in accordance with Chapter 43 of BS 7671.

The inspector should check the presence of RCD protection against fire, where locations with particular risks of fire exist due to the nature of processed or stored materials (Regulation 422.3). For example, where an installation is in a location:

- containing combustible materials (such as hay in a barn or stable), or

- constructed of combustible materials (such as a wooden structured thatched cottage).

Where the above described fire risks exist, except where mineral insulated cables are installed, protection against insulation faults to earth in a TN or TT system should be provided by an RCD with a rated residual operating current ($I_{\Delta n}$) not exceeding 300 mA. Where a resistive fault may cause a fire, for example, for overhead heating with heating film elements, the rated residual operating current must not exceed 30 mA (Regulation 422.3.9).

Voltage-operated earth-leakage circuit-breakers

In 1981 voltage-operated earth-leakage circuit-breakers ceased to be recognized by *BS 7671*, as a protective device against electric shock. The reason being, that a parallel earth path (such as from a water service pipe) may prevent effective operation of the voltage device under earth fault conditions. Such a parallel earth path does not affect the operation of an RCD.

The inspector should report the presence of a voltage-operated earth-leakage circuit-breaker in the observations and recommendations part of the report, where an appropriate recommendation code should be entered.

Immersion heaters

It is estimated that there are about 20 million homes in the UK that have electric immersion heaters.

INSPECTION

Although in these days of central heating many of these immersion heaters will run only occasionally, failure of the thermostat in older systems having no over-temperature cut-out can lead to danger.

In particular, there have been cases where, due to the failure of a thermostat, water in the cylinder has been heated to boiling point, causing it to be discharged into the cold water storage tank via the open vent pipe.

Where the tank is constructed of plastic, the rise in water temperature can cause the tank material to soften. This in itself should not be a problem if the tank base is adequately supported, but there have been cases where the tank has slumped due to inadequate support, causing scalding water to cascade into the space below.

The risk of injury, or even death, from such an event is likely to be higher in homes that were built between 1945 and 1975 because, usually having been linked to back boilers, cisterns are more likely to be located over bedrooms.

Also, with older 'combi boiler' installations still utilizing a hot water cylinder, there is a risk that the hot water pipework would be unable to cope with the increase in system pressure if a faulty immersion heater caused water in the hot water cylinder to boil.

Regulation 554.2.1 of *BS 7671* requires that every heater for liquid or other substances must incorporate or be provided with an automatic device to prevent a dangerous rise in temperature.

Inspectors are requested to check immersion heaters for signs of overheating or thermostat defects (such as blueing or burning of terminals, deteriorated cable insulation). Other signs are condensation in the roof space, the cylinder being noisy (like a large kettle), cold water taps running warm or hot, and increased electricity bills.

If such signs are evident, the immersion heater does **not** comply with *BS EN 60335-2-73 – Specification for safety of household and similar electrical appliances. Particular requirements for fixed immersion heaters* and the cold water tank is plastic, make an appropriate observation and assign it a Recommendation Code 1 (requires urgent attention).

If **no** such signs are evident, the immersion heater does **not** comply with *BS EN 60335-2-73* and the cold water tank is plastic, make an appropriate observation and assign it a Recommendation Code 2 (requires improvement).

4.6.11 Electrical separation

Electrical separation is a protective measure that may be applied to circuits operating at a voltage of up to 500 V. It should not be confused with extra-low voltage systems, SELV or PELV.

Electrical separation is a protective measure in which:

1 basic protection is provided by basic insulation of live parts or by barriers or enclosures in accordance with section 416 of *BS 7671*. Inspection of these provisions should be carried out as previously identified earlier in this chapter.

2 fault protection is provided by simple separation of the separated circuit from other circuits and from Earth. The inspector should check that the requirements of Regulations 413.3.2 to 413.3.6 are met in order to establish that this is the case.

Particular attention should be given to checking the following.

- The separated circuit is supplied from a source of supply with at least simple separation. This could for example be a double-wound transformer the secondary winding of which is not earthed.

- That no live part is connected at any point to another circuit or to Earth, either deliberately or unintentionally, as could occur due to a damaged cable.

- Flexible cables and cords liable to mechanical damage are visible throughout their length.

INSPECTION

- The wiring comprises either a separate wiring system (preferably) or one of the alternatives given in Regulation 413.3.5 (such as suitable cables in insulating conduit), the rated voltage is not less than the highest nominal voltage, overcurrent protection is provided, and electrical separation from other circuits is provided – see Chapter 5 (testing).

Use of electrical separation to supply an individual item of equipment

Where electrical separation is used to supply an individual item of equipment, the inspector should verify that no exposed-conductive-part of the separated circuit, such as any metal casing of an item of equipment fed by the circuit, is connected to the protective conductor or exposed-conductive-parts of another circuit, or to Earth.

4.6.12 Additional protection

Presence of residual current devices (RCDs)

The inspector should check that additional protection has been provided by a residual current device (RCD) for the following, as required by Regulation 411.3.3:

1   Socket-outlets with a rated current not exceeding 20A that are for use by ordinary persons and are intended for general use, and

2   Mobile equipment with a current rating not exceeding 32 A for use outdoors.

An exception is permitted by Regulation 411.3.3 to (1) above, for a specific labelled or otherwise suitably identified socket-outlet provided for connection of a particular item of equipment, such as a fridge or freezer.

An RCD should not be relied upon as the sole means of protection against electric shock (Regulation 415.1.2). One or more other protection measures (see item 4.6.1) should also have been provided

Each RCD should be inspected to confirm that it has a rated residual operating current not exceeding 30 mA and that it meets a product standard which requires the device to operate under type-test conditions within 40 ms at a residual current of 5 $I_{\Delta n}$ (Regulation 415.1.1). The number of socket-outlets or items of equipment controlled by a single RCD should be such that the operation of that RCD does not result in unreasonable inconvenience in the event of a fault or, exceptionally, due to excessive protective conductor currents (Regulation 314.1).

Example of equipment used outdoors that should be connected to a socket-outlet having additional protection by an RCD

Presence and cross-sectional area of supplementary bonding conductors

The requirement for supplementary bonding is generally applicable only to installations and locations where there is an increased risk of electric shock. Some of these installations and locations are covered in Part 7 of *BS 7671*.

Supplementary equipotential bonding may be required for several of the locations and installations covered by Part 7. The most common of these locations in a domestic installation are rooms containing a bath or shower. It needs to be remembered that the particular requirements laid down in Part 7 of *BS 7671* **supplement** or **modify** the general requirements set out elsewhere in that Standard.

Where the circuit protective conductor in a short length of flexible cord has been used also to provide supplementary bonding to a fixed appliance as permitted by Regulation 544.2.5, it must be confirmed that a supplementary bonding conductor has been connected to the circuit protective conductor for that circuit, at the earthing terminal in the connection unit, or other accessory.

INSPECTION

The purpose of checking for the presence of supplementary bonding conductors in bathrooms and shower rooms, where required, is to confirm that exposed-conductive-parts, extraneous-conductive-parts and circuit protective conductors have been connected together with suitably sized and correctly colour-coded (green-and-yellow) supplementary bonding conductors as required by *BS 7671*. Some of the supplementary bonding may have been intended to be provided by extraneous-conductive-parts, subject to the requirements of Regulation 543.2.6 being met, such as:

- electrical continuity is assured, either by construction or suitable connection
- its cross-sectional area is adequate
- it cannot be removed
- it is suitable for use.

In other special installations or locations, such as a swimming pool the purpose is to check that supplementary bonding has been provided as required by the appropriate section in *BS 7671* (such as Section 702).

Assessing whether supplementary bonding is required for plastic pipework

In recent years there has been a significant increase in the use of plastic (non-conducting) pipework for hot and cold water installations and 'wet' central heating systems in domestic premises.

NICEIC is sometimes asked whether, in areas of a dwelling where additional protection: supplementary bonding may be required (usually only bathrooms and shower rooms), it is necessary to install supplementary bonding to metallic parts supplied by plastic water pipework. Examples of such metallic parts may include baths, radiators, taps, and short sections metallic pipework installed for cosmetic purposes.

The inspector will need to assess if the length of plastic pipe supplying a metallic part is sufficient so that its resistance will limit the shock current to 30 mA under earth fault conditions, supplementary bonding of the metallic part is **not** required.

In these circumstances, it is best **not** to supplementary bond the metallic part, as to do so would cause it to be at Earth potential, which would increase the risk of

The NICEIC guide to
Domestic Periodic Inspection, Testing and Reporting

electric shock due contact between a simultaneously accessible live part (with an earth fault) and Earth.

Minimum length of plastic pipe before supplementary bonding is not required

Some measurements of water resistance indicate the following values of resistivity:

- tap water of relatively low resistivity, $\rho = 5.78$ Ωm

- water doped with corrosion inhibitor $\rho = 2$ Ωm

To limit the shock current to 30 mA, the resistance of a plastic pipe and its contents, between a supplied metallic part and either Earth or metalwork connected to the main earthing terminal of the installation, must exceed 230 V/30 mA = 7.67 kΩ (assuming a nominal voltage U_0 of 230 V).

If resistance (R) of plastic pipe and contents is 7.67 kΩ or more, shock current is limited to 30 mA

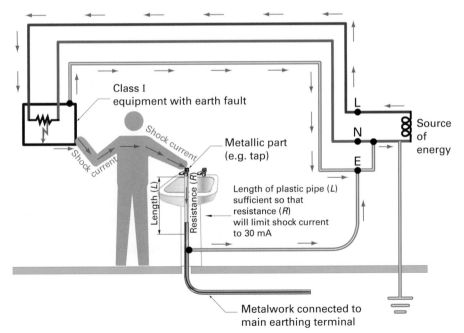

INSPECTION

Table 42 indicates the minimum length pipe, of 15 mm and 25 mm diameters, necessary to produce an impedance of 7.67 kΩ, so that the shock current will be limited to 30 mA.

Table 42 – Minimum lengths of water-filled plastic pipe to produce a resistance of 7.67 kΩ

Pipe diameter D (mm)	Water resistivity ρ (Ωm)	Minimum length L (m)
15 (13.5 internal)	5.78 (tap)	0.19
	2 (with inhibitor)	0.55
25 (23.5 internal)	5.78 (tap)	0.58
	2 (with inhibitor)	1.66

Notes:

1 $L = \dfrac{RA}{\rho} = \dfrac{\pi D^2 R}{4000\rho}$ where D is the internal diameter of the pipe in mm, R is the minimum allowed resistance of 7.67 kΩ, and ρ is the water resistivity in Ωm.

2 The values of L in the table are based on the following values of resistivity: $\rho = 5.78$ Ωm for water of relatively low resistivity, and $\rho = 2$ Ωm for water doped with corrosion inhibitor. Where it is known higher values of resistivity apply, lower values of L may be calculated using the formula in Note 1.

For a metallic part supplied by non-conducting (plastic) water pipework and having no electrical connection to Earth or the main earthing terminal of the installation (other than through the water in the pipe), supplementary bonding is not required if the following condition is met: The length of plastic pipe between the metallic part and either Earth or metalwork connected to the main earthing terminal of the installation is not less than the applicable value of L given in Table 42.

Supplementary equipotential bonding in a room containing a bath or shower

The requirements for providing supplementary equipotential bonding for final circuits in a room containing a bath or shower changed in *BS 7671: 2008*. In general, where all final circuits of the location containing a bath or shower:

The NICEIC guide to
Domestic Periodic Inspection, Testing and Reporting

- comply with the requirements for automatic disconnection according to Regulation 411.3.2, and

- have additional protection by means of an RCD having the characteristics of Regulation 415.1.1, and

- where all extraneous-conductive-parts are effectively connected to the protective equipotential bonding according to Regulation 411.3.1.2

then no supplementary bonding is required. (Regulation 701.415.2 refers)

4.7 Prevention of mutual detrimental influence

The requirements for prevention against mutual detrimental influence between electrical services and non-electrical services, or segregation/separation between Band I and Band II circuits is explained in items 4.7.1 and 4.7.2 respectively.

4.7.1 Proximity of non-electrical services and other influences

It should be verified that no destructive, damaging or harmful effects have occurred, are actually occurring, or are likely to occur, because of the proximity of any part of the electrical installation to non-electrical services or other influences. For example, it should be checked that:

- any heat, steam, smoke, fumes or condensation (such as may be produced by a central heating condensing boiler) is not likely to damage the electrical installation, or

- electrolytic corrosion is not likely to occur between dissimilar metal parts of the electrical installation and the building structure or mechanical plant which are in contact with each other in damp situations (such as may arise from a steel enclosure or conduit installed outdoors).

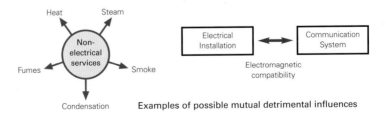

Examples of possible mutual detrimental influences

INSPECTION

Where the equipment or wiring of an electrical installation is in the vicinity of a communication or control system (such as a radio transmitter or intruder alarm system respectively), it should be checked that the relevant electromagnetic compatibility (EMC) requirements have been complied with, so that one system will not cause interference to the other. Regulations 515.3.1 and 515.3.2 require that equipment, when installed, will:

- be able to withstand interference levels present in the vicinity, and

- not interfere with other equipment in the vicinity.

4.7.2 Segregation of Band I and Band II circuits or Band II insulation used

It is necessary to verify by inspection that Band I and Band II circuits are separated or segregated from each other either by containment in separate wiring systems or by adopting a method of insulating (either individually or collectively) the Band I conductors for the highest voltage present, according to Regulation 528.1.

Voltage Band I covers installations where protection against electric shock is provided under certain conditions by the value of voltage. It extends also to installations where the voltage is limited for operational reasons such as in telecommunication, signalling, bell, control and alarm installations. Circuits operating at voltages not exceeding extra-low voltage (50 V a.c. or 120 V ripple-free d.c.) will normally fall within Band I.

Voltage Band II includes low-voltage supplies to domestic installations. Low voltage is defined as exceeding extra-low voltage but not exceeding 1000 V a.c. or 1500 V d.c. between conductors, or 600 V a.c. or 900 V d.c. between conductors and Earth.

Segregation or separation may be achieved in the following ways:

- By containment of a Band I circuit, insulated for its system voltage, in a separate conduit or trunking system.

- By containment of Band I and Band II circuits insulated for their respective system voltage in separate compartments of a common trunking or conduit system.

The NICEIC guide to
Domestic Periodic Inspection, Testing and Reporting

- By installation of Band I and Band II circuits where physical separation is provided by a partition.

- Where Band I and Band II circuits are contained in a common wiring system, by using circuit conductors all having an insulation rating suitable for the highest voltage present.

- Where Band I and Band II circuits are contained in a multicore cable or cord, by having the cores for Band I circuits suitably insulated for the highest voltage present, either individually or collectively. Alternatively, the cores of the Band I circuits must be separated from the Band II circuits by an earthed metal screen having a current-carrying capacity not less than that of the largest core of the Band II circuits.

Where outlets or controls for Band I and Band II circuits are mounted in or on a common box, block or switchplate of wiring systems formed by conduit or trunking, verification by inspection is required to check that the necessary segregation is maintained by an effective partition and that, where the partition is metal, it is earthed.

4.7.3 Segregation of safety circuits

Fire alarm systems are generally required by building regulations for new and refurbished domestic premises (see item 4.15). However, centralized emergency lighting system circuits are unlikely to be found in domestic premises, except where they may form part of a common landlord's system.

Fire alarm and centralized emergency lighting system circuits are required to be segregated from other circuits and from each other in accordance with *BS 5266* and *BS 5839.* This typically means separation by a distance of not less than 300 mm, by separate enclosures, by continuous partition(s) in a common channel or trunking (with separation being maintained at cross-overs and boxes etc), or by wiring such circuits in mineral insulated cable. Furthermore, *BS 5839 – 1: 2002 Fire Detection and Alarm Systems for Buildings* recognizes cables complying with *BS 7629 – Specification for 300/500 V fire resistant electric cables having low emission of smoke and corrosive gases when affected by fire. Multicore cables* as a means of separating conductors carrying fire alarm power and signals from conductors used for other systems. The segregation requirements also apply to the mains supply to fire alarm and emergency lighting systems.

INSPECTION

Though not directly related to segregation, it must be appreciated that *BS 5266* and *BS 5839* also contain specific requirements concerning the selection and erection of emergency lighting and fire alarm wiring systems respectively. The requirement is to provide both prolonged operation during a fire, and protection against mechanical damage. The electromagnetic compatibility requirements of Regulations 515.3.1 and 515.3.2 of *BS 7671* must also be satisfied. *BS 5839: Part 1* and *BS 5266: Part 1* contain requirements for segregation of the wiring of fire alarm and centralised emergency lighting systems.

If relevant, information on completing Emergency Lighting Periodic and Testing Certificates, and Fire Detection and Alarm System Inspection and Servicing Reports are explained in the NICEIC *Guide to Completing Specialized Certificates and Reports*.

4.8   Identification

The following items include information on appropriate diagrams, instructions, warning notices and labels.

4.8.1   Presence of diagrams, instructions, circuit charts and similar information

The presence of the necessary diagrams, charts or tables, as required by Regulation 514.9.1, or an equivalent form of information for the work being inspected, should be verified. The form of information should be legible and durable, and should indicate all of the following:

1   the type and composition of each circuit (that is, the points of utilization served, number and size of conductors, type of wiring)

2   the method used for compliance with Regulation 410.3.2 (that is, the protective measure(s) used for protection against electric shock)

3   the type of earthing arrangement for example TT, TN-S, TN-C-S, and the types and current ratings and/or rated residual currents of protective devices

The NICEIC guide to
Domestic Periodic Inspection, Testing and Reporting

4 the information necessary for the identification of each device performing the functions of protection, isolation and switching, and its location

5 any circuit or equipment vulnerable to a typical test.

The inspector may occasionally find most of the above information contained on a copy of the completed schedules of a Domestic Electrical Installation Certificate or Electrical Installation Certificate, fixed within or adjacent to the consumer unit.

4.8.2 Presence of danger notices and other warning notices

The inspector should verify that all relevant warning notices required by *BS 7671* have been fitted in the appropriate locations, and that they are durable and clearly visible. Examples of notices that may be required are as follows.

1 voltage warning (Regulation 514.10.1) – this warning is to be visible before gaining access to live parts in an enclosure where a nominal voltage exceeding 230 V to Earth exists and would **not** normally be expected.

2 isolation (Regulation 514.11.1) – Required at each position where there are live parts not capable of being isolated by a single device. The location of each isolating device must be indicated unless there is no possibility of confusion.

INSPECTION

3   Periodic inspection (Regulation 514.12.1) – To be fitted on completion of installation work (including alterations and additions) and on completion of each periodic inspection, in a prominent position at or near the origin, giving the recommended date by which the installation should be reinspected.

IMPORTANT
This installation should be periodically inspected and tested and a report on its condition obtained, as prescribed in the IEE Wiring Regulations BS 7671 Requirements for Electrical Installations.
Date of last Inspection
Recommended date of next inspection

This installation, or part of it, is protected by a device which automatically switches off the supply if an earth fault develops. Test quarterly by pressing the button marked 'T' or 'Test'. The device should switch off the supply and should then be switched on to restore the supply. If the device does not switch off the supply when the button is pressed, seek expert advice.

4   RCD (Regulation 514.12.2) – Required at the origin of an installation which incorporates one or more residual current devices. A similar notice may also be fitted adjacent to an RCD, wherever located.

5   Earthing and bonding (Regulation 514.13.1) – A notice should be fixed near the:

a   connection of an earthing conductor to an installation earth electrode (see illustration in item 4.6.6)

b   connection of a bonding conductor to an extraneous-conductive-part (see illustration below)

c   main earthing terminal, where it is separate from the consumer unit (see illustration opposite).

Connection of a bonding conductor to an extraneous-conductive-part

The NICEIC guide to
Domestic Periodic Inspection, Testing and Reporting

Main Earthing Terminal (MET) separate from the consumer unit (not shown)

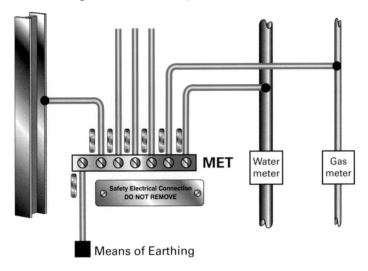

■ Means of Earthing

6   Non-standard colours (Regulation 514.14.1) – If wiring alterations, additions, extensions or repairs are made to an installation such that new wiring uses the latest harmonized colours and there is also wiring to previous editions of *BS 7671*, a warning notice must be fixed at or near the consumer unit, except were there is no possibility of confusion (see item 4.8.4).

CAUTION

This installation has wiring colours
to two versions of BS 7671.

Great care should be taken before
undertaking extension, alteration or repair
that all conductors are correctly identified.

NICEIC
DOMESTIC
INSTALLER

7   High protective conductor currents (Regulation 514.16) – In general, equipment in a domestic installation is unlikely to have a high protective conductor current (that is greater than 10 mA). Where a circuit has, or is likely to have, a high protective conductor current, information should be provided at the distribution board or

consumer unit indicating the circuit or circuits having or likely to have a high protective conductor current. Such information should be positioned so it is visible to a person modifying or extending the circuit (Regulation 543.7.1.5).

8   Dual supply (Regulation 514.15.1) – Where an installation includes a generating set (such a microgenerator), which is used as a secondary source of energy in parallel with the primary source of energy (the supply provided by the distributor), warning notices (see example in the illustration) must be provided and fixed at the following locations in the installation:

- at the origin of the installation
- at the meter position, if remote from the origin
- at the consumer unit, which the sources of energy connect
- at all points of isolation of the sources of energy.

4.8.3   Labelling of protective devices, switches and terminals

The inspector should verify the presence of suitable labelling or marking of protective devices, switches, terminals and the connections of conductors (where necessary). Labels and markings should be legible and durable.

Protective devices

Each fuse, circuit-breaker and residual current device should be checked to ensure that:

- it is arranged and identified so that the circuit protected may be easily recognized, and
- its rated current is indicated on or adjacent to it.

For protective devices incorporated in a distribution board, the above details may be given on the chart within or adjacent to it, provided the devices themselves are identified and arranged to correspond with the chart (see item 1.13).

Switches isolators and similar equipment

The inspector should verify that, except where there is no possibility of confusion, each switch isolator or similar equipment is labelled to indicate its purpose or circuit that it controls.

Example of a fan isolator

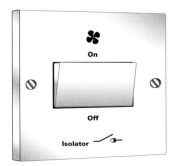

Terminals and connections

The inspector should verify that, so far as is reasonably practicable, the wiring is arranged and/or marked so that it may be readily identified for the purposes of inspection, testing, alteration and repair of the installation (Regulation 514.1.2).

Taking a consumer unit as an example, the wiring within the equipment should be identified by arrangement. This usually means connection of the neutral and cpc of each circuit to the terminals which relate specifically to the associated outgoing fuse or circuit-breaker, by sequence or terminal marking. Where the arrangement does not identify the wiring sufficiently well, for the purposes of the above regulation, the terminations of the conductors should be marked with codings such as '1, 2, 3' or '1L1, 1L2, 1L3' etc, as appropriate. Similarly, conductors connected to a main earthing terminal which is separate from the consumer unit should be identified by arrangement or marking.

INSPECTION

4.8.4 Identification of conductors

(Regulation Group 514.3 refers)

The correct identification of the conductors of cables, and of any bare conductors, in terms of their polarity or protective function, should be verified. This is in addition to the requirements for identification of terminals and connections referred to in item 4.8.3.

With certain permitted exceptions[4], cores of cables must be identified by colour and/or lettering and/or numbering. Every core of a cable must be identifiable at its terminations and preferably throughout its length. Binding or sleeves used for identification must comply with *BS 3858* where appropriate (Regulations 514.3.1, 514.3.2 and 514.6.1 refer). A marking *BS 3858: 1992* on the binding or sleeve is a claim by the manufacturer that it meets the requirements of that standard.

Marking types used to identify conductors may be found as follows.

Colour (installations, installed after March 2006)

Line conductors – For a single-phase installation where identification is to be by colour, the line conductors should be identified by the colour brown. For a three-phase installation where identification is by colour, the line conductors should be identified by the colours of brown, black and grey (Regulation 514.4.4).

Neutral conductors – Where a circuit includes a neutral conductor which is identified by colour, the colour must be blue (Regulation 514.4.1).

Protective conductors – The colours of green-and-yellow must be used for protective conductors and must not be used for any other purpose (Regulation 514.4.2). The single colour green must not be used (Regulation 514.4.5).

---

[4] The permitted exceptions are concentric conductors of cables, metal sheath or armour of cables where used as a protective conductor, certain bare conductors where identification is not practicable, extraneous-conductive-parts used as a protective conductor and exposed-conductive- parts used as a protective conductor (Regulation 514.6.1).

The NICEIC guide to
Domestic Periodic Inspection, Testing and Reporting

CHAPTER **4**

Lettering and/or numbering (installations, installed after March 2006)

Lettering and/or numbering must be in letters or Arabic numerals, must be clearly legible and durable and, in order to avoid confusion; unattached numerals 6 and 9 must be underlined. Where identification is by numbers, the number 0 (zero) is reserved for the neutral conductor (Regulation 514.5.4).

The identification of conductors is summarized in the following table, based on data from part of Table 51 in *BS 7671*, courtesy of the IET:

Bare conductors (installations installed after March 2006)

Bare conductors (for example, as used in decorative lighting suspended wire installations) must be identified, where necessary, by the application of a tape, sleeve, disc or paint, appropriately coloured as shown in Table 51 (Regulation 514.4.6).

Where a sheath of cable incorporating a protective conductor of cross-sectional area up to and including 6 mm^2 is removed adjacent to joints and terminations, the bare protective conductor is to be protected by insulating sleeving complying to *BS EN 60684* series (Regulation 543.3.2).

Older installations (before March 2006)

Single-phase installations – are identified, in general, by the colours of red, black and green-and-yellow for the line, neutral and protective conductors, respectively.

Three-phase installations – are identified by the colours of red, yellow and blue for the three line conductors; and black and green-and-yellow for the neutral and protective conductors, respectively.

Interface between conductors – Except where there is no possibility of confusion, unambiguous marking must be provided at the interface between conductors identified in accordance with *BS 7671* (the harmonized colours) and wiring to previous versions of the Regulations (the 'old' colours).

PART TABLE 51 - Identification of conductors

Function		Colour	Alpha numeric
Protective conductors		Green-and-yellow	
Functional earthing conductor		Cream	
a.c. power circuit[1]			
Line of single-phase circuit		Brown	L
Neutral of single- or three-phase circuit		Blue	N
Line 1 of three-phase circuit		Brown	L1
Line 2 of three-phase circuit		Black	L2
Line 3 of three-phase circuit		Grey	L3
Two-wire unearthed d.c. power circuit			
Positive of two-wire circuit		Brown	L+
Negative of two-wire circuit		Grey	L-
Two-wire earthed d.c. power circuit			
Positive (of negative earthed) circuit		Brown	L+
Negative (of negative earthed) circuit[2]		Blue	M
Positive (of positive earthed) circuit[2]		Blue	M
Negative (of positive earthed) circuit		Grey	L-
Control circuits, ELV and other applications			
Line conductor		Grey	L

	Brown		Orange	White
	Black		Yellow	Pink, or
	Red		Violet	Turquoise

Neutral or mid-wire[4]		Blue	N or M

NOTES: [1] Power circuits include lighting circuits.

[2] M identifies the earthed conductor of a two-wire earthed dc circuit.

[3] Only the middle wire of three-wire circuits may be earthed.

[4] An earthed PELV conductor is blue.

In a single-phase installation at the wiring interface between harmonized colours and old colours, providing the existing cables are correctly identified by the colours of red for the line conductor and black for the neutral conductor and the new cables are correctly identified by the colours of brown for the line conductor and blue for the neutral conductor then the extension, alteration, addition or repair can be considered to be unambiguously marked and further marking at the interface is **not** necessary. A 'Caution' notice in accordance with Regulation 514.14.1 must be provided at the consumer unit, as illustrated below.

Example of identification of mixed harmonized and older colour conductors in a single-phase installation

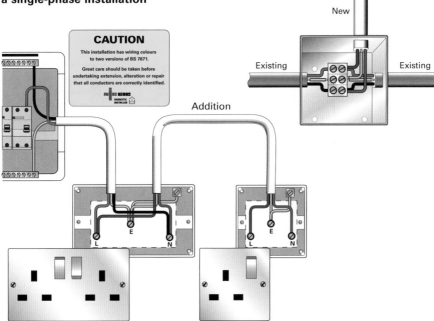

In a three-phase installation, at the wiring interface between harmonized colours and old colours, where an extension, alteration addition or repair is made with the harmonized colours to an installation wired in the old colours, unambiguous identification is required at the interface. Neutral conductors, where identified by colour, must be identified by the colour blue. Old line conductors (red, yellow and

INSPECTION

blue) and new line conductors (brown, black and grey) should be fitted with sleeves marked L1, L2 and L3 and neutral conductors should be fitted with sleeves marked N to avoid any possibility of confusion. As for a single-phase installation a 'Caution' notice should have been provided at the consumer unit.

Example 1 – Identification of mixed harmonized and older colour conductors in a three-phase installation

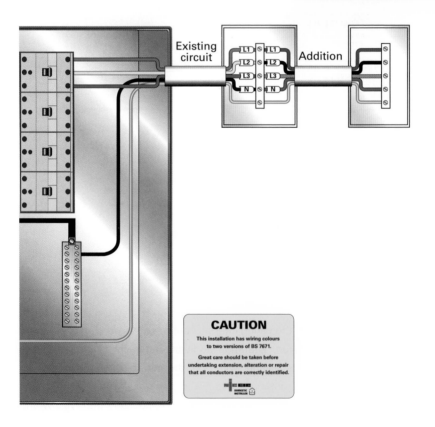

The NICEIC guide to
Domestic Periodic Inspection, Testing and Reporting

Example 2 – Identification of mixed colour conductors in a busbar chamber of a three-phase installation

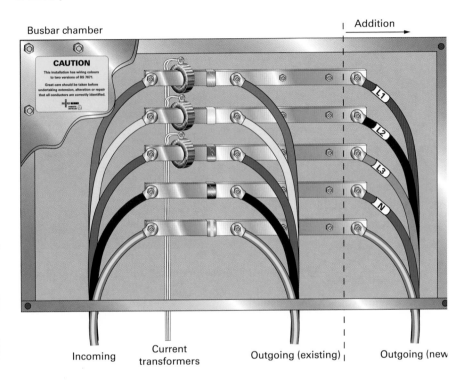

CAUTION
This installation has wiring colours to two versions of BS 7671.

Great care should be taken before undertaking extension, alteration or repair that all conductors are correctly identified.

Busbar chamber

Addition

Incoming | Current transformers | Outgoing (existing) | Outgoing (new

A permitted alternative arrangement is to use three new single-phase conductors with insulation of the same colour, but unambiguous identification must be provided at the terminations. This could be achieved by using numbering or lettering.

Example 3 – Identification of mixed colour conductors in a three-phase installation using new single-phase conductors of the same colour together with numbering and lettering

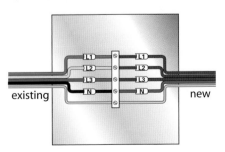

existing

new

INSPECTION

4.9 Cables and conductors

4.9.1 Selection of conductors for current-carrying capacity and voltage drop

The sizes and types of all the installed cables should be checked, in general, to confirm that they have been correctly selected and installed to meet the requirements of Sections 523, 524 and 525 of *BS 7671* with regard to selection of conductors for current-carrying capacity and voltage drop respectively. Particular attention should be given to any visible cables in contact with thermally insulating material (Regulation 523.7), which may have been added since the installation was installed.

Example of cables in contact with thermal insulation

Current-carrying capacity of a cable

In general, the current-carrying capacity of a cable for continuous service under the particular conditions concerned (I_z) should be equal or greater than the circuit design current (I_b) and the nominal current of the circuit protective device (I_n). For example, a cable with a current-carrying capacity of 6 A would be unsatisfactory if it supplied a heating load of 10 A or was protected by a 15 A fuse

In general, the current carried by any conductor for sustained period should not cause the conductor temperature to exceed 70 °C. The inspector might measure the temperature of a suspect conductor using an infrared thermometer (which enables temperature measurement without making contact with the conductor. Readings in excess of 70 °C might indicate an inadequate cross-sectional area of a conductor (or a poor conductor connection to an item of equipment), which would be unsatisfactory.

The NICEIC guide to Domestic Periodic Inspection, Testing and Reporting

Voltage drop between the origin of the installation and a socket-outlet or the terminals of fixed current-using equipment

For a supply of a nominal voltage (u_0) of 230 V a voltage not exceeding:

- 3 % (that is, 6.9 volts) for lighting, or

- 5 % (that is, 11.5 volts) for other uses,

is permitted in a low voltage installation, supplied directly from a public low voltage distribution system, between the origin of the installation (usually the supply terminals) and any load point. Such as at the socket-outlet or the terminals of fixed current-using equipment. (Regulation 525.3 and Table 12 A in Appendix 12 of *BS 7671* refer.)

Voltage drop is generally unlikely to be a problem in a domestic premises installation. However, a problem may occur when long cables are installed and the load current is at its maximum value. For example, sensitive equipment such as a computer may not function correctly in a remote detached annexe building that contains high current-using items of equipment (such as an electric cooker, electric heater or a washing machine). Particularly if the annex is supplied from a main house that is on a TT system, and the supply to the house is supplied by overhead lines that connect to a remote pole mounted transformer.

In similar circumstances to those described above, the inspector might, measure the voltage at a socket-outlet (under maximum load conditions) remote from the consumer unit and compare it with the voltage at a socket-outlet near the consumer unit (under similar load conditions). For example, if the inspector measured a voltage 218 volts at the remote socket-outlet and 230 volts at the socket-outlet near the consumer unit, the difference in these voltages would indicate an approximate voltage drop of 12 volts. As 12 volts is more than the permitted value of 11.5 volts, it is likely that the cross-sectional area of the circuit conductors is inadequate in size. However, the inspector may not consider this voltage drop to be a defect if it does **not** impair the safe functioning of the equipment used at that socket-outlet (Regulation 525.2).

INSPECTION

If required, the inspector might carry out further checks on voltage drop by measuring the circuit resistance and calculating the voltage drop (Regulation 612.14).

If the inspector considers that the voltage drop impairs the safe functioning of equipment, an appropriate observation and recommendation code should be included in the report.

4.9.2 Erection methods

Adequate inspection of erection methods can usually be achieved only if the installation is inspected at appropriate intervals during its construction. Compliance with the relevant requirements of Chapter 52 of *BS 7671* should have been considered at each stage.

The inspector should confirm that, in general, installed equipment and materials:

- comply with the appropriate British Standard or equivalent,

- have been properly selected and erected (for example, the cables in the previous photograph have **not** been properly erected), and

- are not visibly damaged or defective so as to impair safety.

Matters to be checked should include, for example:

- the existence of manufacturer's markings or certification signifying compliance to British or Harmonised Standards

- cables and conduits etc are adequately supported at appropriate intervals and are not subject to mechanical stresses. Cable supports should be sufficient in number to prevent the cables from being damaged by their own weight or by electromechanical forces associated with fault conditions. There should be no appreciable strain on the terminals.

- points, accessories and switchgear are securely fixed

- items of equipment are not cracked, broken or otherwise defective, and

- conduit bushes are tight

- visible cables are not damaged

- radii of bends in cables are not less than the minimum recommended for the particular type and overall diameter of cable.

4.9.3 Ferrous enclosures

Single core cables of a.c. circuits run in steel conduit or any other form of steel enclosure should have been installed so that all line, neutral conductors and separate protective conductors are together within the same enclosure (Regulation 521.5.2). This requirement also applies to cables passing through a hole in a ferromagnetic enclosure, such as the meter tails and earthing conductor entering a cable entry in the metallic enclosure of a consumer unit.

4.9.4 Cables

Cables of imperial (non-metric) sizes

Up until the beginning of the 1970s, cables could still be purchased having imperial, rather than metric, sized conductors. Many such cables are still to be found in older installations.

Their conductors may be single-stranded (as in 1/.044) or may have three, seven or more strands (as in 3/.029, 7/.029 and 19/.044). The first number in the cable conductor reference gives the number of strands in the cable conductor and the second number gives the diameter of each strand in inches. To the inexperienced eye these cables may be difficult to recognize, other than perhaps by comparison of their conductors with those of metric cables. The important thing to appreciate, however, is that their current carrying capacity and voltage drop characteristics are likely to be different from those which may at first be expected and reference is necessary to appropriate cable data tables such as in earlier editions of the IEE Wiring Regulations to determine their current-carrying capacities and voltage drops.

INSPECTION

Examples of imperial cable conductor reference types (number of strands/diameter of each strand in inches)

The equivalent metric cross-sectional area (csa) of any imperial cable conductor may also be determined by:

1 measuring the diameter of one conductor strand, in mm (such as by using a micrometer),

2 calculating the csa of one conductor strand by squaring the diameter, multiplying it by π (pi, is approximately = 3.142) and dividing it by 4, to give the answer in mm^2, and

3 multiplying the csa of one conductor strand by the number of strands, to give the conductor csa, in mm^2.

The rating of the nearest metric conductor below the calculated metric csa could then be used to give an approximation of the cables current carrying capacity rating or voltage drop.

Finally, it should be noted that copper conductors of imperial cables may be of the tinned type, giving them an unfamiliar colour.

The NICEIC guide to
Domestic Periodic Inspection, Testing and Reporting

Cables exposed to direct sunlight or to the effects of ultra-violet radiation

Cables which are exposed to direct sunlight or to the effects of ultra-violet radiation should have been selected for such application. Generally, PVC-sheathed cables may require some protection from ultra-violet radiation, but bare mineral insulated cables usually do not.

Tough rubber sheathed (TRS), vulcanised rubber insulation (VRI) cables

Prior to the use of pvc insulated cables becoming common in the 1960s, most cables installed in domestic dwellings were of the rubber insulated, tough-rubber sheathed (TRS) type. These are easily recognizable by their black exterior.

The extent to which the insulation and sheath deteriorate in service depends very much on whether the cable has been subjected to overloading and/or excessive temperature, or the rubber has been exposed to direct sunlight. Deterioration results in a loss of insulating properties, with the rubber becoming dry and inflexible – perhaps with a tendency to crumble.

As such cables are beyond their normally expected safe working life an appropriate observation and recommendation code should be given in the inspection report, depending on the condition of the cables.

TRS (shown at top of illustration) and VRI (shown at bottom of illustration) cables

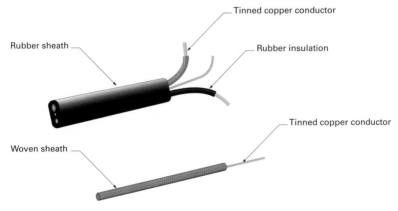

Tinned copper conductor

Rubber sheath

Rubber insulation

Tinned copper conductor

Woven sheath

INSPECTION

Lead-sheathed cables

Lead sheathed cables may be found in some installations dating from before about 1948. These have rubber insulated, tinned copper conductors and an outer sheath of lead.

For fault protection it is essential that the lead sheath of such a cable is properly earthed.

The conductor insulation, being made of rubber, is prone to deterioration as described above for TRS cables.

Again, as for TRS cables, lead cables are beyond their normally expected safe working life an appropriate observation and recommendation code should be given in the inspection report, depending on the condition of the cables.

Lead sheathed cable

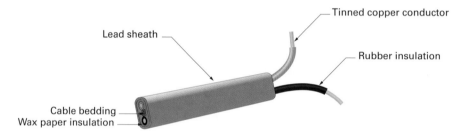

Tinned copper conductor

Lead sheath

Rubber insulation

Cable bedding
Wax paper insulation

2.5 mm² twin-and-earth cables incorporating circuit protective conductor of only 1.0 mm²

For some years, 2.5 mm² twin & earth pvc/pvc cables to *BS 6004* were manufactured with a circuit protective conductor (cpc) of only 1 mm², rather than 1.5 mm² as is incorporated today.

The size of the cpc was increased to 1.5 mm² in *BS 6004* because in certain circumstances the 1 mm² cpc may not always be properly protected against thermal effects in the event of an earth fault. This is where the cable is used in a ring final circuit protected by a 30 A semi-enclosed (rewireable) fuse. If this is the case,

**The NICEIC guide to
Domestic Periodic Inspection, Testing and Reporting**

an observation and appropriate recommendation code should be entered in the inspection report.

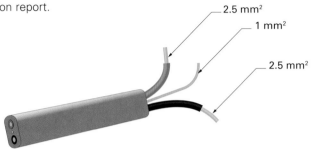

2.5 mm²

1 mm²

2.5 mm²

2.5 mm² twin & earth pvc/pvc cable with a circuit protective conductor (cpc) of only 1 mm²

4.9.5 Routing of cables in prescribed zones

Cables concealed in the fabric of the building at a depth of 50 mm or less from the surfaces of a wall or partition should have been checked at the appropriate stage during the installation to verify that they were routed within prescribed zones, unless cables of a permitted type were used (Regulation 522.6.6).

In general it is **not** possible for the inspector to check if concealed cables are routed in the prescribed zones, and such checks are a limitation (LIM) on the report. However, there may be visible signs to show if a concealed cable is in a prescribed zone or not, such as an unpainted cable chase in a painted wall (illustrated in the following photograph). If a cable is outside a prescribed zone the inspector should report it as a defect in the observation and recommendations code section as appropriate, except if there are signs of other protective measures against impact (AG) to the cable (Regulation 522.6.6) and subsequent risk of electric shock to a person or animal. Such other protective measures include the cable:

 i incorporating an appropriate earthed metallic covering, or

 ii being enclosed in an earthed conduit, or

 iii being enclosed in earthed trunking or ducting, or

 iv being mechanically protected to prevent penetration of nails, screws and the like.

INSPECTION

Where a cable is concealed in a wall or partition at a depth of less than 50 mm from the surface of the wall or partition in an installation not under the supervision of a skilled or instructed person, as would normally be the case in a domestic installation, and the cable is installed in a prescribed zone, but does not comply with indents (i), (ii), (iii) or (iv) on the previous page, the inspector must check that additional protection by means of an RCD having the characteristics specified in Regulation 415.1.1 has been provided (Regulation 522.6.7).

If agreed by the inspector and the client (as extra work to the inspection), for example if the client is planning to drill or cut a wall or floor in the future, the inspector may use a cable detector to help to determine the route of possible concealed cables. Any concealed cable found in a non-permitted zone should be reported as a defect in the observation and recommendations code section as appropriate, except if there are signs of other protective measures (as explained above).

Zoning within a wall or a partition

The positions of the zones in which it is permitted to install a cable not having an earthed metallic covering, not being of insulated concentric construction, not being enclosed in an earthed metallic enclosure or not having sufficient mechanical protection are as follows:

A zone within 150 mm from the top of the wall or partition, and

A zone within 150 mm of an angle formed by two adjoining walls or partitions, and

A zone running either horizontally or vertically to a point, accessory or switchgear on the wall or partition, containing a cable connected to the point, accessory or switchgear.

This zone extends to the reverse side of a wall or partition of 100 mm thickness or less if the location of the point, accessory or switchgear can be determined from that reverse side

(Regulation 522.6.6 refers.)

The NICEIC guide to
Domestic Periodic Inspection, Testing and Reporting

Consider an accessory mounted on a wall in Room 1 as shown in the diagram. The wall is 100 mm thick. A pvc/pvc insulated and sheathed cable has been run to the accessory. On the side of the thin wall where the accessory is mounted, in Room 1, a permitted zone runs both horizontally and vertically to the accessory, as shown ▬▬. In the example, a pvc cable has been run in this zone at a depth of 50 mm or less from the surface in the wall in Room 1.

Prescribed zones for concealing cables

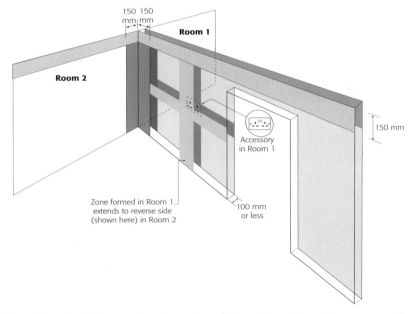

A 'mirror image' of the permitted zone is considered to exist on the reverse side of the wall (in Room 2) provided the location of the accessory can be determined from that reverse side. The 'mirror image' in Room 2 is shown in the diagram as ▭. Referring to the diagram, the open doorway means that from the reverse side of the wall (ie in Room 2) the location of the accessory can be determined. Thus, the cross-shaped permitted zone in Room 1 is also considered to exist on the reverse side of the wall in Room 2. Because of access through the open doorway a person in Room 2 can reasonably be expected to establish that the accessory is present and that the pvc/pvc cable will have been run in the 'mirror-image' of the permitted zone.

INSPECTION

Example of an incorrectly concealed cable (on the right hand side) extending outside the 150 mm permitted zone formed by the vertical walls (and the cable route cannot be determined from the reverse side of the wall)

Irrespective of the depth of the cable from a surface of a wall or partition, where a cable is concealed in a wall or partition metallic parts having an internal metal frame, metal noggins or similar internal metal parts, in an installation in a domestic dwelling, the inspector should check that the cable complies with the requirements of Regulation 522.6.8, and:

- incorporates an appropriate earthed metallic covering, or

- is enclosed in earthed trunking or ducting, or

- is enclosed in an earthed conduit, or

- is mechanically protected to prevent penetration of nails or the like, or

- is protected by an RCD with a rated residual operating current not exceeding 30 mA in accordance with Regulation 415.1.1.

Zoning within a floor or ceiling:

In general a cable installed within a floor or ceiling is concealed, and is not visible to the inspector, and such checks are a limitation (LIM) on the report. However, in some circumstances, such as when building improvement or repair work is in progress,

The NICEIC guide to
Domestic Periodic Inspection, Testing and Reporting

the cable may be visible, enabling the inspector to check if the cable is a minimum of 50 mm from the top or bottom of a joist or batten.

BS 7671 requires that where a cable is installed under a floor or above a ceiling, the cable should have been run in such a position that it is not liable to be damaged by the floor or ceiling, or their fixings. Where a cable passes through a timber joist or batten etc, it should have been installed at least 50 mm from the top or bottom as appropriate (measured vertically), of the timber member (that is, the surface(s) of the joist or batten or other timber member into which fixings are liable to be made), Regulation 522.6.5 (i) refers.

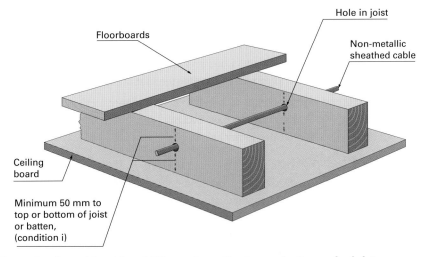

Example of a cable at least 50 mm from the top or bottom of a joist

If a cable is less than 50 mm to the top or bottom of a joist, the inspector should report it as a defect in the observation and recommendations code section as appropriate, except if there are signs of other protective measures against impact (AG) to the cable (Regulation 522.6.5). Such other protective measures include, the cable being:

• enclosed in an earthed armour or metal sheath, or

• mechanically protected to prevent penetration of nails or the like.

INSPECTION

4.9.6 Connection of conductors

Many fires are caused by poor connections in installations, so the following checks are essential.

The inspector should check an appropriate sample to confirm the following.

1   Connection between conductors and between a conductor and equipment is sound, both mechanically and electrically, for example by checking that cable connection screws are tight at appropriate equipment (such as accessories and the consumer unit), after isolating the supply source(s). These checks should include connections in protective conductors, particularly (where provided) those involving metallic wiring systems such as steel conduit and trunking or the metallic sheaths or armouring of cables.

2   Conductor(s) and insulation is undamaged and the condition such that the connection is likely to remain secure for the lifetime of the installation.

3   The method of connection is suitable for the external influences such as moisture, vibration and thermal cycling, and there is no appreciable mechanical strain on the terminations.

4   Connections are accessible, except for compound-filled or encapsulated joints, brazed, welded or compression joints, cold tail connections of underfloor and ceiling heating systems and joints forming part of equipment complying with the appropriate product standard.

5   For purposes of protection against fire and thermal effects:

   •   every joint or connection in a live conductor or PEN conductor is made in an enclosure complying with the requirements of Regulation 526.5 of *BS 7671*. It should be noted that this requirement applies not only to connections in low voltage circuits, but also to connections in extra-low voltage circuits

   •   the enclosure provides adequate protection against mechanical damage and any other external influence or stress to which it may be subjected (Regulation 526.7)

The NICEIC guide to
Domestic Periodic Inspection, Testing and Reporting

- the cores of sheathed cables from which the sheath has been removed do not extend outside the enclosure. In other words, the sheath, which is intended to provide mechanical protection, does extend into the enclosure (Regulation 526.9).

Example of incorrectly installed cable sheaths not entering the enclosure

4.9.7 Presence of fire barriers, suitable seals and protection against thermal effects

Fire barriers

The presence of the required fire barriers should be verified.

Where the wiring system or other equipment passes through an element of building construction (such as a wall or floor) having a specified fire resistance, the space around it should have been sealed to a degree of fire resistance which is no less than that (if any) prescribed for the building element concerned. The inspector should check for the presence of fire resistance measures. For example, at:

- back-to-back accessories, such as lighting switches on staircases, or

- recessed luminaires, such as downlighters.

INSPECTION

If a wiring system has an internal space, such as in trunking, and it passes through an element of a building having a specified fire resistance, the wiring system should have been sealed internally to the appropriate degree of fire resistance. The exception to this requirement is that a non-flame-propagating wiring system, with an internal cross-sectional area of not more than 710 mm², need not be sealed internally (Regulation 527.2.7).

Example of a cable trunking fire-stopped where it passes through a compartment wall

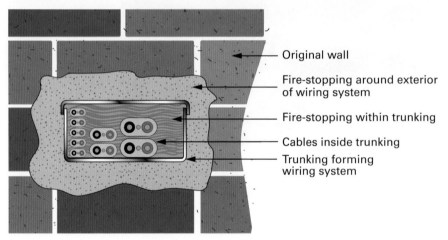

- Original wall
- Fire-stopping around exterior of wiring system
- Fire-stopping within trunking
- Cables inside trunking
- Trunking forming wiring system

Internal barriers may have been made from a type of intumescent packing which expands to fill the space when heated to the temperatures likely to occur under fire conditions. Solidifying foam may also have been used.

Protection against thermal effects

Protection against thermal effects, such as the proximity of hot surfaces to electrical equipment, should be checked. Sufficient clearance or an appropriate form of permanent heat shield or barrier may have been provided to prevent adverse effects on wiring systems.

The NICEIC guide to
Domestic Periodic Inspection, Testing and Reporting

Accessories on wooden mounting blocks

It was commonplace up to the mid 1960s for accessories such as socket-outlets, lighting switches and ceiling roses to be fixed to wooden mounting blocks.

The design of the accessories is often such that the wooden block is used to form part of the enclosure for the unsheathed cores and terminations of cables connecting to the accessory. However, depending on the particular characteristics of the material from which the block is made, it may not satisfy the ignitability requirements of the current Wiring Regulations (*BS 7671*), in which case the inspector needs to include the observation and an appropriate recommendation code in the inspection report.

Accessories on wooden mounting blocks

Overheating luminaires

The inspector should make sample checks to look for any signs of overheating of luminaires, particularly in and behind recessed luminaires.

4.10 Presence and correct location of appropriate devices for isolation and switching

The inspector should check that all devices for isolation and switching are present and correctly located (and identified).

INSPECTION

'Isolation and switching' is the general term used to cover four basic functions, namely:

- isolation,

- switching off for mechanical maintenance

- emergency switching and

- functional switching

These functions are considered separately for the purposes of inspection, as described in the following items. It should be remembered, however, that two or more of the functions may be performed by a single device, provided that the arrangement and characteristics of the device satisfy all the requirements of *BS 7671* for the particular functions concerned. Whilst checking the items referred to below, it should also be confirmed that all devices for isolation and switching are suitable for the currents they will have to carry. For example, if a switch is suitable for disconnecting a full load current of 5 A but the full load current controlled by that switch is 7 A, the switch would be unsatisfactory for continued use.

4.10.1   Isolation

The purpose of isolation is to enable skilled persons to carry out work on, or in the vicinity of, parts that are normally live in service without risk of injury from electric shock from those parts. *BS 7671* requires that every circuit is capable of being isolated (Regulation 537.2.1.1).

The inspector should confirm that the installation has a main linked switch or linked circuit-breaker positioned as near as practicable to the origin (Regulation 537.1.4). This is intended as a means of switching the supply on load, and as a means of isolation. Where the installation is supplied from more than one source (such as where a microgenerator is installed), a main switch or main circuit-breaker is required for each source (Regulation 537.1.6).

**The NICEIC guide to
Domestic Periodic Inspection, Testing and Reporting**

The inspector should verify the presence of the correct number of poles in the main switch or circuit-breaker (Regulation 537.2.2.5). For example, a two pole single-phase main switch in a TT system would be correct.

The main switch or circuit-breaker is required to interrupt all live conductors of the supply except as follows:

- in a TN-S or TN-C-S system, the neutral conductor generally need not be switched where this can be regarded as being reliably connected to Earth through a suitable low impedance provided that, in all cases, a single-phase main switch intended for operation by ordinary persons (such as in a consumer unit) must interrupt both the line and neutral conductors (which will be the general case in domestic premises)

- no switching device is permitted in a protective conductor or the PEN conductor in a TN-C system[5] (Regulation 537.1.2).

Where the main switch or circuit-breaker does not interrupt the neutral conductor, *BS 7671* requires provision to be made for the disconnection of the conductor for testing purposes.

Although the main switch or circuit-breaker provides a means of isolation for the whole installation, additional isolating devices are likely to be provided for individual items of equipment, circuits or groups of circuits to be isolated independently, such as a bathroom extractor fan that is connected to a lighting circuit. The presence of these additional devices, where appropriate, should be verified.

---

[5] TN-C systems are rarely found in domestic premises but if one is found an appropriate observation and recommendation code should be included in the report, because regulation 8(4) of the *Electrical Safety, Quality and Continuity Regulations 2002* requires that consumers must not combine the neutral and protective functions in a single conductor in their installation.

INSPECTION

The additional isolating devices must interrupt all live conductors except, generally, the neutral conductor in TN-S and TN-C-S systems where this can reliably be regarded as being at Earth potential. In a TN-C system, the PEN conductor must not be isolated or switched. It should be checked that each device used for isolation is of a type which *BS 7671* permits for this purpose. Such devices include:

- an isolator (disconnector),

- isolating switch (switch disconnector),

- suitable circuit-breaker,

- plug and socket-outlet,

- (withdrawable) fuse, or

- disconnectable link.

The isolating distance between contacts or other means of isolation when in the open position is to be not less than that determined for an isolator (disconnector) in accordance with the requirements of appropriate standards, such as:

- *BS 1363-4 – 13 A plugs, socket-outlets and adaptors. Specification for 13A fused connection units switched and unswitched,*

- *BS 3676 – Switches for household and similar fixed electrical installations. Specification for general requirements,*

- *BS EN 60669-2-4 – Switches for household and similar fixed electrical installations. Particular requirements. Isolating switches,*

- *BS EN 60898 – Electrical accessories. Circuit-breakers for overcurrent protection for household and similar installations. Circuit-breakers for a.c. and d.c. operation,*

- *BS EN 60947-2 – Low-voltage switchgear and control gear. Circuit-breakers,*

The NICEIC guide to
Domestic Periodic Inspection, Testing and Reporting

- *BS EN 60947-3 – Low voltage switchgear and controlgear. Switches, disconnectors, switch-disconnectors and fuse-combination units,*

- *BS EN 61008-1 – Specification for residual current operated circuit-breakers without integral overcurrent protection for household and similar uses (RCCBs). General rules, or*

- *BS EN 61009-1 – Electrical accessories. Residual current operated circuit-breakers with integral overcurrent protection for household and similar uses (RCBO's). General rules.*

The position of the contacts must be either externally visible or clearly and reliably indicated when the specified isolation has been obtained in each pole (Regulation 537.2.2.2). As a rule of thumb, a contact separation of 3 mm is generally considered to be sufficient, but if there is any doubt as to whether a device is designed to provide isolation (such as may be the case with an older device not complying to any of the above standards) its suitability should be confirmed by enquiry to the manufacturer, where appropriate.

The inspector should check that isolating devices, which are remote from the equipment to be isolated, have a means to secure the isolator in the off (open) position (see item 1.7.1).

4.10.2 Devices for switching off for mechanical maintenance

The purpose of switching off for mechanical maintenance is to enable persons to safely replace, refurbish or clean lamps, and to maintain non-electrical parts of electrical equipment.

The inspector should check that a means of switching off for mechanical maintenance is provided where any of the above operations may involve a risk of burns, or a risk of injury from mechanical movement (Regulation 537.3.1.1). For example, a means of switching off for mechanical maintenance would be required to enable a person to clean luminaires having lamps that may cause burns, or to enable an extractor fan to be cleaned. It should be noted, however, that a suitable means of

INSPECTION

isolation would also be required if any of these operations were likely to involve a need to work on or near live parts (see item 4.10.1), such as could be the case if equipment needs dismantling for repair or replacement.

The inspector should check that devices used for switching off for mechanical maintenance are;

- of the types permitted for this function by *BS 7671*, namely switches, circuit-breakers or suitable socket-outlets. Switches and circuit-breakers should be capable of cutting off the full load current of the relevant part of the installation, and either have an externally-visible contact gap, or give a clear and reliable indication of the OFF or OPEN position when each pole of the contacts is properly opened (Regulation 537.3.2.2). Socket-outlets are permitted for such purposes only if their rating does not exceed 16 A.

- positioned locally to the equipment requiring maintenance.

4.10.3 Devices for emergency switching

The purpose of emergency switching is to remove, as quickly as possible, danger which may have occurred unexpectedly (Regulation 537.4.1.1).

The inspector should check that a means of emergency switching is readily accessible at places in the installation where it is necessary to cut off the supply rapidly, to prevent or remove danger (Regulation 537.4.2.5), and where appropriate remote from the danger. For example, a cooker control switch might be located to one side of a cooker (not behind it), so that the cooker supply can be safely isolated in an emergency (such as if liquid is accidentally spilt over the cooker).

4.10.4 Devices for functional switching

Devices for functional switching are actually the subject of the final item in the Schedule of Items Inspected in the Domestic Electrical Installation Periodic Inspection Report (item 3.8.5). It is against that item that the corresponding tick should be placed, once the provisions have been checked.

The NICEIC guide to
Domestic Periodic Inspection, Testing and Reporting

Table 53.2 of *BS 7671* gives guidance on the selection of devices for protection, isolation and switching and is reproduced below for ease of reference.

Device	Standard	Isolation	Emergency switching[2]	Functional switching
Switching devices	BS 3676: Pt 1 1989	Yes[4]	Yes	Yes
	BS EN 60669-1	No	Yes	Yes
	BS EN 60669-2-1	No	No	Yes
	BS EN 60669-2-2	No	Yes	Yes
	BS EN 60669-2-3	No	Yes	Yes
	BS EN 60669-2-4	Yes	Yes	Yes
	BS EN 60947-3	Yes[1]	Yes	Yes
	BS EN 60947-5-1	No	Yes	Yes
Contactors	BS EN 60947-4-1	Yes[1]	Yes	Yes
	BS EN 61095	No	No	Yes
Circuit-breakers	BS EN 60898	Yes	Yes	Yes
	BS EN 60947-2	Yes[1]	Yes	Yes
	BS EN 61009	Yes	Yes	Yes
RCDs	BS EN 60947-2	Yes[1]	Yes	Yes
	BS EN 61008	Yes	Yes	Yes
	BS EN 61009	Yes	Yes	Yes
Isolating switches	BS EN 60669-2-4	Yes	Yes	Yes
	BS EN 60947-3	Yes	Yes	Yes
Plugs and socket-outlets (> 32 A)	BS EN 60309	Yes	No	Yes
	IEC 60884	Yes	No	Yes
	IEC 60906	Yes	No	Yes
Plugs and socket-outlets (>32 A)	BS EN 60309	Yes	No	No
Devices for the connection of luminaires	IEC 61995-1	Yes[3]	No	No
Control and protective switching devices for equipment (CPS)	BS EN 60947-6-1	Yes	Yes	Yes
	BS EN 60947-6-2	Yes[1]	Yes	Yes
Fuses	BS EN 60269-2	Yes	No	No
	BS EN 60269-3	Yes	No	No
Devices with semi-conductors	BS EN 60669-2-1	No	No	Yes
Luminaire Support coupler	BS 6972	Yes[3]	No	No
Plugs and unswitched socket-outlets	BS 1363-1	Yes[3]	No	Yes
	BS 1363-2	Yes[3]	No	Yes
Plugs and switched socket-outlets	BS 1363-1	Yes[3]	No	Yes
	BS 1363-2	Yes[3]	No	Yes
Plugs and socket-outlets	BS 5733	Yes[3]	No	Yes
Switched fused connection unit	BS 1363-4	Yes[3]	Yes	Yes
Unswitched fused connection unit	BS 1363-4	Yes[3] (Removal of fuse link)	No	No
Fuse	BS 1362	Yes	No	No
Cooker Control Unit switch	BS 4177	Yes	Yes	Yes

Yes Function provided
No Function not provided
(1) Function provided if the device is suitable and marked with the symbol for isolation (see IEC 60617 identity number S00288.)
(2) See 537.4.2.5
(3) Device is suitable for on-load isolation, i.e. disconnection whilst carrying load current.
(4) Function provided if the device is suitable and marked with

Table data courtesy of IET

INSPECTION

The inspector should check that the devices to switch 'on' and 'off' or to vary the supply of electrical energy for normal operating purposes are appropriate in quantity, type, function and location (Regulation 537.5.1.1).

Functional switching is required for any circuit or part of a circuit that may require to be controlled independently of other parts of the installation. Devices for functional switching may be single-pole or multi-pole; they need not control all live conductors but must not solely control the neutral conductor. Suitable devices include switches, plugs and socket-outlets rated at up to 16 A (except for control of d.c.) and semiconductor devices (Regulation 537.5.2.2).

Off-load isolators, fuses or links should not be used for functional switching (Regulation 537.5.2.3).

4.11   Adequacy of access to equipment

The inspector should check that adequate and safe means of access and working space have been afforded to every piece of electrical equipment requiring operation, inspection, testing or maintenance. If these have not been afforded the inspector should include an appropriate observation and recommendation code in the report.

Example of inadequate safe access and working space for a person requiring access to the consumer unit

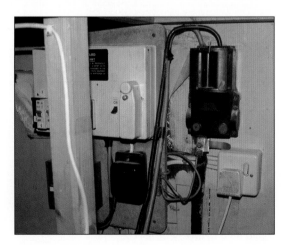

4.12 Particular protective measures for special installations and locations

The special installations and locations referred to in this section are those where the risks associated with electric shock are increased due to wetness; absence of, or minimal clothing; presence of earthed metal; arduous conditions; and where other risks, such as that of fire, may also be increased. Some of these locations and installations are included in Part 7 of *BS 7671*, where the particular protective measures associated with them are also given. These measures modify or add to the general requirements for safety.

The installations and locations included in Part 7 of *BS 7671* – such as locations containing a bath or shower are not the only ones where there may be increased risk of electric shock. An installation may have other locations of increased shock risk where additional measures, have been provided (in accordance with Section 415 of *BS 7671*), such as 30 mA RCD protection to the lighting installation in an inspection pit in a garage.

The inspector should carefully examine all of the special locations and installations within the particular installation being inspected, including any additional locations of increased shock, to verify that the associated protective measures are present in accordance with the relevant Sections in Part 7 of *BS 7671*.

'Special installations and locations' are fairly common, and the inspector will need to think carefully before putting an N/A in the relevant box on the Report. It should be remembered that a room containing a bath or shower is a special location and a tick in this box is normally applicable for every domestic installation.

INSPECTION

4.13 Connections at equipment

4.13.1 Connection of single-pole devices for protection or switching in line conductors only

This is a visual check, to check that all single-pole switching and control devices are connected in the line conductor only. No single-pole switching device, circuit-breaker, fuse, solid link which can be removed without the use of a tool or key, or the like should interrupt or control the neutral conductor. This check should be made in addition, and not as an alternative, to the polarity test which will be conducted later in the periodic inspection process.

4.13.2 Connection of accessories and equipment

The inspector should examine samples of the installation to check that the conductors at accessories and other items of equipment are connected to the correct terminals, and that the connections are well made both electrically and mechanically.

4.13.3 Contact connection of Edison screw or single centre bayonet cap lampholders

The inspector should check a sample of any Edison screw or single centre bayonet cap type lampholders, to determine that the outer contact connects to the neutral conductor, except for E14 and E27 lampholders complying with *BS EN 60238* (Regulation 559.6.1.8).

4.14 Selection of equipment appropriate to external influences

The inspector should confirm that the installed equipment and protective measures have been selected and erected to operate safely, given whatever external influences are reasonably likely to occur during the remaining lifetime of the installation.

The NICEIC guide to
Domestic Periodic Inspection, Testing and Reporting

An external influence is defined in Part 2 of *BS 7671* as any influence external to an electrical installation which affects the design and safe operation of that installation'. Examples of external influences include ambient temperature, external heat sources, solar radiation, impact, vibration, the presence of water, high humidity, solid foreign bodies, corrosive or polluting substances, or other factors such as structural movement.

The inspector should check that all wiring and other equipment is of a design appropriate to the situation in which it is used, and/or that its mode of installation has taken account of the conditions likely to be encountered (as required by *BS 7671*). Moreover, any equipment which does not meet these requirements by its own construction is provided with appropriate additional protection. For example, in an installation such as an electrically heated greenhouse where there may be dusty or wet conditions, the selected luminaires and wiring system may, by their own construction, be suitable for the arduous conditions, whereas the distribution and heating control equipment may be of a standard pattern, but housed within a suitable cupboard or additional electrical enclosure appropriate for both the equipment and the conditions.

The inspector should check that additional protection provided against external influences, for example by an enclosure, has not caused overheating of the protected equipment, impaired its operation, nor impeded its inspection, testing and maintenance.

A concise list of external influences is given in Appendix 5 of *BS 7671*.

INSPECTION

4.15 Presence of a fire alarm and detection systems

The inspector should check if a fire alarm and detection system in present, or not, and it meets the requirements of *BS 7671*, such as segregation (see item 4.7.3).

Information on fire alarms in dwellings in given in NICEIC *Pocket Guide 10 – Fire alarms in dwellings*, which is reproduced as follows, for ease of reference:

NICEIC POCKET GUIDE 10 FIRE ALARMS IN DWELLINGS

Example of a Grade D or E, Category LD2 fire detection and alarm system

**The NICEIC guide to
Domestic Periodic Inspection, Testing and Reporting**

NOTES

1   This guide addresses some of the recommendations in *BS 5839-6: 2004 – Fire detection and alarm systems for buildings, Code of practice for the design, installation and maintenance of fire detection and fire alarm systems in dwellings.*

2   The minimum standard of protection recommended in the 2004 edition of *BS 5839-6* is, for new dwellings, that **smoke alarms** should be provided within the circulation areas of most single-family dwellings and small houses in multiple occupation (HMOs), and that **heat alarms** should be provided in the kitchen and the principal habitable room (eg, the lounge).

3   The Standard recommends that smoke alarms and heat alarms installed within new single-family dwellings and small HMOs are mains powered with, in addition, a standby power supply in the form of a battery or capacitor.

4   There are six Grades of system in the Standard. The Grades identify the equipment incorporated. Grades A, B and C are systems that include fire detectors, alarm devices and central control equipment. Grades D and E are mains-powered smoke alarm systems (as summarised in Table 1). A Grade F system includes a battery-powered smoke alarm.

5   Categories of system (used to describe the principles of operation) in the Standard are summarised in Table 2.

6   In the context of fire detection and alarm systems in dwellings, attention is drawn to the relevant requirements of national building regulations and, in the case of small HMOs, to the relevant housing legislation.

7   Guidance on fire alarm requirements in building regulations is given in Approved Document B in England and Wales, the Technical Standards that support the relevant building regulations in Scotland, and in Technical Booklet E in Northern Ireland.

INSPECTION

FIRE ALARMS IN DWELLINGS

Table 1 - *BS 5839-6: 2004* Grade D and E systems

Grade of system	Summary of equipment incorporated
Grade D	A system of one or more mains-powered smoke alarms, each with an integral standby supply. (The system may, in addition, incorporate one or more mains-powered heat alarms, each with an integral standby supply.)
Grade E	A system of one or more mains-powered smoke alarms with no standby supply. (The system may, in addition, incorporate one or more heat alarms, with or without standby supplies.)

Table 2 - *BS 5839-6: 2004* Categories of system

Category of system	Principles of operation
Category LD	A fire detection and fire alarm system intended for the protection of life.
Category PD	A fire detection and fire alarm system intended for the protection of property.
Note: the above Categories are further subdivided, for example LD2	An LD2 system incorporates detectors in all circulation spaces that form part of the escape routes from the dwelling, and in all rooms or areas that present a high fire risk to the occupants.

Guidance on inspection, testing and reporting of fire alarm and detection systems is given in NICEIC *Guide to Completing Specialized Certificates & Reports* book.

The NICEIC guide to
Domestic Periodic Inspection, Testing and Reporting

TESTING

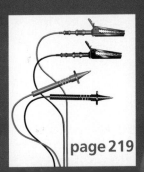

An NICEIC publication © Electrical Safety Council (JAN 2008)

TESTING

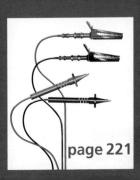

An NICEIC publication © Electrical Safety Council (JAN 2008)

TESTING

5.1   General

This chapter gives guidance on the testing of domestic electrical installations in accordance with *BS 7671*. It includes information on safety precautions, accuracy of instruments, sequence of tests and various testing methods.

Before an installation is tested, it is necessary for safety reasons to carry out a careful and thorough inspection as described in previous chapters. However, during testing, further inspection should be carried out, for example when accessories are removed for measuring $R_1 + R_2$ on lighting final circuits (see item 5.10.1).

The content of this chapter is limited to the tests necessary to complete the schedule in a Domestic Electrical Installation Periodic Inspection Report (see items 3.8 to 3.11).

Guidance on inspection, testing and reporting on portable appliances and fixed equipment is given in the NICEIC *Guide to electrical equipment maintenance* and the IEE *Code of Practice for In-service Inspection and Testing of Electrical Equipment.*

5.2   Safety

Electrical testing inherently involves a degree of risk. Persons carrying out electrical testing have a duty to ensure the safety of themselves and others from any possible danger resulting from the tests or from access to live parts. This requires strict adherence to safe working practices (see item 1.7), including checking that the:

- test equipment: such as test instruments, leads, probes and crocodile clips are safe and suitable for the intended purpose (see item 1.8)

- installed equipment is safe for the inspector to carry out tests on the installation, for example a consumer unit with a damaged main switch would be unsafe to operate the supply to carry out insulation tests on final circuits, and

- working environment does not impair safety.

Particular care is needed where secondary sources of energy form part of the installation, such as microgeneration systems (see item 4.6.11).

Guidance on safety issues is included in items in previous chapters, such as those referenced above and the following:

- legal aspects (see item 1.5)

- the inspector and competence (see item 1.6)

- competence and safety (see item 2.3)

- safety (see item 4.2), and

- accessible live equipment parts (see item 4.3).

5.3 Instrument accuracy

It is essential to ensure the accuracy and consistency of test instruments used to carry out the range of tests and measurements required by *BS 7671*.

The accuracy of each test instrument first needs to be confirmed, such as by formal calibration/re-calibration supported by calibration certificates issued by recognized organizations, with measurements traceable to national standards. Certificates issued by UKAS accredited laboratories are preferable. It should be noted that new or repaired test instruments may not be supplied with calibration certificates unless specifically requested.

Given the arduous conditions in which test instruments often have to be used, such formal calibration checks described above used alone will **not** provide any assurance of continuing accuracy and consistency over the period between calibration checks.

There should be a system in place which enables confirmation of the continuing accuracy and consistency of all test instruments used for testing purposes. There are several options for such a system, including:

TESTING

- Maintaining records over time of comparative cross-checks with other test instruments.

- Maintaining records over time of measurements of the characteristics of designated reference circuits or devices. For example, the consistency of continuity, insulation resistance and earth electrode test instruments can be checked against a proprietary resistance box (as illustrated below) or a set of suitable resistors. Earth fault loop impedance test instruments can be checked by carrying out tests on a designated socket-outlet (on a non-RCD protected circuit), for example in the contractor's premises. RCD test instruments can be checked by carrying out tests on an RCD unit plugged into the designated socket-outlet.

Either of the above systems will provide a measure of confidence in the consistency of test measurements over time.

NICEIC proprietary instrument resistance check box

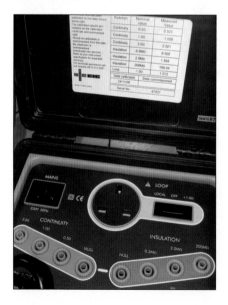

The NICEIC guide to
Domestic Periodic Inspection, Testing and Reporting

Regular calibration checks of test instruments by the inspector using the systems described above should help to identify any test instruments that are out of calibration. Thereby, minimizing potential revisits to installations incorrectly tested by using out of calibration instruments.

It is also essential to maintain records of the formal calibration/re-calibration of test instruments at the intervals recommended by the instrument manufacturers, supported by calibration certificates, together with the checks carried out by the inspector.

Such records should be entered in a test instrument log book, such as that available from NICEIC Direct, as shown below.

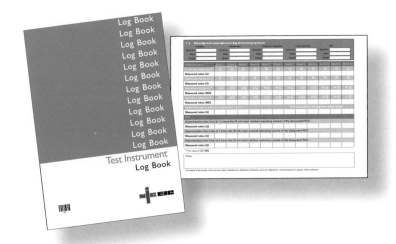

5.4   **Sequence of tests**

The overall sequence of inspection and testing is given in item 1.12.

The sequence for testing follows.

After completing the bulk part of the visual inspection (see earlier chapters) tests should, in general, be carried out in the following order:

TESTING

1. Function of final circuit protective devices (see item 5.17).

2. External earth loop impedance (Z_e), or earth electrode resistance (R_A), see items 5.8 or 5.9 respectively.

3. Prospective fault current (I_{pf}), see item 5.5.

4. R_2 to check continuity of protective conductors (see item 5.10.2) in circuits that do **not** contain socket-outlets (that can be used to plug in an earth fault loop impedance test instrument).

5. $R_1 + R_2$ and polarity (see item 5.10.1) of circuits that do **not** contain socket-outlets (that can be used to plug in an earth fault loop impedance test instrument and a live polarity test instrument).

6. Continuity of ring final circuits (see item 5.10.4).

7. Insulation resistance (see item 5.11).

8. Polarity and phase sequence (see item 5.14).

9. Earth fault loop impedance (Z_s), see item 5.15, of final circuits, containing socket-outlets, used to plug in an earth fault loop impedance tester.

10. RCD operation (see item 5.16).

11. Functional testing of remaining items (see item 5.17).

12. Assessment of maximum demand (see item 5.6).

If any periodic inspection test indicates a failure to comply with the requirements of that test, the result must be accurately recorded on the Domestic Electrical Installation Periodic Inspection Report and associated schedule. The report should include observations, recommendation codes and summary comments as appropriate.

The NICEIC guide to
Domestic Periodic Inspection, Testing and Reporting

5.5   Maximum prospective fault current (I_{pf})

The maximum prospective fault current is one of the 'supply characteristics and earthing arrangements' to be recorded in Section J of the Domestic Electrical Installation Periodic Inspection Report (see item 2.25).

I_{pf} is the current that would flow in the event of a fault at that location, either between live conductors (maximum prospective short-circuit current) or between live conductors and Earth (maximum prospective earth fault current), whichever is the greater.

Why do we have to determine maximum prospective fault current?

A fault current protective device, particularly when fitted close to the supply intake position, must be capable of safely interrupting the fault current which would flow under conditions of short-circuit or earth fault. Otherwise there may be a serious risk of arcing, damage and fire, particularly for circuits having high prospective fault currents.

Accordingly, the fault current capacity (sometimes referred to as the breaking capacity or rated short-circuit capacity) of a protective device must be **not** less than the prospective fault current at the point in the circuit at which it is installed. The only exception to this rule is where a device having a lower fault current capacity is installed in conjunction with what is sometimes called 'back-up' protection. (For example, a consumer unit might be backed-up by an appropriately rated *BS 1361* Type II fuse in the distributor's cut-out, which will protect the consumer unit by limiting the energy let-through during a fault.)

Measurement of prospective fault current and identification of the fault current capacity of circuit protective devices is addressed in the following items 5.5.1 to 5.5.5 and 5.5.6 respectively.

TESTING

5.5.1 Measurement of maximum prospective fault current (I_{pf})

The maximum prospective fault current in an installation, in general, occurs at the origin of that installation (that is, at the point of supply). The measurement should, therefore, be made at the main switch.

Particular care needs to be taken when measuring prospective fault current, because of potential high fault currents, typically in excess of 1000 Amperes (1 kA), that might occur under fault conditions.

Note: that a measurement of prospective fault current made at a point down stream of the main switch, such as at the load side of a final circuit protective device, in general, would **not** be the maximum value for the installation.

The earthing conductor, protective bonding conductors and circuit protective conductors should all remain connected to the main earthing terminal (MET) during this test, because the presence of these and any other parallel paths to Earth may reduce the impedance of the fault loop and so increase the prospective fault current.

An earth fault loop impedance test instrument should be used for this test, with or without a prospective fault current range.

Prospective fault current may be measured using either a two-lead or three-lead instrument (see items 5.5.2 or 5.5.3 respectively).

In general, *Procedure A* or *Procedure B* is used to measure I_{pf}.

Procedure A may be used for measuring prospective fault current at the **supply side** of the consumer unit main switch. However, if access to the live parts being tested is restricted, such as where the consumer unit is located in a small cupboard under the stairs or located at high level (requiring the use of steps), it may be preferable to use *Procedure B*.

If while following *Procedure A*, it is found at step 5 (or before) that:

1   basic protection is **below** the requirements of IP2X (for example IP1X),

or

2   the main switch supply side terminal insulated covers are likely to be accidentally displaced during testing.

Then it may also be preferable to use *Procedure B*.

Procedure A

*Used where basic protection meets the requirements of IP2X (or exceeds it, for example, IP4X), terminal insulated covers are unlikely to be accidentally displaced and access to equipment is **not** restricted.*

1   Read and carefully follow the test instrument manufacturer's instructions.

2   Check that the test instrument, leads, probes and/or crocodile clips are suitable for the purpose, and in good serviceable condition (see item 1.8).

3   Select the appropriate test type and scale (for example, prospective fault current 20 kA).

4   Isolate the supply to final circuit protective devices using the main switch and the isolation procedure given in item 1.7.1.
   Note: that if the installation is supplied by a secondary source(s) of supply, such as a microgenerator, the other source(s) of supply must also be isolated.

5   Remove the consumer unit outer cover[1] and check that the;

   •   basic protection inside the consumer unit meets or exceeds the requirements of IP2X or IPXXB, (see item 5.13), and

---

[1] When the consumer unit cover is removed the inspector must prevent unskilled persons gaining access to the consumer unit.

TESTING

- the main switch supply side terminal insulated covers are unlikely to be accidentally displaced during testing.

If the checks are positive continue with step 6 in this procedure. If **not** continue with step 6 in *Procedure B*.

6   Observing all precautions for safety (such as wearing insulated gloves and eye protection), firmly connect the test instrument leads to measure prospective short-circuit fault current, as explained in item 5.5.2 for a two-lead test instrument or item 5.5.3 for a three-lead test instrument.

   Notes: 1   The order of connection of the test instrument leads should be Earth, neutral and line, and the order of disconnection line, neutral, Earth.

   2   In general, a test instrument lead connection to an Earth or neutral conductor is made using a suitable crocodile clip (for example, be insulated, except for inside the jaws). The connection to a line conductor is made using a suitable test probe (for example, one with a finger guard and short exposed metal tip).

7   Check the test instrument polarity indicator (if any) for correct connection.

8   Press the test button (repeat test as a check if appropriate, in accordance with manufacturer's instructions).

   Note: that a test button may be available on the test probe.

9   Record the prospective short-circuit fault current measured value (if the test is repeated, use the highest value).

10   Repeat steps (6) to (9) but with the instrument connected to measure the prospective earth fault current, as explained in item 5.5.2 for a two-lead test instrument or item 5.5.3 for a three-lead test instrument.

11   Replace the consumer unit cover.

12   Reinstate the supply to the final circuit protective devices using the main switch, and reinstate any secondary source of energy, such as a microgenerator.

The NICEIC guide to
Domestic Periodic Inspection, Testing and Reporting

Procedure B has more steps to follow compared with *Procedure A*. However, using *Procedure B* prevents the need to work **on** live parts, except for proving the supply is isolated by use of a suitable voltage detector (see item 1.8).

Procedure B should also reduce the risk of accidentally displacing main switch supply side terminal insulated covers. However, when the supply is re-energized large areas of accessible exposed live parts may be present so it is essential to take appropriate precautions when working **near** these live parts (see item 8 in *Procedure B* and the illustrations in item 5.5.5).

Using *Procedure B* should enable prospective fault current to be measured where access is **not** restricted, such as outside a cramped cupboard (containing a consumer unit) or at the bottom of a pair of steps (which are used to access a consumer unit mounted above normal reach).

Procedure B involves measuring the prospective fault current at the **load side** of the consumer unit main switch, such as at the busbars supplying the final circuit protective devices (see the illustrations in item 5.5.5). However, all final circuit protective devices must be isolated.

TESTING

Procedure B

(Used where basic protection is below the requirements of IP2X, there are terminal insulated covers that may be displaced or access to equipment is restricted.)

1 Read and carefully follow the test instrument manufacturer's instructions.

2 Check that the test instrument, leads and crocodile clips are suitable for the purpose, and in good serviceable condition (see item1.8).

3 Select the appropriate test type and scale (for example, prospective fault current 20 kA).

4 Isolate the supply to final circuit protective devices using the main switch and the isolation procedure given in item 1.7.1.

Note: that if the installation is supplied by a secondary source(s) of supply, such as a microgenerator, the other source(s) of supply must also be isolated.

5 Remove the consumer unit outer cover² and check that:

a the basic protection inside the consumer unit meets or exceeds the requirements of IP2X or IPXXB, (see item 5.13), **and**

b the main switch supply side terminal insulated covers are **unlikely** to be accidentally displaced during testing, **and**

c access to the live parts being tested is **not** restricted.

If checks a, b **and** c are positive, continue with step 6 of *Procedure A*. If **not** continue with step 6 opposite.

---

² When the consumer unit cover is removed the inspector **must** prevent unskilled persons gaining access to the consumer unit.

6 Isolate **all** final circuit protective devices, such as by switching circuit-breakers OFF or by withdrawing fuses, and use the isolation procedure given in item 1.7.1.

7 Securely connect the test instrument leads to measure prospective short-circuit current, as explained in item 5.5.5.

> **Note:** that in general, test instrument lead connections to Earth, neutral and line conductors are made using suitable crocodile clips (for example, they are insulated, except for the gripping metal surface inside the jaws).

8 Observing all precautions for safety (such as by wearing eye protection and insulated gloves, and/or fitting temporary insulating barriers), re-energize the supply to the final circuit protective devices using the main switch.

> **Note:** Leave the final circuit protective devices isolated.

9 Check the test instrument polarity indicator (if any) for correct connection.

10 Press the test button (repeat test as a check if appropriate, in accordance with manufacturer's instructions).

11 Record the prospective short-circuit fault current measured value (if the test is repeated, use the highest value).

12 Isolate the supply to final circuits using the main switch and the isolation procedure given in item 1.7.1.

13 Repeat steps (7) to (12) but with the test instrument leads connected to measure the prospective earth fault current, as explained in item 5.5.5.

14 Remove the test instrument leads from the consumer unit.

15 Replace the consumer unit cover.

TESTING

16 Reinstate the supply to the final circuits using the circuit protective devices, as appropriate (such as by switching on circuit-breakers or inserting fuses).

17 Reinstate the supply to the final circuit protective devices using the main switch, and reinstate any secondary source of energy, such as a microgenerator.

In **exceptional** circumstances, if it is **not** considered safe by the inspector to undertake either *Procedure A* or *B*, an appropriate limitation, observation and recommendation should be entered on the report. A value of prospective fault current obtained by enquiry should also be entered in the report

If the test instrument does **not** have a prospective fault current range, the readings may be measured as fault loop impedances (in ohms) using the above procedures. To convert each of these readings into a prospective fault current, divide them into the measured value of line to neutral voltage.

For example, if the voltage measured at the time of the test is 230 V (for a **single-phase** incoming supply), and the measured value of fault loop impedance between line and neutral at the origin of the installation is 0.05 Ω, therefore:

Prospective short-circuit current (line to neutral) = 230/0.05 = 4600 A (or 4.6 kA)

(This value would have been given directly if the test instrument had a prospective fault current range).

The same procedure is now repeated, taking readings between **line and earth** to determine the prospective earth fault current.

The higher value of the two prospective fault currents (line to neutral or line to earth) should be recorded on the certificate or report.

Special care is required when measuring the maximum prospective fault current for a three-phase supply (see item 5.5.4).

5.5.2 Measurement of prospective fault current using a two-lead instrument and *Procedure A*

To measure the prospective short-circuit current, in general, the red and black leads of a two-lead instrument (as illustrated below) are connected to the line and neutral terminals respectively of the incoming supply (as shown in the following illustration).

To measure the prospective earth fault current, in general, the red lead also is connected to the line terminal of the incoming supply but the black lead is connected to the main earthing terminal, which is in connected to Earth.

The conditions and use of *Procedure A* to measure prospective fault current are explained in item 5.5.1.

Measurement of prospective short-circuit current using a two-lead instrument and *Procedure A*

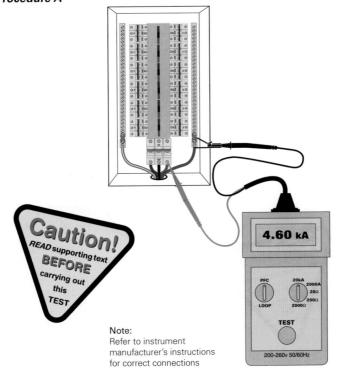

Caution!
READ supporting text
BEFORE
carrying out
this
TEST

4.60 kA

PFC   20kA   2000A
                20Ω
LOOP   2000Ω   200Ω

TEST

200-260v 50/60Hz

Note:
Refer to instrument
manufacturer's instructions
for correct connections

TESTING

5.5.3 Measurement of prospective fault current using a three-lead instrument and *Procedure A*

To measure the prospective short-circuit current or prospective earth fault current, in general, the red, black and green leads of a three-lead test instrument (as shown in the following illustration) are connected to the line and neutral of the incoming supply, and the main earthing terminal respectively.

Other three-lead test instruments may also require the red lead to be connected to the line terminal of the incoming supply, but the black and green leads to be connected together at the:

- neutral of the incoming supply (to measure prospective short-circuit fault current), or

- main earthing terminal (to measure the prospective earth fault current).

The conditions and use of *Procedure A* to measure prospective fault current are explained in item 5.5.1.

Measurement of prospective earth fault current using a three-lead instrument and *Procedure A*

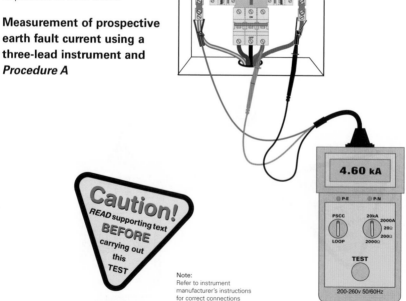

Caution!
READ supporting text
BEFORE
carrying out
this
TEST

Note:
Refer to instrument
manufacturer's instructions
for correct connections

4.60 kA

P-E   P-N

PSCC   20kA   2000A
                20Ω
LOOP   2000Ω   200Ω

TEST

200-260v 50/60Hz

**The NICEIC guide to
Domestic Periodic Inspection, Testing and Reporting**

5.5.4 Measurement of prospective fault current of a three-phase supply

Unless a test instrument designed to operate at 400 V is available, it will be necessary to calculate the prospective fault current between lines.

Measurement of prospective short-circuit current, between two lines of a three-phase supply. This method of measurement is NOT permitted using a test instrument rated at less than 400 Volts

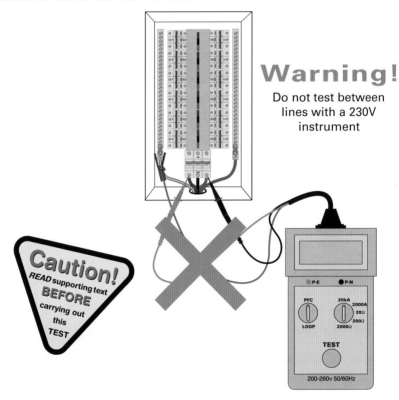

Warning!

Do not test between
lines with a 230V
instrument

Caution!
READ supporting text
BEFORE
carrying out
this
TEST

P-E   P-N

PFC   20kA   2000A
              20Ω
LOOP   2000Ω 200Ω

TEST

200-260v 50/60Hz

Where an installation is supplied by two or more lines, the maximum prospective fault current is likely to be between line conductors. If this is found to be the case, then this is the value to be recorded on the periodic inspection report.

TESTING

The prospective fault current between lines can be determined by using the measured value of the **line to neutral** prospective fault current (obtained as described in item 5.5.1). However, there is a complex relationship between the line to neutral and the line to line values of prospective fault current, which is beyond the scope of this book. As a first approximation, which tends to err on the safe side, the calculated prospective fault current line to line can be taken as **twice** that of the measured prospective fault current line to neutral.

Example, if a three-phase incoming supply has the same single-phase prospective fault current as that used in the previous single-phase example (see item 5.5.1), that is, 4.6 kA, then multiplying it by two gives:

$$\textbf{4.6 kA x 2 = 9.2 kA}$$

Therefore, the approximate value of the prospective fault current between the lines of the three-phase incoming supply would be **9.2 kA.**

5.5.5 Measurement of prospective fault current using *Procedure B*

The conditions and use of *Procedure B* to measure prospective fault current are explained in item 5.5.1.

General connections are shown in the following illustrations for two-lead and three-lead test instruments.

To measure the prospective short-circuit fault current, in general, the red and black leads of a two-lead instrument (as illustrated opposite) are connected to the load side line busbar and neutral terminal bar (as shown in the following illustration).

To measure the prospective earth fault current using a two-lead test instrument, in general, the red lead is also connected to the load side line busbar but the black lead is connected to the main earthing terminal.

Measurement of prospective short-circuit fault current using a two-lead test instrument at the load side of a consumer unit and *Procedure B*

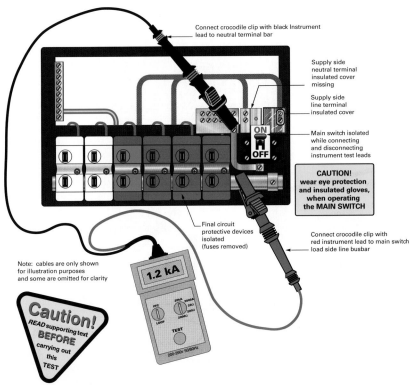

Connect crocodile clip with black Instrument lead to neutral terminal bar

Supply side neutral terminal insulated cover missing

Supply side line terminal insulated cover

Main switch isolated while connecting and disconnecting instrument test leads

CAUTION! wear eye protection and insulated gloves, when operating the MAIN SWITCH

Final circuit protective devices isolated (fuses removed)

Connect crocodile clip with red instrument lead to main switch load side line busbar

Note: cables are only shown for illustration purposes and some are omitted for clarity

Caution! READ supporting text BEFORE carrying out this TEST

1.2 kA

To measure the prospective short-circuit current or prospective earth fault current, in general, the red, blue and green leads of a three-lead test instrument (as shown in the following illustration) are connected to the load side line busbar, neutral terminal bar and main earthing terminals respectively.

Other three-lead test instruments may also require the red lead to be connected to the load side line busbar, but the blue and green leads to be connected together at the:

• neutral terminal bar (to measure prospective short-circuit fault current), or

• main earthing terminal (to measure the prospective earth fault current).

TESTING

Measurement of prospective fault current using a three-lead test instrument at the load side of a consumer unit and *Procedure B*

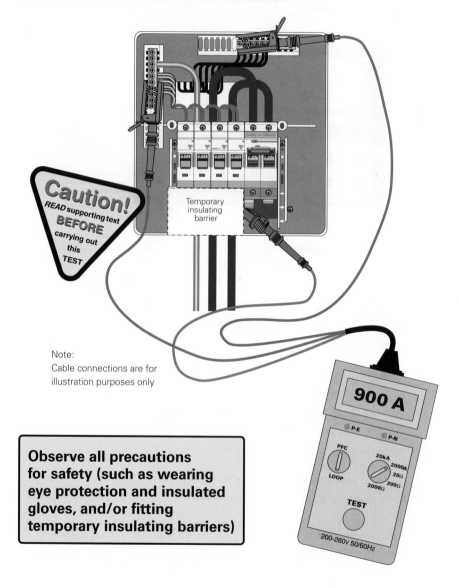

Temporary insulating barrier

Caution!
READ supporting text
BEFORE
carrying out this TEST

Note:
Cable connections are for illustration purposes only

900 A

P-E   P-N

PFC
20kA 2000A
LOOP   20Ω
2000Ω 200Ω

TEST

200-260v 50/60Hz

Observe all precautions for safety (such as wearing eye protection and insulated gloves, and/or fitting temporary insulating barriers)

The NICEIC guide to Domestic Periodic Inspection, Testing and Reporting

5.5.6 Rated short-circuit capacity of overcurrent protective devices

The short-circuit capacity of typical devices is as follows:

Circuit-breakers to *BS EN 60898* have a declared value in a small rectangular box indelibly marked on the device, for example:

$$\boxed{6000}$$

This is the 'rated short-circuit capacity' of the device, I_{cn}, assigned by the manufacturer (in amperes, not kA). The value is determined on the basis of type-tests. It is the ultimate short-circuit capacity. The device may be designed to break a fault of this magnitude only once.

Typical circuit-breaker identification

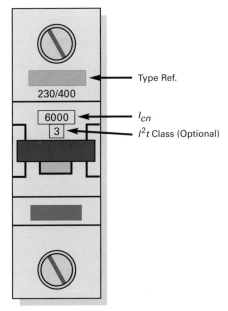

Type Ref.

230/400

I_{cn}

I^2t Class (Optional)

Front view only

TESTING

The maximum fault current the device is designed to break more than once, called the 'service short-circuit capacity', I_{cs}, may be less than the ultimate short-circuit capacity marked on devices (in general, where I_{cn} exceeds 6000 A). The manufacturer's data should be consulted for details.

A circuit-breaker manufactured to *BS 3871* will have an 'M' number marked on it. This indicates its short-circuit capacity in kA.

For example: M4 denotes 4000 A (4 kA). M9 denotes 9000 A (9 kA).

Note: In older installations type B push button operated circuit-breakers to *BS 3871* (see Annex F) may be found. These generally have a 1 kA short-circuit capacity for a 5 A nominal current rated device and 2 kA for 15 A to 45 A rated devices.

Fuses are not so straightforward: Typical values are:

BS 3036 – 1 kA to 4 kA (depending on nominal current rating)

BS 1361 – 16.5 kA

BS 88 – 40 kA to 80 kA (depending on nominal current rating)

The above values are given only as a guide, and the manufacturer's data or other relevant information for the particular device should be consulted.

Note: Overcurrent final circuit protective devices having current ratings up to 50 A incorporated in a consumer unit conforming to Annex ZA Corrigendum June 2006 of *BS EN 60439-3 – Specification for low-voltage switchgear and controlgear assemblies. Particular requirements for low-voltage switchgear and controlgear assemblies intended to be installed in places where unskilled persons have access to their use. Distribution boards* are considered adequate for a prospective fault current of up to 16 kA, provided the consumer unit is fed by a service cut-out having a high breaking capacity (HBC) fuse to *BS 1361* Type II, rated at not more than 100 A, on a single-phase supply of nominal voltage up to 250 V.

5.6   Maximum demand (load current)

This is not, as is sometimes assumed, the rating of the electricity distributor's cut-out fuse(s). The maximum demand is a value, expressed in amperes (or volt amperes) per phase, evaluated on the basis of the connected load with an allowance for diversity. Guidance on estimating maximum demand is given in IEE Guidance Note 1: Selection and Erection. There are, however, other methods by which the maximum demand current may be assessed, and these are not precluded provided they give realistic values. Methods of assessing the maximum demand of a domestic electrical installation are given in Appendix G.

A test may be also carried out on an existing installation to measure the maximum demand, subject to agreement with the client, by switching on most of the major current using equipment in the dwelling, such as the electric heater, electric cooker, washing machine, tumble dryer and immersion heater. The load current can then be measured using a suitable clamp meter, which should be carefully clamped around the line conductor of the incoming supply (such as the 'meter tail') in accordance with the instructions of the manufacturer. Such measurement can help to support the accuracy of the assessment of maximum demand made by the inspector.

Note: This type of measurement of maximum demand only gives a limited snapshot of the load current, as most current using equipment has a cyclic load, for example, cookers, washing machines and dishwashers.

It is essential that the maximum load current (design current) of the installation does **not** exceed the nominal current of the distributor's protective device or the current carrying capacity of the meter tails for a significant period of time, for example, in excess of half an hour.

Clamp meter used for measuring load current

TESTING

5.7   Leakage current

Why do we need to measure leakage currents?

The inspector may wish to investigate the unwanted tripping of an RCD. For example, a leakage current between line and Earth of around 21 mA may cause an RCD with a residual operating current of 30 mA to trip.

Leakage currents between line and Earth can be detected using a clamp meter with low current settings (measuring micro/milli amperes).

Leakage current between line and Earth is measured by using a low current clamp meter (with suitable accuracy), which is clamped carefully around the line and neutral conductors, in accordance with the instructions of the manufacturer. Clamp meter readings in excess of 3 mA may indicate equipment has a high protective current (see listed item 7, in item 4.8.2) or that there is a breakdown in insulation resistance of a conductor(s), and further investigation may be necessary.

5.8   External earth fault loop impedance (Z_e)

The external earth fault loop impedance is another of the 'supply characteristics and earthing arrangements' to be recorded in Section J of the Domestic Electrical Installation Periodic Inspection Report (see item 2.25).

Why do we have to measure external earth fault loop impedance?

In order to verify compliance with *BS 7671*, knowledge of the earth fault loop impedance is required for each circuit that relies on protective earthing, equipotential bonding and Automatic Disconnection of Supply (ADS) for fault protection

Without sufficiently low earth fault loop impedance, the magnitude of the earth fault current will not be sufficient to cause the protective device to automatically disconnect the circuit within the maximum time permitted to provide fault protection against electric shock.

The external earth fault loop impedance of an installation forms part of the earth fault loop impedance of every one of its circuits. Thus *BS 7671* requires that Z_e be determined.

Importantly, establishing Z_e by measurement also verifies that the intended means of earthing is present.

5.8.1 Measurement of external earth fault loop impedance (Z_e)

Like the maximum prospective fault current (see item 5.5), Z_e, in general, should only be measured at the origin of the installation (that is, at the point of supply). The measurement should, therefore, be made at the main switch.

An earth fault loop impedance test instrument should be used for this test.

External earth fault loop impedance may be measured using either a two-lead or three-lead instrument (see items 5.8.2 or 5.8.3 respectively).

Most instruments have a facility for polarity indication. Before proceeding with the test, it is necessary to follow the manufacturer's instructions with regard to correct polarity and test procedure.

Particular care needs to be taken when measuring external earth fault loop impedance, because of potential high fault currents, typically in excess of 1000 Amperes (1 kA), that might occur under fault conditions.

Where the supply is provided with an earth connection from the electricity distributor's network, such as from a TN-S or TN-C-S system, it is unlikely that Z_e will exceed one ohm, and the lowest range of the instrument will be the most appropriate (usually 0 to 20 Ω).

Typical maximum values of Z_e published by electricity distributors are:

TN-S   0.80 Ω

TN-C-S 0.35 Ω

In a **TT** system, where the means of earthing for the installation is provided by an installation earth electrode, the value of Z_e will usually fall within a higher range of the test instrument, for example, 20 to 200 Ω.

For safety reasons, before the earthing conductor is disconnected from the main earthing terminal, it is essential that the entire installation is **isolated** from all sources of supply (see item 1.7.1).

TESTING

Before the test, the earthing conductor must be disconnected from the main earthing terminal or otherwise separated from all parallel earth paths such as bonding and circuit protective conductors, as the purpose of the test is to prove that the intended means of earthing is present and of an acceptable ohmic value.

Any parallel earth paths present during the test would result in a false reading of Z_e, and perhaps conceal the fact that the intended means of earthing is defective, or even non-existent.

Do NOT proceed with the test unless the indications on the test instrument show that it is safe to do so.

On completion of testing and **before** the installation is re-energized, the earthing conductor and any other protective conductors disconnected to facilitate the measurement of Z_e must be reconnected.

In general, *Procedure A* or *Procedure B* is used to measure Z_e.

Procedure A may be used for measuring earth fault loop impedance at the **supply side** of the consumer unit main switch. However, if access to the live parts being tested is restricted, such as where the consumer unit is located in a small cupboard under the stairs or located at high level (requiring the use of steps), it may be preferable to use *Procedure B*.

If while following *Procedure A*, it is found at step 5 (or before) that:

1 basic protection is **below** the requirements of IP2X (for example IP1X),

   or

2 the main switch supply side terminal insulated covers are likely to be accidentally displaced during testing.

Then it may also be preferable to use *Procedure B*.

The NICEIC guide to
Domestic Periodic Inspection, Testing and Reporting

*Used where basic protection meets the requirements of IP2X (or exceeds it, for example, IP4X), terminal insulated covers are unlikely to be accidentally displaced and access to equipment is **not** restricted.*

1 Read and carefully follow the test instrument manufacturer's instructions.

2 Check that the test instrument, leads, probes and/or crocodile clips are suitable for the purpose, and in good serviceable condition (see item 1.8).

3 Select the appropriate test type and scale (for example: loop, impedance 20 Ω).

4 Isolate the supply to final circuit protective devices using the main switch and the isolation procedure given in item 1.7.1

   Note: that if the installation is supplied by a secondary source(s) of supply, such as a microgenerator, the other source(s) of supply must also be isolated.

5 **Carefully** disconnect the earthing conductor from the main earthing terminal or otherwise separate it from all protective bonding conductors and circuit protective conductors.

   Note: that on a TN-C-S system with a network fault (such as a broken neutral in the supply cable to another installation) the earthing conductor may be live and carry a high earth fault current (in **exceptional** circumstances perhaps in excess of 30 amperes). Such a fault current may be measured by connecting a clamp meter to the earthing conductor before it is removed. If it is unsafe to remove the earthing conductor to test Z_e, the inspector should report the high earth fault current to the distributor. If the earth fault cannot be cleared, an appropriate limitation, observation and recommendation code should be entered in the report.

6 Remove the consumer unit outer cover[3] and check that basic protection inside the consumer unit:

   • meets or exceeds the requirements of IP2X or IPXXB, (see item 5.13), and

---

[3] When the consumer unit cover is removed the inspector **must** prevent unskilled persons gaining access to the consumer unit.

**Procedure A
continued**

- that the main switch supply side terminal insulated covers are unlikely to be accidentally displaced during testing.

If the checks are positive continue with step 6 in this procedure. If **not** continue with step 6 in *Procedure B*.

7 Observing all precautions for safety (such as wearing insulated gloves and eye protection), firmly connect the test instrument leads to measure earth fault loop impedance, as explained in item 5.8.2.

Notes: 1 The order of connection of the test instrument leads should be Earth, neutral and line, and the order of disconnection line, neutral, Earth.

2 In general, test instrument lead connections to the Earth and neutral conductors are made using suitable crocodile clips (for example, they are insulated, except for inside the jaws). The connection to a line conductor is made using a suitable test probe (for example, one with a finger guard and short exposed metal tip).

8 Check the test instrument polarity indicator (if any) for correct connection.

9 Press the test button (repeat test as a check if appropriate, in accordance with manufacturer's instructions).

Note: that a test button may be available on the test probe.

10 Record the external earth fault loop impedance (if the test is repeated, use the highest value).

11 **Carefully** reconnect the earthing conductor.

12 Replace the consumer unit cover.

13 Reinstate the supply to the final circuit protective devices using the main switch, and reinstate any secondary source of energy, such as a microgenerator.

Procedure B has more steps to follow compared with *Procedure A*. However, using *Procedure B* prevents the need to work **on** live parts, except for proving the supply is isolated by use of a suitable voltage detector (see item 1.8).

CHAPTER **5**

Procedure B should also reduce the risk of accidentally displacing main switch supply side terminal insulated covers. However, when the supply is re-energized large areas of accessible exposed live parts may be present so it is essential to take appropriate precautions when working **near** these live parts (see item 8 in *Procedure B* and the illustrations in item 5.5.5).

Using *Procedure B* should enable external earth fault loop impedance to be measured where access is **not** restricted, such as outside the cupboard or at the bottom of the steps.

Procedure B involves measuring the external earth fault loop impedance at the **load side** of the consumer unit main switch, such as at the busbars supplying the final circuit protective devices (see the illustration in item 5.8.3). However, all final circuit protective devices and other sources of supply **must** be isolated.

Procedure B

(Used where basic protection is below the requirements of IP2X, there are terminal insulated covers that may be displaced or access to equipment is restricted.)

1 Read and carefully follow the test instrument manufacturer's instructions.

2 Check that the test instrument, leads and crocodile clips are suitable for the purpose, and in good serviceable condition (see item 1.8).

3 Select the appropriate test type and scale (for example: loop, impedance 20 Ω).

4 Isolate the supply to final circuit protective devices using the main switch and the isolation procedure given in item 1.7.1.

   Note: that if the installation is supplied by a secondary source(s) of supply, such as a microgenerator, the other source(s) of supply must also be isolated.

TESTING

5 Remove the consumer unit outer cover[4] and check if:

    a basic protection inside the consumer unit meets or exceeds the requirements of IP2X or IPXXB, (see item 5.13), **and**

    b the main switch supply side terminal insulated covers are **unlikely** to be accidentally displaced during testing, **and**

    c access to the live parts being tested is **not** restricted.

If checks **a, b and c** are positive, continue with step 6 of *Procedure A* above. If **not** continue with step 6 below.

6 Isolate **all** final circuit protective devices, such as by switching circuit-breakers OFF or by withdrawing fuses, and use the isolation procedure given in item 1.7.1.

7 **Carefully** disconnect the earthing conductor from the main earthing terminal or otherwise separate it from all protective bonding conductors and circuit protective conductors.

    Note: that on a TN-C-S system with a network fault (such as a broken neutral in the supply cable to another installation) the earthing conductor may be live and carry a high network earth fault current (in exceptional circumstances, perhaps in excess of 30 amperes). Such a fault current may be measured by connecting a clamp meter to the earthing conductor before it is removed. If it is unsafe to remove the earthing conductor to test Z_e, the inspector should report the high earth fault current to the distributor. If the fault cannot be cleared, an appropriate limitation, observation and recommendation code should be entered in the report.

8 Securely connect the test instrument leads to measure external earth fault loop impedance, as explained in item 5.8.3.

    Note: that in general, test instrument lead connections to Earth, neutral and line conductors are made using suitable crocodile clips (for example, they are insulated, except for the gripping metal surface inside the jaws).

---

[4] When the consumer unit cover is removed the inspector **must** prevent unskilled persons gaining access to the consumer unit.

The NICEIC guide to
Domestic Periodic Inspection, Testing and Reporting

9   Observing all precautions for safety (such as by wearing eye protection and insulated gloves, and/or fitting temporary insulating barriers), re-energize the supply to the final circuit protective devices using the main switch.

   Note: Leave the final circuit protective devices (and any other source of supply, such as a microgenerator) isolated.

10 Check the test instrument polarity indicator (if any) for correct connection.

11 Press the test button (repeat test as a check if appropriate, in accordance with manufacturer's instructions).

12 Record the external earth fault loop impedance (if the test is repeated, use the highest value).

13 Isolate the supply to final circuits using the main switch and the isolation procedure given in item 1.7.1.

14 Remove the test instrument leads from the consumer unit.

15 **Carefully** reconnect the earthing conductor.

16 Replace the consumer unit cover.

17 Reinstate the supply to the final circuits using the circuit protective devices, as appropriate (such as by switching on circuit-breakers or inserting fuses).

18 Reinstate the supply to the final circuit protective devices using the main switch, and reinstate any secondary source of energy, such as a microgenerator.

In **exceptional** circumstances, if it is **not** considered safe by the inspector to undertake either *Procedure A* or *B*, an appropriate limitation, observation and recommendation should be entered on the report. A value of prospective fault current obtained by enquiry should also be entered in the report.

TESTING

5.8.2 Measurement of external earth fault loop impedance using *Procedure A*

The conditions and use of *Procedure A* to measure prospective fault current are explained in item 5.8.1.

To measure the external earth fault current using a **two-lead** instrument (see Fig 1), in general, the red lead is connected to the line terminal of the incoming supply and the green lead is connected to the earthing conductor, which is in connected to Earth.

To measure the external earth fault current using a **three-lead** instrument (see Fig 2), in general, the red, black and green leads are connected to the line and neutral of the incoming supply, and the earthing conductor respectively.

Other **three-lead** test instruments may also require the red lead to be connected to the line terminal of the incoming supply, but the black and green leads to be connected together at the earthing conductor.

The NICEIC guide to
Domestic Periodic Inspection, Testing and Reporting

Measurement of external earth fault loop impedance using *Procedure A*

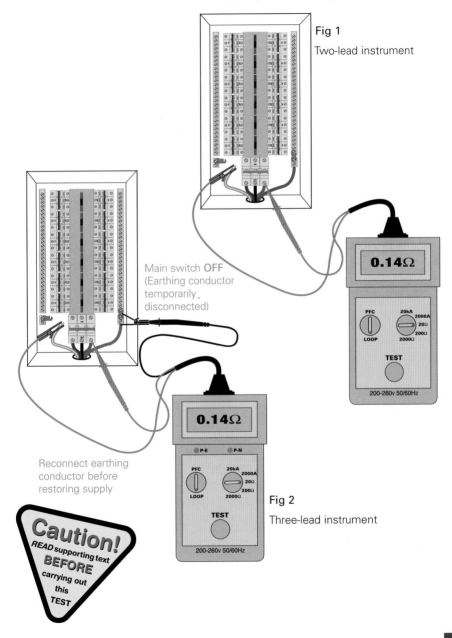

Fig 1

Two-lead instrument

Main switch **OFF**
(Earthing conductor
temporarily
disconnected)

0.14Ω

PFC   20kA   2000A
           20Ω
LOOP   2000Ω   200Ω

TEST

200-260v 50/60Hz

0.14Ω

P-E   P-N

PFC   20kA   2000A
           20Ω
LOOP   2000Ω   200Ω

TEST

200-260v 50/60Hz

Reconnect earthing
conductor before
restoring supply

Fig 2

Three-lead instrument

Caution!
READ supporting text
BEFORE
carrying out
this
TEST

An NICEIC publication © Electrical Safety Council (JAN 2008)

TESTING

5.8.3 Measurement of external earth fault loop impedance using Procedure B

The conditions and use of *Procedure B* to external earth fault loop impedance are explained in item 5.8.1.

General connections are shown in the following illustration for a **three-lead** test instrument. Connections for a **two-lead** would be similar but there would be **no** connection to the neutral terminal bar.

To measure the earth fault loop impedance using a **three-lead** test instrument, in general, the red, blue and green leads (as shown in the following illustration) are connected to the load side line busbar, neutral terminal bar and earthing conductor respectively.

Other three-lead test instruments may also require the red lead to be connected to the load side line busbar, but the blue (or black) and green leads to be connected together at the earthing conductor.

Measurement of external earth fault loop impedance using a three-lead test instrument and *Procedure B*

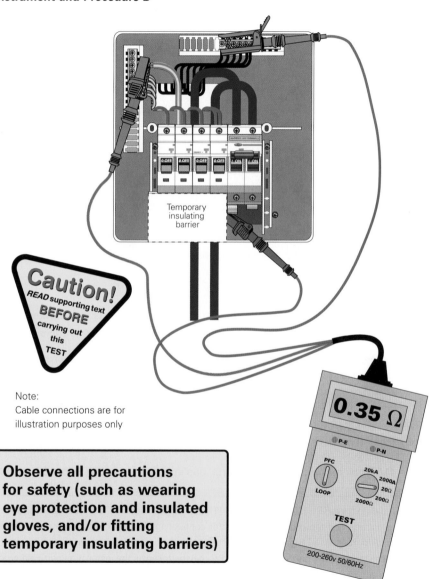

Note:
Cable connections are for
illustration purposes only

Caution!
READ supporting text
BEFORE
carrying out
this
TEST

Temporary
insulating
barrier

0.35 Ω

P-E   P-N

PFC   20kA   2000A
              20Ω
LOOP   2000Ω   200Ω

TEST

200-260v 50/60Hz

**Observe all precautions
for safety (such as wearing
eye protection and insulated
gloves, and/or fitting
temporary insulating barriers)**

TESTING

5.9 Installation earth electrode resistance (R_A)[5]

Why do we have to measure the resistance of the installation earth electrode?

Regulations 411.5.3 and 411.5.4 require certain conditions to met. For example, Regulation 411.5.3 requires that the following condition is fulfilled for each circuit that is protected by an RCD:

R_A multiplied by I_a is not to be more than 50 V ($R_A\,I_a \leq 50\,V$)

Where:

> R_A is the sum of the resistance to earth of the electrode and the resistance of the protective conductor(s), including circuit protective conductor(s), connecting it to the exposed-conductive-part, in units of ohms,

> I_a is the current causing automatic operation of the protective device within 5 seconds, in units of amperes, and

> V is the symbol used for volts.

Knowledge of the resistance of the installation earth electrode is therefore essential in order to be able to verify that the installation satisfies these safety requirements.

Note: When this condition is satisfied, it does not indicate that the touch voltages under earth fault conditions will be limited to 50 V.

Regulation 411.5.3 states that the requirements of this regulation are met if the maximum value of earth fault impedance for a final circuit protected by an RCD does **not** exceed the values given in Table 41.5 of *BS 7671*.

Table 41.5 gives maximum values of earth loop impedance of 1667, 500, 167 and 100

---

[5] R_A is defined in *BS 7671* (Regulation 411.5.3) as the sum of the resistances of the earth electrode and the protective conductor connecting it to the exposed-conductive-parts (in ohms). In most installations the resistance of the protective conductors is small compared to the resistance of the earth electrode and R_A can be taken as the installation earth electrode resistance.

The NICEIC guide to
Domestic Periodic Inspection, Testing and Reporting

ohms for RCDs with rated residual operating currents of 30, 100, 300 and 500 mA respectively that are connected to a maximum nominal 230 volt supply.

The resistance of the installation earth should be as low as practicable and a value exceeding 200 ohms may **not** be stable (Note 2 to Table 41.5 of *BS 7671* refers).

A TT system should be equipped with an installation earth electrode as its means of earthing. The function of the earth electrode is to make electrical contact with the general mass of the Earth to provide a suitable path for earth fault current to return to the source (such as via the earth electrode at the distribution transformer).

Measurement of the resistance of the installation earth electrode to the general mass of the Earth provides information necessary for verifying that the earthing arrangement satisfies the requirements of both *BS 7671* and the particular installation design. The method of measurement and the measured resistance value need to be recorded, together with the type of electrode and its location, in Section J of the Domestic Electrical Installation Periodic Inspection Report (see item 2.25).

Two methods of measuring the resistance of an earth electrode are recognised in IEE Guidance Note 3:

- Method 1: using a proprietary earth electrode test instrument (see item 5.9.1)

- Method 2: using an earth fault loop impedance test instrument (see item 5.9.2).

Where sufficient and suitable ground area is available, a proprietary earth electrode test instrument may be used. However, where there is insufficient space, or where hard surfaces make the use of such a test instrument impracticable, the use of an earth fault loop impedance test instrument may be appropriate. The use of a spikeless earth electrodes test instrument may be considered where more than one earth electrode is installed.

For safety reasons, these methods require the installation to be isolated from the supply (see item 1.7.1) before the means of earthing is disconnected.

TESTING

5.9.1 Method 1 (using a propriety earth electrode test instrument)

Having first isolated the installation, the earth electrode should preferably be disconnected from the earthing conductor which connects it to the main earthing terminal. If this is not possible, the earthing conductor must be disconnected from the protective bonding conductors and other protective conductors at the main earthing terminal, to remove any parallel paths to the general mass of the Earth. If such parallel paths are not removed before the measurement is made, a false (low) reading of the resistance of the electrode to Earth will be obtained.

If the test instrument is a four-terminal device, the terminals marked C1 and P1 are linked together and connected to the electrode under test. The remaining two terminals are connected to temporary electrodes as shown in the following illustration.

Where the instrument is a three-terminal device, the corresponding configuration is shown in the following illustration. Many proprietary instruments have a facility for checking the resistance of the temporary electrodes. Where the resistance of a temporary electrode is found to exceed the limit stated in the instrument manufacturer's instructions, the resistance should be reduced to a value within the stated limit.

A sufficient reduction in the resistance of the temporary electrodes may be achieved by driving longer temporary rods into the ground, or by watering the ground in the immediate vicinity of the temporary rods. The ground adjacent to the installation earth electrode must **not** be treated with water or brine, as this would make the resistance measurement invalid for the purpose of periodic inspection reporting.

Where possible, the test instrument should be situated close to the installation earth electrode under test. If the test instrument has to be situated some considerable distance from that electrode, two separate leads should be run out from C1 and P1 to minimise the effect of lead resistance, with the link being formed at the installation earth electrode.

The NICEIC guide to
Domestic Periodic Inspection, Testing and Reporting

In principle, the instrument passes a current through the ground between the two current terminals C1 and C2. At the same time, the voltage drop between the installation earth electrode and the general mass of Earth is determined by means of the voltage (potential) at terminals P1 and P2. The instrument then has sufficient information to calculate and display an ohmic value for the resistance of the installation earth electrode under test.

The temporary (current) electrode C2 is placed in the ground some distance away from the installation earth electrode under test. Unless the soil resistivity is very high, 20 metres is usually sufficient for this purpose. The temporary (potential) electrode P2 is placed approximately mid-way between the other two electrodes.

One reading is taken with P2 in the mid-way position, and a further two readings are taken with P2 approximately 2 metres on either side of the mid-way point.

The average of these three resistance readings should then be calculated, and compared with the individual readings. None of the individual readings should differ from the average by more than 5%. If they do, and there is a clear progression in the readings from one position of P2 to the next, it may mean that the resistance area of the installation earth electrode is overlapping that of temporary electrode C2.

To overcome this problem, electrode C2 should be moved further away from the installation earth electrode, and the test procedure repeated. When three acceptable resistance readings have been obtained, record the average value on the report.

*Re-connect the earthing conductor and all bonding and protective conductors on completion of the test, **before** the installation is re-energized.*

TESTING

Measurement of installation earth electrode resistance

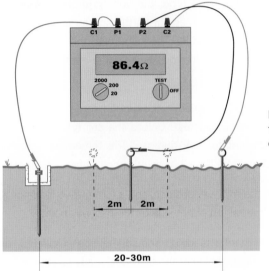

Method 1 (using a four-terminal proprietary earth electrode test instrument)

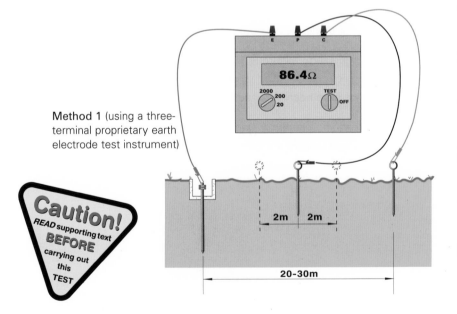

Method 1 (using a three-terminal proprietary earth electrode test instrument)

Caution!
READ supporting text
BEFORE
carrying out
this
TEST

The NICEIC guide to
Domestic Periodic Inspection, Testing and Reporting

5.9.2 Method 2 (using an earth fault loop impedance test instrument)

This method is essentially the same as the method used to measure the external earth fault loop impedance, Z_e (see item 5.8). The measured value of Z_e for a TT system may therefore also be used as the approximate value of the resistance of the installation earth electrode (R_A).

The test method measures the impedance of the earth fault loop from the earthing conductor via the installation earth electrode, the earth return path, the source earth electrode, the supply distribution transformer, and the supply line conductor back to the line supply terminal at the origin of the installation.

As the impedance of the other parts of the earth fault loop can be expected to be relatively low, the measurement given by the earth fault loop impedance test instrument may be taken as the resistance of the installation earth electrode. (The measurement, which will include the resistance of the means of earthing at the source distribution transformer and circuit loop line conductors, will err on the safe (high) side).

Procedure A described in item 5.8.2 may be used for approximately measuring R_A provided that all of the conditions given in 5.8.1 apply, that is,

1   basic protection meets the requirements of IP2X (or exceeds it, for example, IP4X), and

2   the requirements of, terminal insulated covers are unlikely to be accidentally displaced, and

3   access to equipment is **not** restricted.

If any of the conditions listed above are **not** met than *Procedure B*, as explained in items 5.8.1 and 5.8.3, may be used.

TESTING

Measurement of approximate earth electrode resistance R_A, in ohms, of an installation using *Procedure A* (see items 5.8.1 and 5.8.2 for information on measuring external earth fault loop impedance)

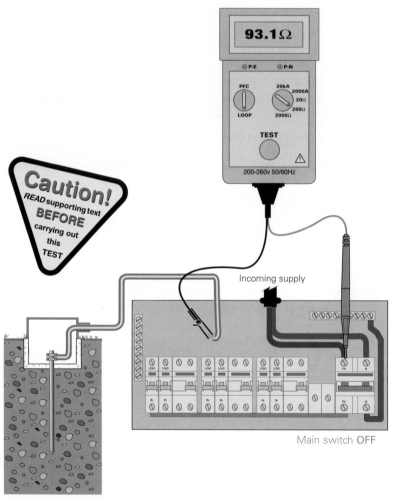

Method 2 (using an earth fault loop impedance test instrument).

The NICEIC guide to
Domestic Periodic Inspection, Testing and Reporting

5.10 Continuity of conductors

Why do we need to test the continuity of protective conductors?

It is essential to ensure that all circuit protective conductors and bonding conductors are continuous. Otherwise, an exposed-conductive-part, an extraneous-conductive-part or the earthing terminal of a point or accessory could be left without an effective connection to Earth, giving no earth fault protection.

Whilst the primary purpose of testing for protective conductor continuity is to ensure that such continuity exists, the result of an $R_1 + R_2$ test (see item 5.10.1) can be used to determine the earth fault loop impedance (Z_s) and confirm polarity at the point or accessory at which the test is applied. Information to determine Z_s and confirm polarity is explained in items 5.15 and 5.14 respectively.

Errors caused by parallel paths

Before carrying out a test to confirm the continuity (or to measure the resistance) of a protective conductor, care should be taken to locate and disconnect (if practical) any conductive paths which may be connected in parallel with all or part of it. Such parallel paths could lead to incorrect test results and may even conceal the fact that a protective conductor is not electrically continuous.

An example of parallel paths is between the earthing terminal of a metallic boiler and the main earthing terminal (MET). Where the parallel paths are the boiler:

- circuit protective conductor (which connects directly to the MET), and
- gas and water metallic pipework (which both connect to the MET through the gas and water protective bonding conductors respectively).

In the above example, before checking the continuity (or measuring resistance) between the boiler earthing terminal and the MET, it may be possible to temporarily remove these parallel paths by disconnecting the:

- gas and water protective bonding conductors, or circuit protective conductor, from the MET, or
- circuit protective conductor from the boiler earthing terminal.

Such temporary disconnections must only be carried out if it practical and safe to do so, and after all sources of energy have been isolated, using the procedure explained in item 1.7.1. Any items disconnected **must be securely** reconnected after testing, before restoring the supply.

TESTING

Test instrument

The test instrument to be used is an ohmmeter having a low ohms range, or an insulation and continuity test instrument set to the continuity range. It is recommended that the instrument has a short-circuit output current of not less than 200 mA (a.c. or d.c.) and an open-circuit voltage of between 4 V and 24 V.

Continuity test readings of less than 1 Ω are common. Therefore, the resistance of the test leads is significant, and should not be included in any recorded test result. If the particular test instrument does not have provision for correcting for the resistance of the test leads, it will be necessary to measure the resistance of the leads when connected together, and for this measured value to be subtracted from all the test readings. See the following illustration.

Measuring resistance of the leads of a continuity test instrument

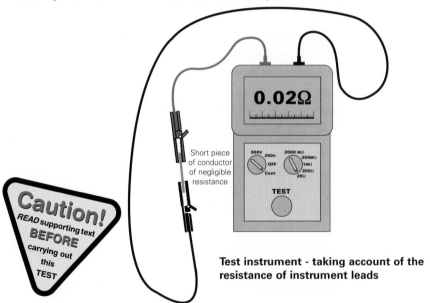

Test instrument - taking account of the resistance of instrument leads

Measuring the resistance of the leads of a continuity test instrument is necessary so that this value can be subtracted from test results for protective conductor continuity. Some test instruments have a built in facility to 'zero out' the lead resistance, making subtraction from test results unnecessary.

**The NICEIC guide to
Domestic Periodic Inspection, Testing and Reporting**

5.10.1 The $R_1 + R_2$ method

This method is applicable to circuit protective conductors and their associated line conductors. It is not applicable to main or supplementary bonding conductors. The $R_1 + R_2$ method of testing the continuity of circuit protective conductors has the following advantages:

- the information required to complete the $R_1 + R_2$ column of the Schedule of Test Results is obtained directly

- polarity may be verified as each continuity test is performed

- the method may be more convenient than the 'wander lead' method (see item 5.10.2).

The test provides a measured value of resistance for the line conductor and the circuit protective conductor of a circuit, in series.

The test should be carried out, having **first securely isolated the supply** (see item 1.7.1), by temporarily connecting together the line conductor and the circuit protective conductor (at the supply end of the final circuit being measured), and then connecting the test instrument to the terminals of the line conductor and the circuit protective conductor at each point and accessory on the final circuit in turn, as appropriate.

The value of $R_1 + R_2$ measured at the point or accessory electrically most remote from the supply will be the maximum value, and it is this value that should be recorded on the Schedule of Test Results. The test readings at the other points and accessories on the circuit serve to confirm that the protective conductor is continuous to each of them, and that the polarity is correct.

TESTING

Testing continuity of the protective conductor to a lighting point by the $R_1 + R_2$ method

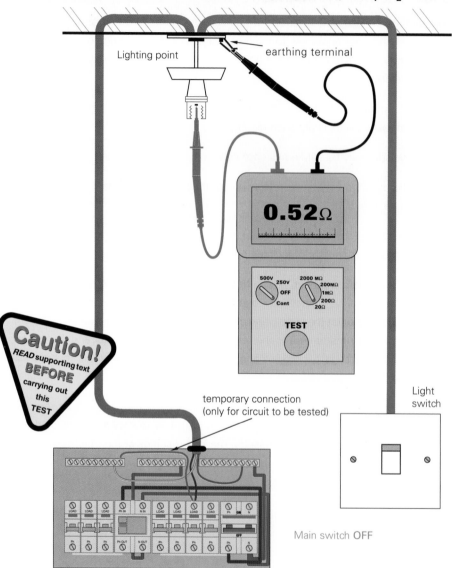

Lighting point

earthing terminal

0.52Ω

500V 250V
OFF
Cont

2000 MΩ
200MΩ
1MΩ
200Ω
20Ω

TEST

Caution!
READ supporting text
BEFORE
carrying out
this
TEST

temporary connection
(only for circuit to be tested)

Light
switch

Main switch OFF

This test procedure also enables correct polarity to be verified.

The NICEIC guide to
Domestic Periodic Inspection, Testing and Reporting

Procedure:

1 Securely isolate the supply (see item 1.7.1).

2 Disconnect any bonding connections that could affect the test readings.

3 Make a temporary connection, at the supply end of the circuit (for example, at a consumer unit) between the line of the circuit to be tested and the circuit protective conductor.

4 Measure the resistance between line and protective conductor at each point and accessory on the circuit (thereby also confirming correct polarity).

5 Record the reading at the electrically most remote point or accessory (the highest value) of the circuit (and confirm correct polarity for the circuit).

6 Re-connect any bonding conductors disconnected for the test.

7 Remove the temporary connection **before** the supply is restored.

5.10.2 The R_2 (or wander lead) method

This method is used principally for testing protective conductors that are connected to the main earthing terminal (such as main equipotential bonding conductors and circuit protective conductors). It can be a useful method to easily determine the earth continuity of exposed-conductive-parts such as metallic luminaires or accessories, without the need to dismantle them. However, the correct polarity of circuit connections will need to be verified separately.

Testing continuity of the protective conductor at a lighting switch by the wander lead method

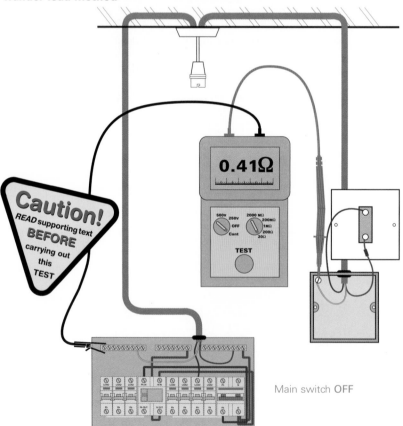

Main switch OFF

Danger may occur from access to live parts, for example:

- while removing a consumer unit cover,

- while removing an accessory from its mounting box,

- when testing equipment that has a reverse polarity connection, or

- when testing equipment with an accessible metallic enclosure, such as a Class I luminaire, which has a line to earth fault at the metallic enclosure, and a broken protective conductor. That is, there is **not** a path to Earth for the fault to operate the automatic protective device. Meaning that the enclosure is live!

To ensure that accessible exposed-conductive-parts are **not** live, supplies to the circuits concerned need to be securely isolated (see item 1.7.1) **before** continuity testing is carried out.

One terminal of the continuity test instrument is connected to the main earthing terminal with a long lead (or 'wander lead') and, with a lead from the other terminal, contact is made with the protective conductor at every position to which it is connected in that circuit, such as at socket-outlets, lighting points, fixed equipment points, switches, exposed-conductive-parts and extraneous-conductive-parts. By this means, provided that no parallel paths are present, the continuity of the protective conductor back to the main earthing terminal can be verified, and its resistance measured.

An earthing conductor, circuit protective conductor, protective bonding conductor or supplementary bonding conductor can be tested by simply attaching the leads of the test instrument to each end of the conductor, after securely isolating the supply and having temporarily disconnected one end of that conductor to remove parallel paths as appropriate (see items 5.10.5 to 5.10.8 respectively).

Replace any temporary disconnected conductors before the supply is re-energized.

TESTING

5.10.3   Ferrous enclosures

Where inspection and testing of ferrous enclosures used as protective conductors is undertaken, the inspector should make every effort to verify the compliance of these conductors with the requirements of *BS 7671* by careful inspection, so far as is reasonably practicable, and testing by the $R_1 + R_2$ (see item 5.10.1) or wander lead method (see item 5.10.2).

One lead of the continuity test instrument would connect to the protective conductor of the enclosure (shown below) and the other lead would connect to the line conductor at the enclosure for the $R_1 + R_2$ method (or main earthing terminal for the wander lead method).

Test lead from a continuity test instrument connected to a ferrous enclosure used as a protective conductor

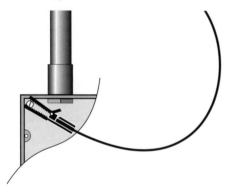

If, after this inspection and testing, the inspector has reasonable doubt about the soundness of any part of these conductive paths, such as the ability of any of the joints to provide durable electrical continuity and adequate mechanical strength, the inspector should include an appropriate observation and recommendation code in the report.

5.10.4   Ring final circuit conductors

Ring final circuit conductors start at the appropriate outgoing terminals in a

**The NICEIC guide to
Domestic Periodic Inspection, Testing and Reporting**

consumer unit, connect to all the points in the ring, and return to the same outgoing terminals. The live (line and neutral) conductors must form a complete unbroken loop (ring) without interconnections (known as bridges), as must the circuit protective conductor unless it is formed by a continuous metal covering or enclosure (such as a steel conduit) containing all the live conductors.

Why do we need to check the continuity of ring final circuit conductors?

Incorrectly connected or open circuit conductors in an installed ring final circuit can lead to overloading of those conductors. Testing by the following procedure verifies continuity and correct connection, as well as correct polarity.

Test instrument for checking continuity

The test instrument to be used for checking continuity is one of the types described earlier in this Chapter for testing the continuity of protective conductors. The test instrument needs to be capable of distinguishing between resistances differing by as little as 0.05 Ω, and due allowance needs to be made for the resistance of the test leads.

Checking ring final circuit continuity, interconnections, spurs and polarity, and measuring $R_1 + R_2$

Loop resistance of ring final is, in general, measured at the ends of the ring circuit at a consumer unit as explained in Step 1 of the following procedure. However, it may be necessary to measure the loop resistance at a socket-outlet position (as illustrated in the following photograph), perhaps for safety reasons as explained after the procedure below.

Procedure:

Step 1 (Confirming ring continuity)

   1   Securely isolate the installation (see item 1.7.1), or the part of the installation to be tested.

TESTING

2 Identify and disconnect the line, neutral and circuit protective conductors of the ring final circuit.

3 Measure the resistance of the line and neutral conductors separately, between ends. If the circuit protective conductor is a ring conductor not made up of metal conduit, trunking or cable covering, also measure its resistance.

4 Note the readings obtained as **end to end** resistance of the:

    a line conductor = r_1

    b Circuit protective conductor = r_2

    c Neutral conductor = r_n.

The values of r_1, r_2 and r_n will indicate whether or not the conductors are continuous. The line and neutral conductors should have equal resistances. If the circuit protective conductor has a smaller cross-sectional area than the line and neutral, its resistance should be higher.

In the case of a ring circuit having 2.5 mm² live conductors and a 1.5 mm² circuit protective conductor, the resistance of the protective conductor should be around 1.67 times that of the line or neutral conductor.

Exceptionally, the resistance of the protective conductor may be less than the resistance of the line or neutral conductor if parallel earth paths are present. For example, if the protective conductors and water (and/or gas) installation pipework for several current using items of equipment have an unintentional common metallic connection.

An example of such a parallel earth path is a Class I gas fired central heating system and a separate Class I mains ignition gas heater, which are both connected to the same ring circuit and metallic gas pipework.

If the appropriate resistance conditions cannot be confirmed, then either the ring conductors may **not** have been correctly identified, or there may be a wiring defect

**The NICEIC guide to
Domestic Periodic Inspection, Testing and Reporting**

in the ring circuit. So an appropriate observation and recommendation code should be included on the report.

Step 1

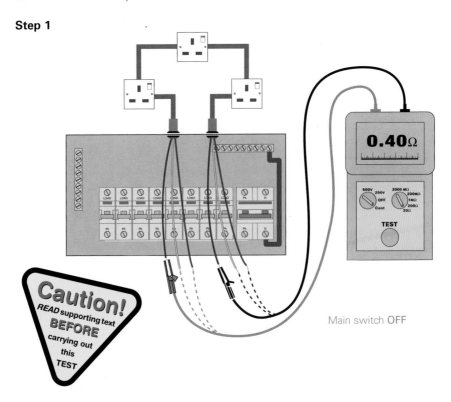

Main switch OFF

Step 2 (Checking ring continuity and interconnections)

1   Connect the incoming neutral to the outgoing line of the circuit, and vice versa, so that the conductors are 'cross-connected'

2   Measure the resistance (line to neutral) between the pairs at the point at which the cross-connection is made, and note the result. The reading obtained should be approximately **half** that obtained for either the line or neutral conductor in Step 1.

TESTING

Step 2

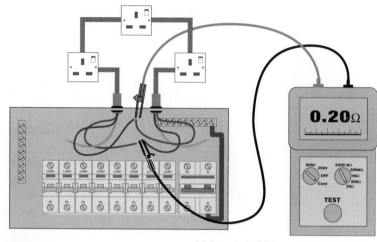

0.20Ω

Main switch OFF

Caution!
READ supporting text
BEFORE
carrying out
this
TEST

Step 3 (Checking ring continuity, interconnections and spurs)

With the circuit conductors still connected as in Step 2, measure the resistance between the line and neutral at each point on the ring. The reading should be substantially the same as that measured in Step 2.

Socket-outlets wired as spurs (cable branches) will give a slightly higher resistance reading depending on the length of the cable branch. Where the presence of a cable branch is identified from such a resistance reading, the inspector should assess whether adequate protection against overload has been afforded for that branch.

The NICEIC guide to
Domestic Periodic Inspection, Testing and Reporting

CHAPTER **5**

If the resistance measurements increase with the distance from the starting point, it is usually an indication that the ends of the ring have not been crossed-over as intended. If this is the case, go back to the starting point of Step 2 and reverse the connections so that one line is connected to the other neutral and vice versa, and then repeat the test.

It should now be found that the value is the same as in Step 2 at all points in the ring circuit.

Note: Instrument leads may be connected to the socket-outlet terminals using a socket interface adaptor (such as that illustrated), which avoids the need to remove the socket-outlet to gain access to the line, neutral and protective conductors. Such an adaptor may be obtained from NICEIC Direct.

Socket interface adaptor

TESTING

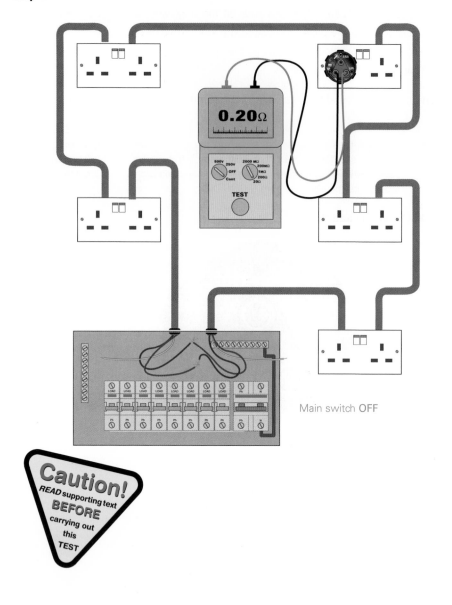

Main switch OFF

Caution!
READ supporting text BEFORE carrying out this TEST

The NICEIC guide to
Domestic Periodic Inspection, Testing and Reporting

CHAPTER **5**

Step 4 (Checking ring continuity, interconnections, spurs and polarity, and measuring $R_1 + R_2$)

Repeat the procedure as in Steps 2 and 3, but using the line and protective conductors.

With the line and protective conductors cross-connected, the resistances measured between the line and protective conductor at each point on the ring will differ slightly from each other.

Resistances measured at points connected to a spur will be higher than the resistance measured at the nearest point on the ring, and will increase with the length of the spur.

The highest value (measured in this step) represents the maximum $R_1 + R_2$ value for the circuit, and can be recorded as such on the Schedule of Test Results.

Note: Out of interest, the measured value of $R_1 + R_2$ measured in this step should be equal to $(r_1 + r_2)/4$, where r_1 and r_2 are the end-to-end resistances of the line and circuit protective ring conductors respectively (as measured in Step 1).

This test sequence also verifies polarity and circuit protective conductor continuity to all points in the ring final circuit.

TESTING

Step 4

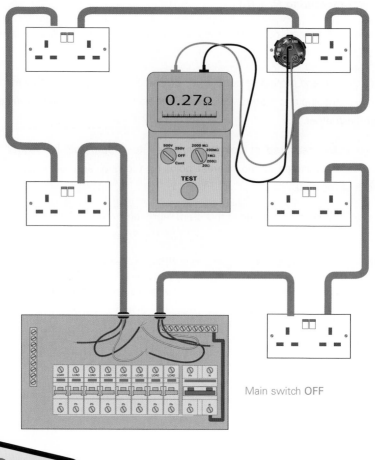

0.27Ω

Main switch OFF

Caution!

READ supporting text
BEFORE
carrying out
this
TEST

The NICEIC guide to
Domestic Periodic Inspection, Testing and Reporting

Step 5 (Reconnecting conductors)

Reconnect the conductors to the correct terminals **before** re-energizing the supply.

Measuring continuity of ring final circuit protective conductors at a socket-outlet, with the supply isolated

If it is necessary to measure the loop resistance at a socket-outlet position (as illustrated in the above photograph) ring continuity may be determined using a procedure similar to that explained in Steps 1 and 5 of the previous procedure. If it is impractical to use similar steps to Steps 2 to 4 of the procedure it would mean that ring interconnections, spurs or polarity are **not** checked, and $R_1 + R_2$ is not measured. However, alternative tests may be carried out to check and measure similar items, for example, by using:

- a plug in earth fault loop impedance test instrument:

   - incorrect ring interconnections or spurs can be indicated, by comparing measured values of Z_s at socket-outlets on different parts of the ring, and

   - the maximum value of Z_s (see item 5.15) can be measured

TESTING

- a continuity test instrument, continuity of protective conductors at points or accessories can be confirmed, by measuring R_2 (see item 5.10.2)

- a plug in polarity indicator, polarity of socket-outlets (see item 5.14) can be confirmed.

5.10.5 Earthing conductor

In practice the continuity of the earthing conductor is checked when the external earth fault loop impedance (Z_e) is measured (see item 5.8). However, in the unlikely event that the continuity of an earthing conductor is required to be measured, the following procedure might be used:

1   Isolate the supply at the main switch (see item 1.7.1).

2   Disconnect the earthing conductor from the main earthing terminal.

3   Measure the resistance between the earthing conductor ends using the R_2 (wander lead method), see item 5.10.2.

4   Check the measured value of continuity against the calculated value of the conductor resistance (see below).

5   Reconnect the earthing conductor at the main earthing terminal **before** the supply is re-energized

The calculated value of conductor resistance in ohms (Ω) is determined by multiplying the length of the conductor (in metres) by its resistance per metre (in ohms per metre). That is:

Conductor resistance = length x resistance per metre

Values of conductor resistance per metre are given in Annexe E.

The NICEIC guide to
Domestic Periodic Inspection, Testing and Reporting

Example of calculating conductor resistance

A single-core pvc insulated earthing conductor with a cross-sectional area of 16 mm^2 is 2 metres long.

From Table E1 in Annex E, a copper conductor with a cross-sectional area of 16 mm^2 has a resistance of 1.15 milliohms per metre (mΩ per m).

Using the above formula:

Conductor resistance = 2 x 1.15 = 2.3 mΩ

In practice the measured value of the earthing conductor resistance displayed on the continuity test instrument is likely be around 0.1 Ω, depending on the resolution and accuracy of the test instrument. If the earthing conductor resistance measured was higher than 0.1 Ω, for example 0.4 Ω, an appropriate observation and recommendation code should be entered in the report.

5.10.6 Circuit protective conductors (cpc)

The procedure for measuring the resistance of protective conductors is explained in item 5.10.2.

Example of calculating conductor resistance

The cpc of cross-sectional area of 1 mm^2 in a pvc flat insulated and sheathed cable is approximately 20 metres long.

From Table E1 in Annex E, a copper conductor with a cross-sectional area of 1 mm^2 has a resistance of 18.1 milliohms per metre (mΩ per m).

Using the previously mentioned formula:

Conductor resistance = 20 x 18.1 = 362 mΩ

Therefore the measured value of the cpc should be around the value of 360 mΩ (0.36Ω) depending on the resolution and accuracy of the continuity test instrument. If the circuit protective conductor resistance measured was higher than 0.4 Ω, for

TESTING

example 0.7 Ω, an appropriate observation and recommendation code should be entered in the report.

5.10.7 Protective bonding conductors

The procedure and method of calculating and measuring the resistance of a Protective bonding is similar to that for an earthing conductor (see item 5.10.5), except that the protective bonding conductor is temporary disconnected (step 2) and reconnected to the MET (step 5), rather than the earthing conductor.

5.10.8 Additional protection: supplementary bonding conductors

Where additional protection: supplementary bonding is required (that is, in installations installed before *BS 7671*: 2008) visual inspection may, in general, be used to confirm the presence of supplementary bonding (see item 4.6.10). However, if supplementary bonding is **not** visible, or doubt exists of the effectiveness of supplementary bonding (for installations installed to an edition of *BS 7671* before 2008) the following test procedure may be used to confirm the presence of supplementary bonding.

Similarly the same test procedure may be used to assess the effectiveness of the connection of extraneous-conductive-parts of the location and the main earthing terminal, if necessary (for installations installed to Regulation 701.415.2 of *BS 7671*: 2008).

Procedure:

1   Isolate the supply at the main switch (see item 1.7.1). Isolation is necessary in case there is **no** supplementary bonding or protective bonding present, and there is a fault on the installation. Thereby, producing a possible touch voltage of 230 volts between a live exposed-conductive-part (such as a Class I luminaire) and an extraneous-conductive-part (such as a metallic radiator connected to a water pipe), which is not bonded to the main earthing terminal.

2 Measure the resistance between the simultaneously accessible exposed-conductive-part (such as a Class I luminaire) and the extraneous-conductive-part (such as a metallic radiator connected to metallic pipework), using the R_2 (wander lead method (see item 5.10.2).

3 Verify that the resistance between the simultaneously accessible exposed-conductive-parts and extraneous-conductive-parts is less or equal to 50 volts divided by the operating current (I_a) in amperes of the protective device[6] (Regulation 415.2.2). An example of how to calculate and verify if the resistance is adequate is shown below.

4 Re-energize the supply when safe to do so.

Example, to verify if the resistance measured between a Class I luminaire and a metallic radiator connected to the water pipe (which is an exposed-conductive-part) is adequate

Consider a Class I luminaire protected by a 5A semi-enclosed (rewireable) fuse to *BS 3036*. Using the procedure given in item 3 above:

1 the operating current (I_a) of the 5 A fuse is 13 A for an operating time of 5 s, as determined from the time/current characteristics table for a 5 A semi-enclosed fuse given in Fig 3.2A of Appendix 3 of *BS 7671*

2 The maximum permitted resistance is 50 V divided by
I_a = 50 V/13 A = 3.8 Ω

If the measured resistance between the Class I luminaire and a metallic radiator that is connected to the metallic water pipe (which is an exposed conductive part) is greater than 3.8 Ω, say 5 Ω, the result would be unacceptable and an appropriate observation and recommendation code should be included in the report.

---

[6] The operating current I_a of an RCD is the residual operating current ($I_{\Delta n}$), and for an overcurrent device it is the 5 second operating current (taken from the time/current characteristics of the device).

TESTING

5.11 Insulation resistance

Why do we need to test insulation resistance?

The insulation resistance tests give an indication of the condition of the insulation of the installation. Effective insulation is required to provide basic protection, and to prevent short-circuits, earth faults and fires.

Leakage currents due to inadequate insulation can present a risk of electric shock to persons. They can also cause further deterioration to the insulation and conductors if allowed to persist, when they may present a fire risk. It is therefore important that insulation resistances are tested when assessing the condition of an existing installation.

Precautions should be taken to avoid damage to electronic devices during insulation resistance tests. For example, by:

- inserting a temporary link between the line and neutral conductors of a circuit fitted with a lighting dimmer control, and

- disconnecting equipment fitted with a surge protective device (SPD), which connects between a line conductor and Earth. An SPD might be used to protect equipment such as a computer.

In general, the installation would be initially tested as a whole. However, for practical reasons it may be necessary or desirable to sub-divide the installation in order to carry out insulation resistance testing.

The instrument to be used is an insulation resistance test instrument capable of supplying the test voltage indicated in Table 61 of *BS 7671* (which is partly reproduced as follows).

The NICEIC guide to
Domestic Periodic Inspection, Testing and Reporting

Part Table 61 - Minimum values of insulation resistance

Circuit nominal voltage (V)	Test voltage d.c. (V)	Minimum insulation resistance (MΩ)
SELV and PELV	250	≥ 0.5
Up to and including 500 V	500	≥ 1.0

Reproduced courtesy of the IET

Regulation 612.3.2 considers that the measured value of insulation resistance of an installation is satisfactory if it is **not** less than the appropriate minimum value given in Table 61. The insulation resistance value being measured with all the final circuits connected to the consumer unit, but with all current-using equipment disconnected.

The insulation resistance is normally measured between live conductors (line and neutral), see item 5.11.1, and between live conductors and Earth, see item 5.11.2.

5.11.1 Resistance between live conductors

To test the insulation resistance between live conductors (line and neutral for a single-phase circuit), a voltage is applied between the conductors at the origin of the circuit.

Any reduction in insulation resistance (compared to previous test measurements) indicates an increase in leakage current from one conductor to the other.

Very low values of insulation resistance (possibly a few ohms or less) indicate incorrect connections or damaged cables, and leakage current between conductors is very high current (possibly hundreds of amperes), that is, a short-circuit.

Very high values of insulation resistance (200 MΩ or more, beyond the upper range of the instrument) indicate that the insulation is satisfactory, and leakage current between conductors is very low (possibly a few microamperes).

TESTING

It is likely to be impracticable to disconnect all electronic devices from a circuit to measure the insulation resistance between live conductors. For this reason, the neutral and line conductors should be temporary connected together, and insulation resistance **only** measured between this connection of live conductors and Earth (see item 5.11.2).

However, if there is an **exceptional** requirement to measure the insulation resistance between live conductors the following procedure may be used.

Procedure:

1   Read and carefully follow the test instrument manufacturer's instructions.

2   Check that the test instrument and leads are in sound condition (see item 1.8).

3   Check the condition of the batteries in the test instrument.

4   Select the appropriate test voltage and range.

5   Securely isolate the circuit under test from the supply (see item 1.7.1), including the neutral.

6   Disconnect all equipment that may be vulnerable to the test voltage, such as fire detection alarm systems, security systems and lighting controls.

7   Unplug all electrical equipment including appliances and surge protection devices. Disconnect all current-using equipment including fluorescent and other discharge luminaires. Remove filament and compact fluorescent lamps and check that all switches are closed (two-way switches should be operated to include all live conductors in the test). Where the disconnection of current-using equipment or removal of lamps is impracticable, the local switches controlling these items should be opened.

8   Disconnect all pilot or indicator lamps that are likely to interfere with the test

The NICEIC guide to
Domestic Periodic Inspection, Testing and Reporting

9 Connect the test instrument, and measure and record the insulation resistance, in units of Ω, kΩ or MΩ as appropriate:

a For a single-phase installation:

- Line 1 to neutral

b For a three-phase installation:

- Line 1 to Line 2

- Line 2 to Line 3

- Line 3 to Line 1

- Each line in turn to the neutral.

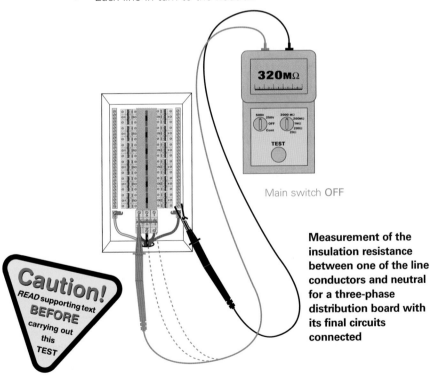

320MΩ

Main switch OFF

Caution!
READ supporting text
BEFORE
carrying out
this
TEST

Measurement of the insulation resistance between one of the line conductors and neutral for a three-phase distribution board with its final circuits connected

TESTING

5.11.2 Resistance between live conductors and Earth

Protective conductors must be connected to the earthing arrangement, that is, the general mass of Earth (as implied by the capitalized word Earth) to comply with Regulation 612.3.2.

The connection to Earth is typically achieved by the protective conductor being connected to the main earthing terminal (MET) of the installation, to which the earthing, protective bonding and supplementary bonding also connect.

Having protective conductors connected to Earth during the test has the advantage that it might detect any contact between a live conductor and any unearthed[7] metalwork (such as an isolated concealed part of the building structure or a section of pipework). For example, the unearthed metalwork may have some low resistance contact with Earth that is identified as a problem by the inspector using the insulation test instrument. Such a problem might be caused by the penetration of a nail making contact with a live conductor and the unearthed metalwork, making a potential electric shock hazard.

The following procedure may be used to measure insulation resistance between linked live conductors and Earth.

Procedure:

1   Read and carefully follow the test instrument manufacturer's instructions.

2   Check that the test instrument and leads are in sound condition (see item 1.8).

3   Check the condition of the batteries in the test instrument.

4   Select the appropriate test voltage and range.

---

[7] Unearthed – means **not** forming part of the earthed equipotential zone. That is, metalwork that is not connected to Earth through bonding conductors, which form part of the electrical installation.

The NICEIC guide to
Domestic Periodic Inspection, Testing and Reporting

5   Securely isolate the circuit under test from the supply (see item 1.7.1), including the neutral.

6   Disconnect any equipment fitted with a surge protective device (SPD).

> **Note:**   Where it is not practicable to disconnect the equipment (such as, in the case of a fixed-socket outlet containing an SPD) the test voltage may be reduced to 250 V d.c. but the insulation resistance should have a value of **not** less than 1 M Ω.

7   Link together all live conductors (line and neutral)

8   Connect the insulation resistance test instrument between the linked live conductors and the main earthing terminal.

9   Measure and record the insulation resistance, in units of Ω, kΩ or MΩ as appropriate.

10   Reconnect any equipment fitted with a surge protective device (SPD).

11   Remove the link between live conductors **before** the supply is restored.

As may be seen from Table 61 of *BS 7671* (partly reproduced in item 5.11.1), the minimum acceptable value for a 400/230 V installation may be as low as 1 MΩ. However, such a very low value should not be accepted without question.

If any test reveals an insulation resistance lower than 2 MΩ, the circuits should be separated and tested individually in order to identify the cause of the low reading. The overall low reading may, depending on the particular wiring system, be due to an accumulation of individual circuit readings, and hence be considered acceptable. Alternatively, should the low insulation reading be due to one particular circuit, this would merit further investigation, and entering an appropriate observation and recommendation code in the report.

TESTING

5.12 Protection by SELV, PELV or electrical separation

Where SELV (separated extra-low voltage), PELV (protective extra-low voltage), or electrical separation is used for protection against electric shock, the circuits and the source of supply have to provide electrical separation from the live parts of other systems, and (except where exempted by *BS 7671*) from the protective conductors of other systems.

Information on SELV, PELV and electrical separation is given in item 4.6.

In general, protection by electrical separation of circuits is unlikely to be found in installations in domestic premises, and is therefore outside the scope of this book.

Note: Protection by electrical separation of circuits is subject to detailed requirements given in *BS 7671*. Some of these requirements may be unfamiliar, and particular care is needed in the inspection and testing of installations which rely on these protective measures for safety.

Measurement of insulation resistance for circuits protected by SELV or PELV is, in general, unlikely to be necessary for a periodic inspection of a domestic premises installation. However, a procedure for such measurement is explained in item 5.12.1, if it is necessary (for example, to test a garden lighting circuit protected by a SELV source).

5.12.1 Circuits

The instrument used for testing purposes must be capable of supplying the relevant d.c. test voltage when loaded with 1 mA.

For **SELV** circuits a test of insulation resistance is carried out between the live conductors of each SELV circuit connected together and the protective conductors of any adjacent higher voltage system connected together to Earth. The test is applied at 250 V and the minimum acceptable insulation resistance is 0.5 MΩ, as shown in Table 61 (Regulation 612.4.1). Table 61 is partly reproduced in item 5.11 for ease of reference.

For **PELV** circuits, the tests are similar to those for SELV (Regulation 612.4.2).

5.12.2 Sources of supply

For a **SELV** or **PELV** system, the source of supply must be selected from one of those listed in Regulation group 414.3 of *BS 7671*. This means that it must be derived from a source such as a safety isolating transformer complying with *BS EN 61558-2-6 – Safety of power transformers, power supply units and similar. Particular requirements for safety isolating transformers for general use* (which supersedes *BS EN 60742/BS 3535*: Part 1) in which there is no connection between the output winding and the transformer casing or the circuit protective conductor, if any. Alternatively, the source of supply may be one of the other listed types in Regulation group 414.3, giving equivalent electrical separation.

5.12.3 Relays and contactors

Any relays or contactors in electrically separated circuits should provide separation from any other circuits to the standard provided between the input and output of an isolating transformer to *BS EN 61558-2-6*.

5.13 Basic protection by barriers or enclosures

In general, basic protection by barriers or enclosures is determined by inspection rather than testing (see item 4.6.3). In general, a test is **not** necessary.

Exceptionally, a test may be carried out to verify if each barrier or enclosure gives suitable protection against the risk of electric shock through contact with live parts by fingers, solid objects and the like.

All sources of supply must be isolated (see item 1.7.1) before inserting any barrier or enclosure aperture measuring device into equipment, where otherwise danger may occur.

The test also applies to barriers or enclosures of factory-built equipment, which has been modified on site. For example, if an opening has been formed in an enclosure on site for the entry of cables, but is oversized or unused, the enclosure should meet the test criteria in order to comply with the requirements of *BS 7671*.

TESTING

Basic protection provided by each barrier or enclosure must not be less than IP2X or IPXXB. For readily accessible top surfaces basic protection must not be less than IP4X.

IP2X means that the barrier or enclosure provides basic protection by a standard test finger (illustrated), which is 12 mm in diameter, 80 mm long and is capable of bending through 90 degrees twice in the same plane (like a normal finger). The test finger is applied with a force, not exceeding a specified maximum value and is used in conjunction with an electric signalling circuit. IPXXB is equivalent to IP2X in this context.

Use of the test finger (NOT used in general for testing on site, and must NOT be used unless all sources of supply are isolated)

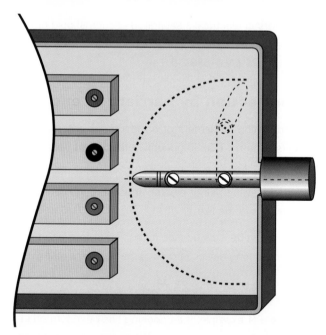

Information on the standard finger test is given in Topic S233-1 of the *Technical Manual* published by The Electrical Safety Council.

The NICEIC guide to
Domestic Periodic Inspection, Testing and Reporting

IP4X is protection against the entry of a wire, strip or similar object which is more than 1 mm thick, or a foreign object which is greater than 1 mm in diameter.

If the barrier or enclosure fails to comply when tested an appropriate observation and recommendation code should be included in the report.

5.14 Polarity and phase sequence

Why do we need to confirm correct polarity?

Incorrect polarity can give rise to danger in a number of ways, including:

- Parts of the installation may remain connected to the line conductor when switched off by a single-pole device but, for all intents and purposes, will appear to be 'dead'.

- In the event of an overload, the circuit-breaker or fuse protecting that part of the installation would disconnect the neutral of the circuit, leaving the load at full line voltage.

- An earth fault current might remain undetected by overcurrent protective devices.

Polarity tests are made to verify that any single-pole control devices or single-pole protective devices are connected in the line conductor only. This includes switches, fuses, thermostats and the like. All non-reversible plugs and socket-outlets also need to be checked for correct connection.

Edison screw and other centre-contact lampholders (except for E14 and E27 lampholders to *BS EN 60238 – Edison screw lampholders*) should be connected in such a way that the line conductor is connected to the centre contact, and the neutral to the screw thread or the part of the lampholder which makes contact with the lamp cap.

Much of the polarity testing can be carried out during the process of testing protective conductor continuity by using the $R_1 + R_2$ test method (see item 5.10.1).

TESTING

If the results of such tests confirm correct polarity, there is no need to undertake other polarity tests separately on those circuits.

There are many types of multifunction test instruments available that can be plugged easily in to a socket-outlet to verify polarity (with the circuit live).

Example of a multifunction test instrument, which includes polarity verification for a live circuit

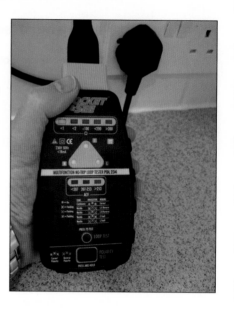

Such a live circuit check at a socket-outlet should be used to ensure that the polarity of the incoming supply is correct; otherwise the whole installation may have the wrong polarity. (Such situations are not unknown).

Why do we check phase sequence?

For multi-phase circuits, we check that phase sequence is maintained throughout the installation, because crossed line conductors might cause multi-phase equipment to malfunction. For example, a three-phase motor connected to crossed line conductors may run in the reverse direction to that intended.

A suitable phase rotation test instrument should be used to verify that the correct phase sequence is maintained at the origin and relevant parts of the installation.

The test instrument manufacturer's instructions should be strictly followed and a safe working procedure used.

The NICEIC guide to
Domestic Periodic Inspection, Testing and Reporting

Example of a three-phase sequence tester

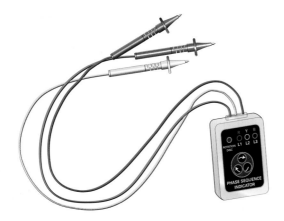

5.15   Earth fault loop impedance (Z_s)

Why do we need to test earth fault loop impedance?

A circuit which relies on protective earthing, equipotential bonding and Automatic Disconnection of supply (ADS) for fault protection, is generally required to disconnect the Supply under earth fault conditions within the **maximum** time permitted by *BS 7671* for that type of circuit or location (see item 5.15.3).
The test procedure for measurement of earth fault loop impedance at the origin of the installation (Z_e) is described in item 5.8.

The type of earth fault loop impedance test instrument to be used is the same as that used for the measurement of Z_e. The earth fault loop impedance, Z_s, should be measured for every final circuit having ADS as its method of fault protection.

The maximum value of Z_s recorded in the test schedule should be the value measured at the point or accessory electrically furthest from the supply to the circuit.

Measured values of Z_s at socket-outlets should be obtained by means of an earth fault loop impedance test instrument (see item 5.15.2).

TESTING

Measured values of Z_s at points and accessories (other than socket-outlets) should be determined by using the $R_1 + R_2$ test results obtained during continuity testing (see item 5.15.1), in conjunction with test results of Z_e, obtained by use of the loop impedance test (see item 5.8).

Both methods of determining Z_s are discussed in items 5.15.1 and 5.15.2, the reasons for using the two methods are:

- $R_1 + R_2$ values are measured on final circuits **without** socket-outlets, to calculate Z_s (in order to avoid the need for live working, for example, at lighting switches, points, or luminaires), and

- Z_s is measured using an earth fault loop impedance test instrument for final circuits **with** socket-outlets (to avoid working inside the consumer unit and for ease of measurement).

The earth fault loop impedance test instrument uses the circuit voltage to pass a test current through the line earth loop. This type of test can cause the unwanted operation of residual current devices or certain overcurrent devices, such as 6 A Type B circuit-breakers which may be in circuit.

In such cases, it may not be possible to obtain a measured value of Z_s. Some instrument manufacturers include features in their earth fault loop impedance test instruments that are intended to avoid some or all of the problems of unwanted tripping. Manufacturers should be consulted for details.

*Under **NO** circumstances shall the **dangerous** practice of short-circuiting the incoming and outgoing line conductors of a circuit protective device to prevent unwanted tripping of an RCD during Z_s testing be used.*

The NICEIC guide to
Domestic Periodic Inspection, Testing and Reporting

5.15.1 Calculation of Z_s using measured values of $R_1 + R_2$ for final circuits without socket-outlets

As previously indicated, an $R_1 + R_2$ test result for a given point in a circuit (generally the point which is electrically furthest from the supply)[8] can be used to determine a measured value for the earth fault loop impedance, Z_s, at that point.

To do this, it is also necessary to know the value of external earth fault loop impedance, Z_e (see item 5.8) at the consumer unit, which is directly supplying the final circuit. The value of Z_e added to the values of $R_1 + R_2$ gives the value of Z_s, in ohms. As shown in the following formula:

$$Z_s = Z_e + (R_1 + R_2)$$

Strictly, it should **not** be $R_1 + R_2$ that is used in the above equations, because this does **not** take account of the a.c. resistance or the reactance of the line conductor and circuit protective conductor. Instead it should be the impedance $Z_1 + Z_2$, which takes these quantities into account. However, this is not of any concern, since $R_1 + R_2$ is approximately equal to $Z_1 + Z_2$ for circuits rated up to about 100 A.

---

[8] **Note:** In the simplified diagram illustrated on the next page, polarity should be verified at both the lighting point (as shown) and the switch. However, the electrically most remote point in this particular circuit will be the switch.

Determination of Z_s using $R_1 + R_2$ measured values

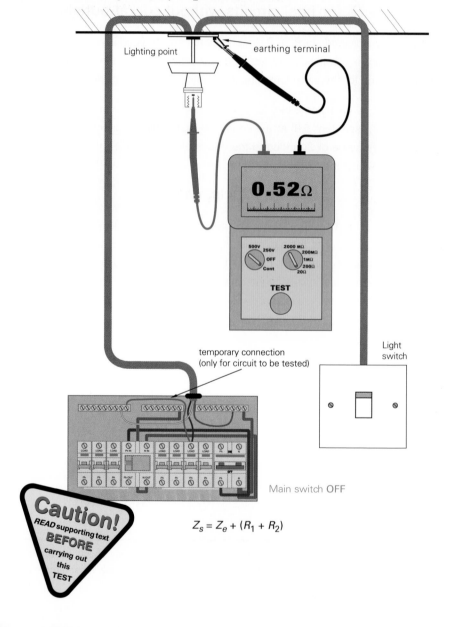

Lighting point

earthing terminal

0.52Ω

500V 250V OFF Cont 2000 MΩ 200MΩ 1MΩ 200Ω 20Ω

TEST

temporary connection
(only for circuit to be tested)

Light switch

Main switch OFF

Caution!
READ supporting text
BEFORE
carrying out
this
TEST

$$Z_s = Z_e + (R_1 + R_2)$$

**The NICEIC guide to
Domestic Periodic Inspection, Testing and Reporting**

5.15.2 Measurement of Z_s at socket-outlets using an earth fault loop impedance test instrument

Testing should only be carried out after a thorough inspection and continuity testing have confirmed, so far as is reasonably practicable, that all circuit protective conductors, and main and supplementary bonding conductors are in place, and if the indicator lights on the instrument indicate that it is safe to proceed. If this procedure is **not** observed, there is a possibility that exposed-conductive-parts and extraneous-conductive-parts may become live during the testing process, thus exposing persons to the risk of electric shock.

Measurement of Z_s at a socket-outlet using an earth fault loop impedance test instrument

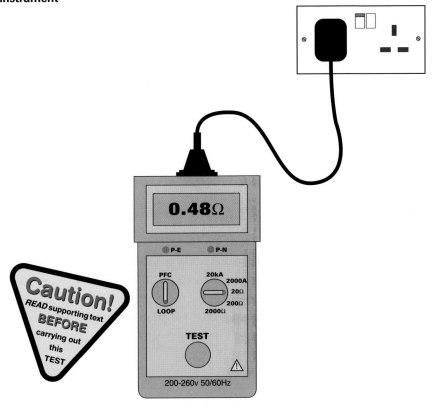

TESTING

Remember that this test is conducted with the circuit live. All necessary precautions must therefore be taken to prevent danger. It is suggested that this test is used only on final circuits containing socket-outlets, to prevent live working on circuits that do **not** have socket-outlets.

All accessible socket-outlets should be tested on each circuit, and the highest value recorded in the schedule of test results. A proprietary instrument test lead with a fitted plug should be used.

Procedure

1   Read and carefully follow the instrument manufacturer's instructions.

2   Check that the test instrument, and its connections, including plug and leads, are in good condition (see item 1.8).

3   Plug the instrument into the socket-outlet to be tested.

4   Check that the lamps or LEDs on the instrument indicate that it is safe to proceed. If they do not, investigate and resolve the situation before proceeding.

5   Press the test button.

6   Record the value of Z_s.

7   Repeat previous steps 3 to 6 for other socket-outlets as appropriate.

The value of Z_s for every circuit must, after adjustment to take into account the heating effects of load current, be sufficiently low to allow the overcurrent device to operate within the maximum time permitted by *BS 7671*, or should not exceed a value which might prevent conformity with the requirements of *BS 7671* relating to RCD-protected circuits. Maximum values of Z_s are given in the next item.

The NICEIC guide to
Domestic Periodic Inspection, Testing and Reporting

CHAPTER **5**

5.15.3 Maximum values of Z_s

Maximum permitted values of Z_s for different types of overcurrent protective devices and different maximum permitted disconnection times are given in Chapter 41 of *BS 7671* (see item 3.10.10).

It is generally necessary to adjust the values obtained by the test before comparing them with the maximum permitted values given in *BS 7671*. This is because the values referred to in *BS 7671* are based on the conductors having been heated up by the passage of load and/or fault current, which increases their resistance; whilst test results are usually obtained when the conductor temperature is somewhat lower. Information on conductor temperature correction factors is given in Annex E of this book.

Alternatively, as a rule of thumb, the measured value of Z_s should not exceed 0.8 times the relevant value given in Tables 41.2, 41.3, 41.4 and 41.5 of *BS 7671*. The following table (included with each pad of NICEIC report forms) gives the limiting values of measured earth fault loop impedance when measured at ambient temperatures up to 20 °C.

TESTING

Maximum earth fault loop impedance values (at 20 °C) for overcurrent protective devices in common use, for fault protection

MAXIMUM EARTH FAULT LOOP IMPEDANCE VALUES FOR OVERCURRENT PROTECTIVE DEVICES IN COMMON USE, FOR FAULT PROTECTION

For fault protection, the limiting values of earth fault loop impedances, Z_s, are given in Tables 41.2, 41.3 and 41.4 of BS 7671, for many commonly-used overcurrent protective devices.

The values given in those tables are the limits that apply under earth fault conditions, when the temperature of the conductors can be expected to be higher than when testing is undertaken (usually under no-load conditions). Consequently, the values of earth fault loop impedance when measured at ambient temperature should be lower than the limits set out in BS 7671.

It is generally accepted that, where the measured earth fault loop impedance of a circuit is not greater than 80% of the relevant limit specified in BS 7671, the impedance can be expected to be sufficiently low under earth fault conditions to meet the relevant limit specified in BS 7671, and for the protective device to automatically disconnect within the time specified.

The following table gives the limiting values of earth fault loop impedance when measured at ambient temperatures up to 20°C. The limits on measured values are 80% of the values given in BS 7671, rounded down. The boxes marked 'N/A' (Not Applicable) indicate either that the overcurrent protective device is not commonly available or that, by virtue of its characteristics, the device is not generally appropriate for fault protection.

The impedance values are based on the 'worst case' limits allowed by BS 7671 and, in certain cases, where the manufacturer of the protective device claims closer limits of fault current necessary for operation of the device than allowed for by the Standard, the values may be modified accordingly.

Where the measured value of the earth fault loop impedance exceeds the relevant tabulated value below, further investigation will be necessary to evaluate the particular circumstances to confirm that compliance with BS 7671 has been achieved.

LIMITING VALUES OF MEASURED EARTH FAULT LOOP IMPEDANCES FOR COMMON OVERCURRENT PROTECTIVE DEVICES, FOR FAULT PROTECTION, OPERATING AT 230 V BASED ON 80% (APPROX.) OF THE VALUES GIVEN IN BS 7671

Rated current (A)	Fuses						Circuit-breakers to BS 3871 or BS EN 60898 or RCBOs to BS EN 61009				
	BS 88 (gG) Parts 2 and 6		BS 1361 or BS 1362		BS 3036		Type 1	Type 2	Type B	Type 3 and C	Type D
	0.4 s	5 s	0.4 s	5 s	0.4 s	5 s	0.4 s and 5 s				
3	N/A	N/A	13.12	18.56	N/A	N/A	N/A	N/A	12.26	N/A	N/A
5	N/A	N/A	8.35	13.11	7.66	14.16	9.20	5.26	N/A	3.68	1.84
6	6.81	10.81	N/A	N/A	N/A	N/A	7.66	4.37	6.13	3.06	1.53
10	4.08	5.93	N/A	N/A	N/A	N/A	4.60	2.63	3.68	1.84	0.92
13	N/A	N/A	1.94	3.06	N/A	N/A	N/A	N/A	N/A	N/A	N/A
15	N/A	N/A	2.63	4.00	2.04	4.27	3.06	1.75	N/A	1.22	0.61
16	2.16	3.34	N/A	N/A	N/A	N/A	2.87	1.64	2.30	1.15	0.57
20	1.41	2.33	1.36	2.24	1.41	3.06	2.30	1.31	1.84	0.92	0.46
25	1.15	1.84	N/A	N/A	N/A	N/A	1.84	1.04	1.47	0.73	0.36
30	N/A	N/A	0.92	1.47	0.87	2.11	1.53	0.87	N/A	0.61	0.30
32	0.83	1.47	N/A	N/A	N/A	N/A	1.44	0.82	1.15	0.57	0.29
40	0.65	1.08	N/A	N/A	N/A	N/A	1.15	0.65	0.92	0.46	0.23
45	N/A	N/A	0.46	0.76	0.47	1.27	1.02	0.58	0.82	0.40	0.20
50	0.48	0.83	N/A	N/A	N/A	N/A	0.92	0.52	0.73	0.36	0.18
60	N/A	N/A	N/A	0.55	N/A	0.89	N/A	N/A	N/A	N/A	N/A
63	0.36	0.65	N/A	N/A	N/A	N/A	0.72	0.41	0.58	0.29	0.14
80	0.24	0.46	N/A	0.39	N/A	N/A	0.57	0.32	0.46	0.23	0.11
100	0.18	0.33	N/A	0.29	N/A	0.42	0.46	0.26	0.36	0.18	0.08
125	0.14	0.26	N/A	N/A	N/A	N/A	N/A	N/A	0.29	0.14	0.07
160	0.11	0.20	N/A	N/A	N/A	N/A	N/A	N/A	N/A	N/A	N/A
200	0.08	0.15	N/A	N/A	N/A	N/A	N/A	N/A	N/A	N/A	N/A

The NICEIC guide to
Domestic Periodic Inspection, Testing and Reporting

These limiting measured values are based on 80% of the values given in *BS 7671* for 0.4 second and 5 second disconnection times, as appropriate.

The final circuit maximum measured values of Z_s should to be recorded in section N of the schedule of test results. The measured values should **not** exceed the limiting values given in the previous table.

If the protective device is **not** of a type whose maximum permitted Z_s value is given in *BS 7671* then, as a rule of thumb, the measured value should **not** exceed 0.8 times the value calculated by using the formula on the first page of Appendix 3 of *BS 7671*.

Reduced sized protective conductors

Insulated and sheathed cables usually have a reduced sized protective conductor compared to the live conductors. For example, a thermoplastic insulated and sheathed flat cable with 2.5 mm^2 cross-sectional area line and neutral conductors may have a protective conductor with a cross-sectional area of 1.5 mm^2 or even 1.0 mm^2.

Reduced sized protective conductors may **not** be protected against fault current (required by Regulation group 543) by certain fuses under fault conditions.

The following table lists protective conductor cross-sectional areas of 1.0 mm^2 to 4.0 mm^2 and related fuses that are known **not** to provide protection against fault current conditions for circuits that require disconnection times of up to 0.4 or 5 s (which apply to TN systems). Protective conductors in TT systems are in general protected by RCDs so should have adequate fault protection.

The table is based on results of comparisons between the time/current characteristic of the fuses and the time/current characteristic derived from the adiabatic equation (Regulation 543.1.3) for the protective conductors listed.

TESTING

Table of reduced sized protective conductors for TN systems NOT protected against fault current by listed fuses at specified disconnection time

	Fuses	Protective conductor cross-sectional area (mm²)			
		1.0	1.5	2.5	4.0
1-1	BS EN 60269-2 or BS 88-6 0.4 second disconnection time (Current rating in amperes)				
	32	✗			
	40	✗	✗		
	50	✗	✗		
1-2	BS EN 60269-2 or BS 88-6 5 second disconnection time (Current rating in amperes)				
	16	✗			
	20	✗	✗		
	25	✗	✗		
	32	✗	✗		
	40	✗	✗	✗	
	50	✗	✗	✗	✗
2-1	BS 3036 0.4 second disconnection time (Current rating in amperes)				
	30	✗			
	45	✗	✗		
	60	✗	✗	✗	
2-2	Fuse to BS 3036 5 second disconnection time (Current rating in amperes)				
	20	✗			
	30	✗	✗		
	45	✗	✗	✗	
	60	✗	✗	✗	
3-1	BS 1361 0.4 second disconnection time (Current rating in amperes)				
	30	✗			
	45	✗	✗		
	60	✗	✗	✗	
3-2	BS 1361 5 second disconnection time (Current rating in amperes)				
	20	✗	✗		
	30	✗	✗		
	45	✗	✗	✗	✗
	60	✗	✗	✗	✗

✗ Denotes an unsatisfactory protective conductor, fuse combination.

The NICEIC guide to
Domestic Periodic Inspection, Testing and Reporting

If any reduced sized protective conductor is **not** adequately protected against overcurrent (see previous table) an appropriate observation and recommendation code should be included on the report.

5.16 Operation of residual current devices

Each residual current device must be tested to confirm that it functions correctly. The procedure comprises two parts, namely:

- Simulating an appropriate fault condition using an RCD test instrument.

- Testing the operation of the device by means of the integral test button.

Note: The test button on the RCD should **not** be operated until the RCD test instrument has completed its automatic processing routine, as this may influence the electrical test results.

Test instrument

The RCD test instrument should be capable of applying the full range of currents required to test the RCD in question, and of displaying the time, in milliseconds (ms), taken for the device to operate. For reasons of safety, the test instrument will normally automatically limit the duration of the test to a maximum of 2 seconds.

The testing of an RCD which incorporates an intentional time delay will only be possible if the test instrument is capable of providing a test duration which exceeds the permitted maximum operating time of the RCD. Owing to the range of time delays, it is **not** possible to specify a maximum test duration, but 2 seconds should normally be found sufficient in practice.

Procedure

1   Established that the earth fault loop impedance of the circuit is sufficiently low to satisfy the requirements of *BS 7671* for the RCD to be tested. That is to say, the earth fault loop impedance, in ohms, when multiplied by the rated residual operating current of the device in amperes, must **not** exceed 50 V as described in Regulation 411.5.3 of *BS 7671*.

TESTING

2   Read and carefully follow the instrument manufacturer's instructions.

3   Check that the test instrument, and its connections, including plug, leads and probes, are in good condition (see item 1.8).

4   Prevent contact by persons to exposed-conductive-parts or extraneous-conductive-parts during the test. This is because potentially dangerous voltages may appear on these parts during the testing procedure.

5   Connect the test instrument to the line, neutral and Earth on the load side of the RCD, with the load disconnected. The connection being made at any convenient point in the circuit, such as by:

   a   Plugging the test instrument into a socket-outlet, which is the preferred point of measurement, or

   b   Using a split 3-lead connection* incorporating suitable probes and/or crocodile clips. Providing that the following *Conditions 1, 2 and 3* **are** met** Steps 1 to 3 (shown below) can be followed:

   ### *Conditions*

   1   basic protection meets the requirements of IP2X (or exceeds it, for example, IP4X), and

   2   the requirements of, terminal insulated covers are unlikely to be accidentally displaced, and

   *3   access to equipment is **not** restricted.*

   Steps (for using a split 3-lead connection)

   1   securely isolate the supply **before** connecting the instrument leads,

   2   re-energize the supply to carry out each test, and

3   securely isolate the supply on completion of each test **before** disconnecting the instrument leads.

*   A split 3-lead connection may be used where the RCD being tested is used as a main switch and the down stream socket-outlets are also protected by another RCD (also down stream).

**   If Conditions 1, 2 and 3 **cannot** be met, then testing should be carried out clear of live conductors (rather than on or near them), by making suitable connections to the RCD. For example, by using all crocodile clip connections. In **exceptional** circumstances, if it is not considered safe by the inspector to undertake this test, an appropriate limitation, observation and recommendation should be entered on the report.

Note: some manufacturer's equipment may only meet the standard if all loads are isolated when measurement is made at the terminals of an RCD

6   Set the instrument to the correct range. Many RCD test instruments have a facility whereby tests can be carried out during the positive or negative half cycles of the supply waveform in turn. For tests 1 and 2 below, the operating time to be noted is the longer of those measured during the positive and negative half cycle tests.

7   Check that the polarity indication on the instrument shows that it is in order to proceed with Test 1, followed by Test 2 and Test 3.

8   On completion of tests refit any equipment covers **before** re-energizing any isolated supplies.

Test 1

Adjust the current setting to 100% of the rated operating (tripping) current of the device, push the button on the test instrument and note the time taken for the RCD to operate (See illustration on next page).

TESTING

Testing of an RCD, where the three conditions described in item 5b of the previous Procedure are met

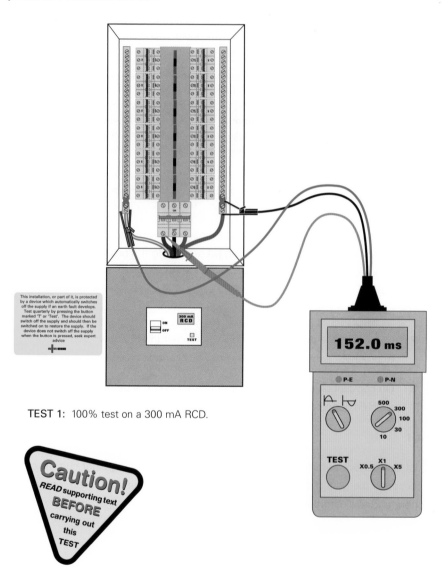

TEST 1: 100% test on a 300 mA RCD.

The NICEIC guide to
Domestic Periodic Inspection, Testing and Reporting

The measured operating time(s) should be compared with the appropriate value(s) in the following tables, which relate to the type-tests carried out under specified conditions by RCD manufacturers in accordance with the relevant product standards.

RCDs - conditions required for a satisfactory test result

General purpose RCDs to *BS 4293,* and RCD-protected socket-outlets to *BS 7288*

Test	Instrument test current setting	Satisfactory result
Test 1	100% of rated operating current	Device should trip in less than 200 ms

RCDs to *BS 4293* (incorporating a time delay)

Test	Instrument test current setting	Satisfactory result
Test 1	100% of rated operating current	Device should trip between 200 ms+ 50% of the time delay and 200 ms+ 100% of the time delay

For example, if the trip has a rated time delay of 100 ms, it should operate between 250 ms and 300 ms

General purpose RCDs to *BS EN 61008,* and RCBOs to *BS EN 61009*

Test	Instrument test current setting	Satisfactory result
Test 1	100% of rated operating current	Device should trip in less than 300 ms

RCDs to *BS EN 61008* and *BS EN 61009* Type 'S'

Test	Instrument test current setting	Satisfactory result
Test 1	100% of rated tripping current	Device should trip between 130 ms and 500 ms

TESTING

Despite manufacturers' recommendations and the presence of the notice required by *BS 7671*, residual current devices may not have been operated by the users at quarterly intervals, by means of the 'test' button on the RCD.

If, during a periodic inspection, a device does not trip within the expected time (including failing to trip at all) when first subjected to a test current equal to the rated operating (tripping) current, but operates satisfactorily when subjected to such a test subsequently (perhaps after manual switching), an appropriate observation and recommendation should be made on the report.

If the inspector considers that the result of the subsequent test is satisfactory and indicates the operating characteristic had the device been operated at quarterly intervals as intended, it would be in order to record the result of the subsequent test, subject to the related observation and recommendation. In particular, the attention of the recipient of the report should be drawn to the safety implications of **not** operating the device at quarterly intervals.

> This installation, or part of it, is protected by a device which automatically switches off the supply if an earth fault develops. Test quarterly by pressing the button marked 'T' or 'Test'. The device should switch off the supply and should then be switched on to restore the supply. If the device does not switch off the supply when the button is pressed, seek expert advice
>
>

Test 2

An RCD provided for additional protection should have a rated residual operating (tripping) current $I_{\Delta n}$ not exceeding 30 mA. Regulation 415.1.1 requires that, when type-tested under specified conditions in accordance with the relevant product standards, such RCDs must operate in a time not exceeding 40 ms at a residual current of $5I_{\Delta n}$.

When testing an installed RCD of this type using an RCD test instrument, the RCD should normally not be considered to be in a satisfactory condition unless it operates in a time not exceeding 40 ms when subjected to a residual (test) current of $5I_{\Delta n}$.

It should be noted, however, that some RCDs intended to provide additional protection are designed such that they operate under type-test conditions in a time only marginally less than 40 ms at a residual operating current of $5I_{\Delta n}$.

Such RCDs may operate under installed conditions in a time marginally exceeding 40 ms at 5$I_{\Delta n}$. In which case the inspector should retest the RCD, and if the RCD operating time continues to exceed 40 ms an appropriate observation and recommendation code should be included on the report.

Test 3

The 50% of rated operating (tripping) current test should be carried out as follows:

1   Adjust the current setting on the test instrument to 50% of the rated operating (tripping) current of the device. (See following illustration)

2   Push the button on the test instrument and wait.

3   The RCD should **not** operate within 2 seconds.

Testing of an RCD, where the three conditions described in item 5b of the previous *Procedure* are met

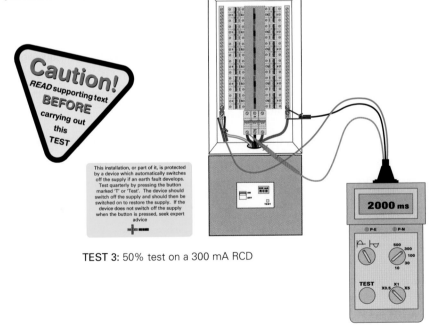

Caution!
READ supporting text
BEFORE
carrying out
this
TEST

This installation, or part of it, is protected by a device which automatically switches off the supply if an earth fault develops. Test quarterly by pressing the button marked 'T' or 'Test'. The device should switch off the supply and should then be switched on to restore the supply. If the device does not switch off the supply when the button is pressed, seek expert advice

TEST 3: 50% test on a 300 mA RCD

TESTING

Test button

Following the electrical test procedure described above, each RCD should be operated by means of its integral test facility. This confirms that the device is responding to its design level of sensitivity and that all the mechanical parts are functioning. The users of installations are advised (by means of a notice at or near the origin of the installations - see Regulation 514.12.2 of *BS 7671*) to carry out this simple test at quarterly intervals, but it is not a substitute for the electrical test procedure as described.

5.17 Equipment functions

All equipment forming part of the installation should be checked to ensure that it functions as intended, and has been properly mounted, adjusted and installed in accordance with the relevant requirements of *BS 7671*. Such equipment may include switches, circuit-breakers, motors (such as fans or pumps), control devices (such as thermostats or photocells), heaters, lamps or luminaires.

If a domestic fire detection and alarm system is installed, the system indicator lights should be checked for correct status and each detector/alarm test button should be pressed to determine satisfactory operation, at a time agreed with the client/occupant(s) of the installation as appropriate.

The inspector should **not** sign the Domestic Electrical Installation Periodic Inspection Report until it has been established that all equipment has been properly tested for satisfactory operation.

The NICEIC guide to
Domestic Periodic Inspection, Testing and Reporting

ANNEXES

INSPECTION AND TESTING
SERVICE LEVELS

ANNEX **A**

The following three star service levels for inspection,
testing and reporting are:

One star ★   Domestic Visual Condition Report
                          (includes inspection only)

Two star ★★   Domestic Electrical Installation
                          Periodic Inspection Report
                          (includes inspection and testing)

Three star ★★★   Domestic Electrical Installation
                          Periodic Inspection Report
                          (includes inspection, testing and
                          additional items, which are to be
                          crossed or ticked in the appropriate
                          boxes, as agreed between the
                          inspector and the client).

INSPECTION AND TESTING SERVICE LEVELS

A table of typical items to be included for each service level is shown below.

Note: Items ticked ✓ are included

Items crossed ✗ are not included

Service levels		One star ★ (Inspection only)	Two star ★★ (Inspection and testing)	Three star ★★★ (Inspection, testing and additional items)
INSPECTION (I) of items as follows:				
I1	Minimum % sample inspection of accessories or points/circuit (opened for internal inspection)	10%	20%	30%
I2	Supply protective devices	✓	✓	✓
I3	System type	✓	✓	✓
I4	Consumer unit (or distribution board)	✓	✓	✓
I5	Main switch including its operation	✓	✓	✓
I6	Final circuit protective devices, including their operation	✓	✓	✓
I7	Means of earthing	✓	✓	✓
I8	Earthing and bonding arrangements	✓	✓	✓
I9	Supplementary bonding	✓	✓	✓
I10	Final circuits, such as for lighting, power, cooking, heating, showers, fire detection and alarm systems, and supplies to outdoor equipment	✓	✓	✓
I11	Lighting points and luminaires	✓	✓	✓
I12	Socket-outlets	✓	✓	✓
I13	Outdoor power supplies and lighting, and installations in outbuildings (such as garages or green houses)	✓	✓	✓
I14	Switches including their operation	✓	✓	✓
I15	Immersion heater thermostats	✓	✓	✓
I16	RCDs including their test button operation	✓	✓	✓
I17	Fire detection and alarm systems including operation of test buttons	✓	✓	✓
I18	Methods of protection against electric shock, such as insulation of live parts, equipotential bonding and earthing, SELV and Class II equipment	✓	✓	✓
I19	Prevention of mutual detrimental influence, such as proximity of non-electrical services	✓	✓	✓

The NICEIC guide to
Domestic Periodic Inspection, Testing and Reporting

Service levels	One star ★ (Inspection only)	Two star ★★ (Inspection and testing)	Three star ★★★ (Inspection, testing and additional items)
I20 Identification, such as labelling, notices and identification of conductors	✓	✓	✓
I21 Cables and conductors, such as routing, connections, selection and presence of fire barriers	✓	✓	✓
I22 General selection, location, connection and protection of equipment	✓	✓	✓
TESTING (T) of items as follows:			
T1 Minimum % sample testing of accessories or points/circuit	0%	20%	30%
T2 External earth loop impedance (Z_e), or earth electrode resistance (R_A),	✗	✓	✓
T3 Prospective fault current (I_{pf}),	✗	✓	✓
T4 Continuity of protective conductors	✗	✓	✓
T5 Polarity of circuits	✗	✓	✓
T6 Ring continuity of ring final circuits	✗	✓	✓
T7 Insulation resistance	✗	✓	✓
T8 Earth fault loop impedance (Z_s)	✗	✓	✓
T9 RCD trip time at rated operating current	✗	✓	✓
T10 RCD trip time at 5 time rated operating current	✗	✓	✓
T11 RCD trip time at 50% rated operating current	✗	✓	✓
T12 Testing polarity and Z_s of **all** accessible socket-outlets	✗	✓	✓
ADDITIONAL (A) items (to be ticked in Three star ★★★ column):			
A1 Testing earth continuity of **all** accessible exposed-extraneous-conductive-parts and exposed-conductive-parts (metal parts that may become live during a fault)	✗	✗	insert ✓ or ✗
A2 Test (separately listed) portable equipment, such as a kettle, iron and toaster	✗	✗	insert ✓ or ✗
A3 Test (separately listed) fixed equipment, such as a cooker and air conditioning unit	✗	✗	insert ✓ or ✗
A4 Maximum load measurement (using clamp meter)	✗	✗	insert ✓ or ✗
A5 Terminal temperatures	✗	✗	insert ✓ or ✗
A6 Produce circuit chart	✗	✗	insert ✓ or ✗

Inspector to add other additional items as appropriate

DOMESTIC VISUAL CONDITION REPORTS

ANNEX **B**

Domestic Visual Condition Report

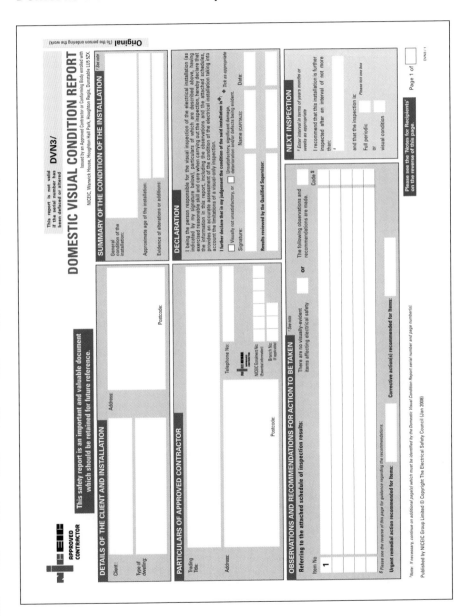

Domestic Visual Condition Report

THIS DOMESTIC VISUAL CONDITION REPORT IS AN IMPORTANT AND VALUABLE DOCUMENT WHICH SHOULD BE RETAINED FOR FUTURE REFERENCE

NOTES FOR RECIPIENT

The purpose of a visual-only inspection of a domestic electrical installation is to determine, so far as is reasonably practicable, whether the installation has any visually-evident defects or has suffered any damage or deterioration which may affect safety. This domestic visual condition report provides an assessment of the condition of the electrical installation identified overleaf at the time it was inspected, taking into account the limitations of a visual-only inspection.

Whilst a visual inspection may reveal defects, damage or deterioration which may present electrical safety hazards, such an inspection alone cannot fully determine whether an installation is safe for continued use.

Furthermore, due to the significant limitations, it is not appropriate to report that an installation is in a satisfactory condition on the basis of visual inspection only.

Visual inspections do not include items that can only be checked with test instruments, such as the adequacy of earthing arrangements.

NICEIC* Approved Contractor performing the visual inspection will recommend that a full inspection and testing be performed if it is suspected that the installation is in an unsafe condition.

Also for safety reasons, the electrical installation will need to be re-inspected at appropriate intervals by a competent person. The recommended maximum time interval to the next inspection and the type of inspection is stated overleaf in the section: *Next inspection*. The recommendation for the interval to the next inspection is conditional on all items which have attracted a Recommendation Code 1 and Code 2 in the section *Observations and recommendations for actions to be taken* being remedied without delay and as soon as practical respectively. Additionally, the recommendation given for the interval to the next inspection and the type of inspection is also to be conditional on all items which have attracted a Recommendation Code 3 being remedied as soon as practicable. NICEIC recommends that you engage the services of an Approved Contractor for this purpose. There should be a notice at or near the consumer unit indicating the latest date by which a full periodic inspection and test of the installation is due.

Where the installation incorporates a residual current device (RCD), there should be a notice at or near the consumer unit stating that the device should be tested at quarterly intervals. For safety reasons, it is important that you carry out the test regularly.

Note that consumer units fitted with cartridge or rewirable fuses may be suitable for continued use provided the consumer unit is in a satisfactory condition and each fuse is correctly rated.

---

* NICEIC is a trading name of NICEIC Group Limited, a wholly owned subsidiary of The Electrical Safety Council. Under licence from The Electrical Safety Council, NICEIC acts as the electrical contracting industry's independent voluntary regulatory body for electrical installation safety matters throughout the UK, and maintains and publishes registers of electrical contractors that it has assessed against particular scheme requirements (including the technical standard of electrical work).

NICEIC Approved Contractors, whose scope of enrolment includes electrical work at filling stations, have been assessed as having the technical capability to carry out electrical work in compliance both with British Standard 7671 – Requirements for Electrical Installations and the guidance given by the Association for Petroleum and Explosives Administration (APEA) and the Energy Institute (EI).

For further information about electrical safety and how NICEIC can help you, visit **www.niceicgroup.com**

Published by NICEIC Group Limited © Copyright The Electrical Safety Council (Jan 2008)

GUIDANCE FOR RECIPIENTS ON THE RECOMMENDATION CODES

Only one Recommendation Code should have been given for each recorded observation.

Recommendation Code 1

Where an observation has been given a Recommendation Code 1 (requires urgent attention), the safety of those using the installation may be at risk.

The person responsible for the maintenance of the installation is advised to take action without delay to remedy the observed deficiency in the installation, or to take other appropriate action (such as switching off and isolating the affected part(s) of the installation) to remove the potential danger. The NICEIC Approved Contractor issuing this report will be able to provide further advice.

NICEIC make available 'dangerous condition' notification forms to enable inspectors to record, and then to communicate to the person ordering the report, any dangerous condition discovered.

Recommendation Code 2

Recommendation Code 2 (requires improvement) indicates that, whilst the safety of those using the installation may not be at immediate risk, remedial action should be taken as soon as possible to improve the safety of the installation. The NICEIC Approved Contractor issuing this report will be able to provide further advice.

Items which have been attributed Recommendation Code 2 should be remedied as soon as possible.

Recommendation Code 3

Where an observation has been given a Recommendation Code 3 (requires further investigation), the inspection has revealed an apparent deficiency which could not, due to the extent or limitations of this inspection, be fully identified. Items which have been attributed Recommendation Code 3 should be investigated by a competent person as soon as possible.

The person responsible for the maintenance of the installation is advised to arrange for the NICEIC Approved Contractor issuing this report (or other competent person) to undertake further inspection and/or testing of the installation to determine the nature and extent of the apparent deficiency.

Recommendation Code 4

Recommendation Code 4 (does not comply with BS 7671 (as amended)) will have been given to observed non-compliance(s) with the current safety standard which do not warrant one of the other Recommendation Codes. It is not intended to imply that the electrical installation inspected is unsafe, but careful consideration should be given to the benefits of improving these aspects of the installation. The NICEIC Approved Contractor issuing this report will be able to provide further advice.

It is important to note that the recommendation given at *Next Inspection* of this report for the maximum interval until the next inspection is conditional upon all items which have been given a Recommendation Code 1 and Code 2 being remedied without delay and as soon as possible respectively.

It would not be reasonable to indicate a 'visually not unsatisfactory' assessment if any observation in the report had been given a Code 1 or Code 2 recommendation.

Continued on the reverse of page 2

DVN3 / I&2B

Domestic Visual Condition Report

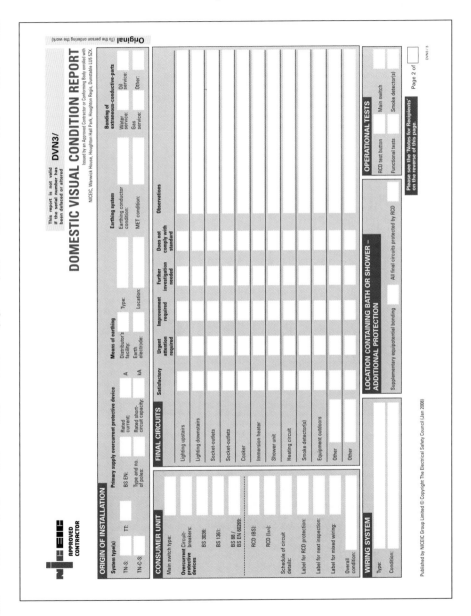

Domestic Visual Condition Report

NOTES FOR RECIPIENT (continued)

The visual-only inspection report

This report is intended to be issued only for the purpose of reporting on the condition of an existing electrical installation. The report should identify, so far as is reasonably practicable, any damage, deterioration and visually-evident defects which:

- may give rise to danger,

- require improvement,

- require further investigation or

- do not comply with the latest edition of the national standard for electrical safety BS 7671: *Requirements for Electrical Installations*

The report consists of at least two numbered pages. Additional numbered pages may have been provided to permit further relevant information concerning the installation to be reported. The report is invalid if any of the identified pages are missing. The report form has a printed seven-digit serial number, which is traceable to the Approved Contractor to which it was supplied by NICEIC.

The report should not have been issued to certify a new electrical installation. A 'Domestic Electrical Installation Certificate' or 'Electrical Installation Certificate' (where appropriate) should be issued for the certification of new installation work.

Only an NICEIC Approved Contractor or Conforming Body is authorised to issue this NICEIC Domestic Visual Condition Report. You should have received the report marked 'Original' and the Approved Contractor should have retained the report marked 'Duplicate'.

If you were the person ordering the work, but not the user of the installation, you should pass this report, or a full copy of it including these notes and additional pages (if any), immediately to the user.

The 'Original' report form should be retained in a safe place and shown to any person inspecting or undertaking further work on the electrical installation in the future. If you later vacate the property, this report will provide the new user with an assessment of the condition of the electrical installation at the time the inspection was carried out.

Understanding the report

Page 1

In the *Summary of the conditions of the installation* box, the inspector should have put a brief summary of the overall condition of the installation, taking into account the specific observations made.

In the *Declaration* box the inspector should have ticked one of the two boxes, namely:

☐ Visually not unsatisfactory, or

☐ Unsatisfactory, significant damage, deterioration and/or defects being evident.

Published by NICEIC Group Limited © Copyright The Electrical Safety Council (Jan 2008)

The declaration should reflect the observations and recommendations made. A list of observations and recommendations for urgent remedial work and corrective action(s) necessary to restore the installation to a satisfactory condition should be given in the box at the bottom of page 1. But, given the limitations of a visual inspection, these recommendations may be incomplete and a full periodic inspection report may be necessary to determine the full extent of the required remedial action.

For further guidance on the recommendations, please see the reverse of page 1.

In the box entitled *Next Inspection* the inspector should have made a recommendation as to the time interval to the next inspection and the type of inspection, such as a visual inspection or a full periodic inspection. This recommendation will depend on circumstances such as the age of the installation or if it is subject to more rapid deterioration.

Page 2. Schedules:

All unshaded boxes should have been completed either by insertion of the relevant details or by entering:

A '✓' meaning a particular inspection has been carried out and the result, as far as can be ascertained from a visual-only inspection, is **not unsatisfactory**

or

A '✗' meaning a particular inspection has been carried out and the result is **unsatisfactory**

or

'N/A' meaning **'Not Applicable'**, where appropriate.

Note that for every '✗' meaning 'unsatisfactory', an observation should have been made in the Section *Observations and recommendations for actions to be taken.*

Should the person ordering the domestic visual condition inspection (eg the client, as identified on Page 1 of this report), have reason to believe that the report issued by the Approved Contractor does not reasonably reflect the condition of the electrical installation reported on given the limitations of a visual only inspection, the person should in the first instance raise the specific concerns in writing with the Approved Contractor. If the concerns remain unresolved, the client may make a formal complaint to NICEIC, for which purpose a standard complaint form is available on request.

The complaints procedure offered by NICEIC is subject to certain terms and conditions, full details of which are available upon application (or visit **www.niceicgroup.com**). NICEIC does not investigate complaints relating to the operational performance of electrical installations (such as lighting levels), or to contractual or commercial issues (such as time or cost).

Jan 2008

DVN3 /3&4B

Domestic Visual Condition Report Continuation Sheet

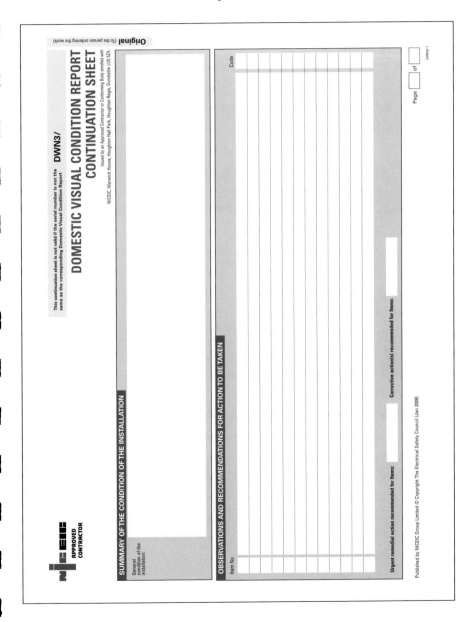

Guidance for Approved Contractors and Conforming Bodies

DOMESTIC VISUAL CONDITION REPORT
GUIDANCE FOR CONTRACTORS

A record of each report used should be made on the record sheet provided. Unused sets of obsolete reports must be destroyed to prevent their misuse.

General

The purpose of a visual-only inspection of a dwelling is to determine, so far as is reasonably practicable, whether an electrical installation has suffered any damage or deterioration or has any visually-evident defects which affect, or may affect, safety. The Domestic Visual Condition Report is intended to be used only for the purpose of reporting on the condition of an existing electrical installation. The report should identify, so far as is reasonably practicable, any damage, deterioration or defects which may give rise to danger.

The practice of 'visual inspection only' is **not non-compliant** with the requirements of the national standard for electrical safety, BS 7671: *Requirements for Electrical Installations*, provided that:

- The visual inspection is carried out in accordance with all the requirements of BS 7671 that are applicable to visual inspection.

- The limitations of 'visual inspection only' which are stated in the Notes for Recipients on the reverse of the report form are made clear in writing to the person ordering the work.

- It is **not** claimed that a 'visual inspection only' can or will fully determine whether an installation is **safe for continued use.**

- An objective report of the findings of the visual inspection is given to the person ordering the work, whether or not specifically requested by that person.

- It is made clear to the person ordering the work that a visual inspection does not include items that can only be checked with test instruments (such as the adequacy of earthing arrangements).

- Any quotation for proposed remedial work is given separately from the visual inspection report.

- A full periodic inspection is recommended to the customer if it is suspected that the installation is in an unsafe condition, or if it is believed that other significant defects cannot be determined, but may be revealed by testing.

The entire electrical installation should be inspected including the loft space(s) and any outside garage, workshop, greenhouse, conservatory etc.

A certain amount of dismantling is normally necessary even though the inspection is 'visual-only'. For example, after appropriate isolation, the cover of the consumer unit should be removed to permit the checking of electrical equipment such as the condition and suitability of the cables employed. In addition, equipment such as socket-outlets, light switches and luminaires should be inspected for signs of deterioration, damage, overheating etc.

The report must not be used instead of an Electrical Installation Certificate or a Domestic Electrical Installation Certificate for certifying a new electrical installation, or in place of a full Periodic Inspection Report for certifying that an electrical installation may continue to be used in safety.

The Domestic Visual Condition Report may be used only where all the following conditions apply:

- The inspection is limited to the installation in a single dwelling (house or individual flat).

- The supply to the installation is single-phase, 50 Hz, and the nominal voltage does not exceed 230 V.

- The installation forms part of a TN-S, TN-C-S (PME) or TT system.

- The protective measure against electric shock is provided by Automatic Disconnection of Supply (ADS).

- The installation is supplied from one source only.

The report form marked 'Original', including any additional pages, is to be given to the person ordering the inspection. The report form marked 'Duplicate' is to be retained by the contractor.

It is the responsibility of the compiler of the report to ensure that the information provided in the report is factual, and that the declaration of the condition of the electrical installation to which the report relates is fair and reasonable in all the circumstances, given the limitations of visual inspection only.

The total number of pages which make up the report must be inserted in the box provided at the foot of each of the pages on the right-hand side.

Completing the report

Page 1

The box entitled *Details of the client and the installation* provides space for the client's name, address and the type of dwelling being inspected; such as a house, flat or bungalow.

continued on reverse

DVN3 / GF

Published by NICEIC Group Limited © Copyright The Electrical Safety Council (Jan 2008)

In the box *Summary of the condition of the installation* the inspector should insert a brief description of the condition of the installation. The summary should adequately describe the overall condition of the installation having considered, for example:

- whether the earthing and bonding is likely to be adequate
- the condition of the consumer unit and the protective devices
- the type of wiring system and its condition
- the serviceability of equipment including accessories
- the presence of adequate identification and notices including a schedule of circuit details
- the extent of any wear and tear, damage or other deterioration.

Where the visual inspection has identified damage or deterioration to an installation or visually-apparent defects which may significantly affect electrical safety, the condition of that installation must be recorded as unsatisfactory. If the space available on the form for the summary of the inspection is insufficient, additional numbered pages are to be provided as necessary. Additional pages must be referenced specifically to this report.

In the box *Particulars of the Approved Contractor*, the Inspector should enter the appropriate details.

A *Declaration* of the overall condition of the installation must be given in this section of the report. The inspector should tick one of the two boxes, namely

☐ Visually not unsatisfactory or

☐ Unsatisfactory, significant damage, deterioration and/or defects being evident.

The declaration must be consistent with the observations and recommendations made. A list of observations and recommendations for urgent remedial work and corrective action(s) necessary to restore the installation to a satisfactory condition should be given. But, given the limitations of a visual inspection, these recommendations may be incomplete and in such a case, a recommendation should be given that a full periodic inspection be performed to determine the full extent of the remedial action required.

Where the second box *'Unsatisfactory, significant damage, deterioration, defects being evident'* is ticked a list of corrective action(s) necessary to maintain the installation in a safe working order should be given. For further guidance on the recommendations to be given, see the reverse of page 1 of the Domestic Visual Condition Report.

Space is provided to insert the appropriate time interval before re-inspection of the installation becomes due. IEE Guidance Note 3 gives guidance on the frequency of inspection of electrical installations in various types of premises, but due account must be taken of factors such as the present condition of the installation and its use and operation. For domestic electrical installations, the maximum time interval from initial inspection is normally 10 years or upon change of occupancy. Your recommendation for the interval to the next inspection is to be conditional on all items that have attracted a recommendation Code 1 and Code 2 in the Section *Observations and recommendations for actions to be taken*

Published by NICEIC Group Limited © Copyright The Electrical Safety Council (Jan 2008)

being remedied without delay and as soon as practical respectively. Additionally, your recommendation for the interval to the next inspection is also to be conditional on all items which have attracted a recommendation Code 3 being remedied as soon as practicable.

Observations and recommendations for actions to be taken includes two boxes at the top, in one of which the inspector is required to enter a 'Yes' or a '✓' to indicate, as appropriate, that *There are no visually-evident items affecting electrical safety* or *'The following observations and recommendations are made'*. In the latter case, the observations and recommendations are to be listed with a Recommendation Code 1, 2, 3 or 4 (see reverse of page 2 of the report forms for further guidance on the recommendations). **Only one Recommendation Code is to be given for each recorded observation.** At the bottom of the Section, two boxes are provided for recording the items which, in the opinion of the inspector, need urgent remedial action and those items requiring corrective action(s), respectively.

Where an Approved Contractor classifies a recommendation as *'Urgent remedial action recommended'*, the client is to be advised immediately, in writing, to satisfy the duties imposed by the Electricity at Work Regulations 1989. It should be noted that, where an existing or a potential danger is observed that may put the safety of those using the installation at risk, Recommendation Code 1 (requires urgent attention) must be used.

If the space available on the form for recording observations and recommendations is insufficient, additional numbered pages are to be provided as necessary. Additional pages must be referenced specifically to this report.

Page 2, Schedule

All unshaded boxes should be completed either by insertion of the relevant details or by entering:

A '✓' meaning a particular inspection has been carried out and the result is, as far as can be ascertained from a visual-only inspection, **not unsatisfactory.**

A 'X' meaning a particular inspection has been carried out and the result is **unsatisfactory.**

or

'N/A' meaning **'Not Applicable'**, where appropriate. It is unlikely that all items will apply, and the range of applicable inspections will depend on the particular installation covered by the report. If an inspection is not applicable, 'N/A' should be recorded in the box.

Note that for every 'X' meaning 'unsatisfactory', an observation should be made in the Section *Observations and recommendations for actions to be taken.*

Further guidance

For further guidance on inspection and testing of electrical installations, refer to the practical advice and guidance in the NICEIC Inspection, Testing and Certification book, the current edition of BS 7671, and IEE Guidance Note 3.

Jan 2008

DVN3 G8

Domestic Visual Condition Report

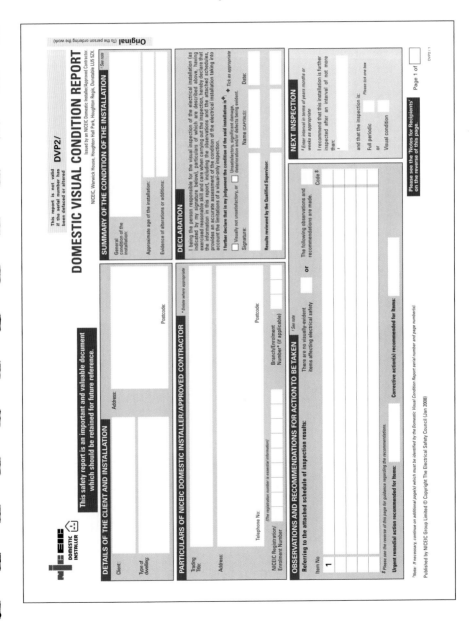

Domestic Visual Condition Report

NOTES FOR RECIPIENT

THIS DOMESTIC VISUAL CONDITION REPORT IS AN IMPORTANT AND VALUABLE DOCUMENT WHICH SHOULD BE RETAINED FOR FUTURE REFERENCE

The purpose of a visual-only inspection of a domestic electrical installation is to determine, so far as is reasonably practicable, whether the installation has any visually-evident defects or has suffered any damage or deterioration which may affect safety. This domestic visual condition report provides an assessment of the condition of the electrical installation identified overleaf at the time it was inspected, taking into account the limitations of a visual-only inspection.

Only NICEIC Domestic Installers registered for Domestic Periodic Inspection Reporting work and NICEIC Approved Contractors working within the scope of their enrolment are authorized to issue these NICEIC Domestic Visual Condition Reports.

Whilst a visual inspection may reveal defects, damage or deterioration which may present electrical safety hazards, such an inspection alone cannot fully determine whether an installation is safe for continued use.

Furthermore, due to the significant limitations, it is not appropriate to report that an installation is in a satisfactory condition on the basis of visual inspection only.

Visual inspections do not include items that can only be checked with test instruments, such as the adequacy of earthing arrangements.

An NICEIC® Domestic Installer/Approved Contractor performing the visual inspection will recommend that a full inspection and test be performed if it is suspected that the installation is in an unsafe condition.

Also for safety reasons, the electrical installation will need to be re-inspected at appropriate intervals by a competent person. The recommended maximum time interval to the next inspection and the type of inspection is stated overleaf in the section: *Next Inspection*. The recommendation for the interval to the next inspection is conditional on all items which have attracted a Recommendation Code 1 and Code 2 in the section *Observations and recommendations for actions to be taken* being remedied without delay and as soon as practical respectively. Additionally, the recommendation given for the interval to the next inspection and the type of inspection is also to be conditional on all items which have attracted a Recommendation Code 3 being remedied as soon as practicable. NICEIC recommends that you engage the services of a Domestic Installer/Approved Contractor for this purpose. There should be a notice at or near the consumer unit indicating the latest date by which a full periodic inspection and test of the installation is due.

Where the installation incorporates a residual current device (RCD), there should be a notice at or near the consumer unit stating that the device should be tested at quarterly intervals. For safety reasons, it is important that you carry out the test regularly.

Note that consumer units fitted with cartridge or rewirable fuses may be suitable for continued use provided the consumer unit is in a satisfactory condition and each fuse is correctly rated.

For further information about electrical safety and how NICEIC can help you, visit www.niceicgroup.com

---

* NICEIC is a trading name of NICEIC Group Limited, a wholly owned subsidiary of The Electrical Safety Council. Under licence from The Electrical Safety Council, NICEIC acts as the electrical contracting industry's independent voluntary regulatory body for electrical installation safety matters throughout the UK and maintains and publishes registers of electrical contractors that it has assessed against particular scheme requirements (including the technical standard of electrical work).

Published by NICEIC Group Limited © Copyright The Electrical Safety Council (Jan 2008)

GUIDANCE FOR RECIPIENTS ON THE RECOMMENDATION CODES

Only one Recommendation Code should have been given for each recorded observation.

Recommendation Code 1

Where an observation has been given a Recommendation Code 1 (requires urgent attention), the safety of those using the installation may be at risk.

The person responsible for the maintenance of the installation is advised to take action without delay to remedy the observed deficiency in the installation, or to take other appropriate action (such as switching off and isolating the affected part(s) of the installation) to remove the potential danger. The NICEIC Domestic Installer/Approved Contractor issuing this report will be able to provide further advice.

NICEIC make available 'dangerous condition' notification forms to enable inspectors to record, and then to communicate to the person ordering the report, any dangerous condition discovered.

Recommendation Code 2

Recommendation Code 2 (requires improvement) indicates that, whilst the safety of those using the installation may not be at immediate risk, remedial action should be taken as soon as possible to improve the safety of the installation. The NICEIC Domestic Installer/Approved Contractor issuing this report will be able to provide further advice.

Items which have been attributed Recommendation Code 2 should be remedied as soon as possible.

Recommendation Code 3

Where an observation has been given a Recommendation Code 3 (requires further investigation), the inspection has revealed an apparent deficiency which could not, due to the extent or limitations of the inspection, be fully identified. Items which have been attributed Recommendation Code 3 should be investigated by a competent person as soon as possible.

The person responsible for the maintenance of the installation is advised to arrange for the NICEIC Domestic Installer/Approved Contractor issuing this report (or other competent person) to undertake further inspection and/or testing of the installation to determine the nature and extent of the apparent deficiency.

Recommendation Code 4

Recommendation Code 4 (does not comply with BS 7671 (as amended)) will have been given to observed non-compliance(s) with the current safety standard which do not warrant one of the other Recommendation Codes. It is not intended to imply that the electrical installation inspected is unsafe, but careful consideration should be given to the benefits of improving these aspects of the installation. The NICEIC Domestic Installer/Approved Contractor issuing this report will be able to provide further advice.

It is important to note that the recommendation given at *Next Inspection* of this report for the maximum interval until the next inspection is conditional upon all items which have been given a Recommendation Code 1 and Code 2 being remedied without delay and as soon as possible respectively.

It would not be reasonable to indicate a 'visually not unsatisfactory' assessment if any observation in the report had been given a Code 1 or Code 2 recommendation.

Continued on the reverse of page 2

DVP2 / 1&2/2

The NICEIC guide to
Domestic Periodic Inspection, Testing and Reporting

Domestic Visual Condition Report

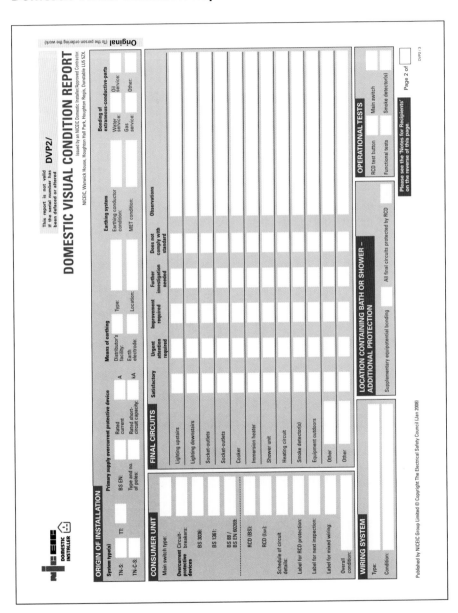

NOTES FOR RECIPIENT *(continued)*

The visual-only inspection report

This report is intended to be issued only for the purpose of reporting on the condition of an existing electrical installation. The report should identify, so far as is reasonably practicable, any damage, deterioration and visually-evident defects which:

- may give rise to danger,
- require improvement,
- require further investigation or
- do not comply with the latest edition of the national standard for electrical safety BS 7671: *Requirements for Electrical Installations.*

The report consists of at least two numbered pages. Additional numbered pages may have been provided to permit further relevant information concerning the installation to be reported. The report is invalid if any of the identified pages are missing. The report form has a printed nine-digit serial number, which is traceable to the NICEIC Domestic Installer/Approved Contractor to which it was supplied by NICEIC.

The report should not have been issued to certify a new electrical installation. A 'Domestic Electrical Installation Certificate' or 'Electrical Installation Certificate' (where appropriate) should be issued for the certification of new installation work.

Only NICEIC Domestic Installers registered for Domestic Periodic Inspection Reporting work and NICEIC Approved Contractors working within the scope of their enrolment are authorized to issue these NICEIC Domestic Visual Condition Reports. You should have received the report marked 'Original' and the Domestic Installer/Approved Contractor should have retained the report marked 'Duplicate'.

Understanding the report

Page 1

In the *Summary of the conditions of the installation* box, the inspector should have put a brief summary of the overall condition of the installation, taking into account the specific observations made.

In the *Declaration* box the inspector should have ticked one of the two boxes, namely:

☐ Visually not unsatisfactory, or

☐ Unsatisfactory, significant damage, deterioration and/or defects being evident.

Published by NICEIC Group Limited © Copyright The Electrical Safety Council (Jan 2008)

The declaration should reflect the observations and recommendations made. A list of observations and recommendations for urgent remedial work and corrective action(s) necessary to restore the installation to a satisfactory condition should be given in the box at the bottom of page 1. But, given the limitations of a visual inspection, these recommendations may be incomplete and a full periodic inspection report may be necessary to determine the full extent of the required remedial action.

For further guidance on the recommendations, please see the reverse of page 1.

In the box entitled *Next Inspection* the inspector should have made a recommendation as to the time interval to the next inspection and the type of inspection, such as a visual inspection or a full periodic inspection. This recommendation will depend on circumstances such as the age of the installation or if it is subject to more rapid deterioration.

Page 2, Schedules:

All unshaded boxes should have been completed either by insertion of the relevant details or by entering:

A '✓' meaning a particular inspection has been carried out and the result, as far as can be ascertained from a visual-only inspection, is **not unsatisfactory**

or

A 'X' meaning a particular inspection has been carried out and the result is **unsatisfactory**

or

'N/A' meaning **'Not Applicable'**, where appropriate.

Note that for every 'X' meaning 'unsatisfactory', an observation should have been made in the Section *Observations and recommendations for actions to be taken.*

Should the person ordering the domestic visual condition inspection (eg the client, as identified on Page 1 of this report), have reason to believe that the report issued by the NICEIC Domestic Installer/Approved Contractor does not reasonably reflect the condition of the electrical installation reported on given the limitations of a visual only inspection, the person should in the first instance raise the specific concerns in writing with the NICEIC Domestic Installer/Approved Contractor. If the concerns remain unresolved, the client may make a formal complaint to NICEIC, for which purpose a standard complaint form is available on request.

The complaints procedure offered by NICEIC is subject to certain terms and conditions, full details of which are available upon application (or visit **www.niceicgroup.com**). NICEIC does not investigate complaints relating to the operational performance of electrical installations (such as lighting levels), or to contractual or commercial issues (such as time or cost).

Jan 2008

DVP2 08AB

Domestic Visual Condition Report Continuation Sheet

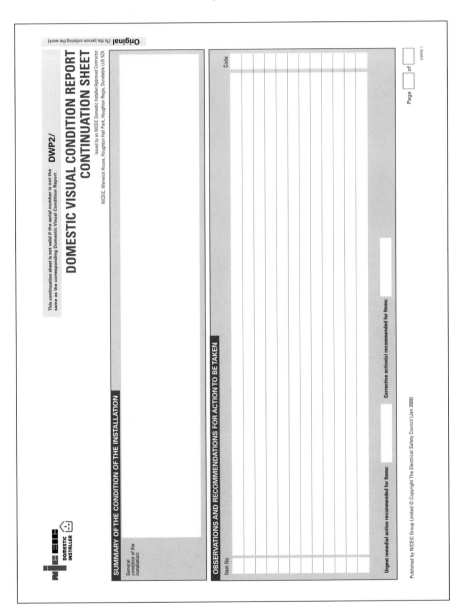

Guidance for Domestic Installers/Approved Contractors

DVP2 GF

continued on reverse

DOMESTIC VISUAL CONDITION REPORT
GUIDANCE FOR NICEIC DOMESTIC INSTALLER/APPROVED CONTRACTOR

NICEIC reports are accountable documents. Unused copies should be kept secure by the Qualified Supervisor. A record of each report used should be made on the record sheet provided. Unused sets of obsolete reports must be destroyed to prevent their misuse.

General

The purpose of a visual-only inspection of a dwelling is to determine, so far as is reasonably practicable, whether an electrical installation has suffered any damage or deterioration or has any visually-evident defects which affect, or may affect, safety. The NICEIC Domestic Visual Condition Report is intended to be used only for the purpose of reporting on the condition of an existing electrical installation. The report should identify, so far as is reasonably practicable, any damage, deterioration or defects which may give rise to danger.

NICEIC considers that the practice of 'visual inspection only' is **not non-compliant** with the requirements of the national standard for electrical safety, BS 7671: *Requirements for Electrical Installations, provided that:*

- The visual inspection is carried out in accordance with all the requirements of BS 7671 that are applicable to visual inspection.

- The limitations of 'visual inspection only' which are stated in the Notes for Recipients on the reverse of the report form are made clear in writing to the person ordering the work.

- It is **not** claimed that a 'visual inspection only' can or will fully determine whether an installation is **safe for continued use.**

- An objective report of the findings of the visual inspection is given to the person ordering the work, whether or not specifically requested by that person.

- It is made clear to the person ordering the work that a visual inspection does not include items that can only be checked with test instruments (such as the adequacy of earthing arrangements).

- Any quotation for proposed remedial work is given separately from the visual inspection report.

- A full periodic inspection is recommended to the customer if it is suspected that the installation is in an unsafe condition, or if it is believed that other significant defects cannot be determined, but may be revealed by testing.

The entire electrical installation should be inspected including the loft space(s) and any outside garage, workshop, greenhouse, conservatory etc.

A certain amount of dismantling is normally necessary even though the inspection is 'visual-only'. For example, after appropriate isolation, the cover of the consumer unit should be removed to permit the checking of electrical equipment such as the condition and suitability of the cables employed. In addition, equipment such as socket-outlets, light switches and luminaires should be inspected for signs of deterioration, damage, overheating etc.

The report must not be used instead of an Electrical Installation Certificate or a Domestic Electrical Installation Certificate for certifying a new electrical installation, or in place of a full Periodic Inspection Report for certifying that an electrical installation may continue to be used in safety.

The NICEIC Domestic Visual Condition Report may be used only where all the following conditions apply:

- The inspection is limited to the installation in a single dwelling (house or individual flat).

- The supply to the installation is single-phase, 50 Hz, and the nominal voltage does not exceed 230 V.

- The installation forms part of a TN-S, TN-C-S (PME) or TT system.

- The protective measure against electric shock is provided by Automatic Disconnection of Supply (ADS).

- The installation is supplied from one source only.

The report form marked 'Original', including any additional pages, is to be given to the person ordering the inspection. The report form marked 'Duplicate' is to be retained by the Domestic Installer/Approved Contractor and made available for review by NICEIC.

It is the responsibility of the compiler of the report to ensure that the information provided in the report is factual, and that the declaration of the condition of the electrical installation to which the report relates is fair and reasonable in all the circumstances, given the limitations of visual inspection only.

The total number of pages which make up the report must be inserted in the box provided at the foot of each of the pages on the right-hand side.

Completing the report

Page 1

The box entitled *Details of the client and the installation* provides space for the client's name, address and the type of dwelling being inspected; such as a house, flat or bungalow.

Published by NICEIC Group Limited © Copyright The Electrical Safety Council (Jan 2008)

Guidance for Domestic Installers/Approved Contractors

In the box *Summary of the condition of the installation* the inspector should insert a brief description of the condition of the installation. The summary should adequately describe the overall condition of the installation having considered, for example:

- whether the earthing and bonding is likely to be adequate
- the condition of the consumer unit and the protective devices
- the type of wiring system and its condition
- the serviceability of equipment including accessories
- the presence of adequate identification and notices including a schedule of circuit details
- the extent of any wear and tear, damage or other deterioration.

Where the visual inspection has identified damage or deterioration to an installation or visually-apparent defects which may significantly affect electrical safety, the inspector should enter the appropriate details.

In the box *Particulars of NICEIC Domestic Installer/Approved Contractor*, the Inspector should enter the appropriate details.

A *Declaration* of the overall condition of the installation must be given in this section of the report. The inspector should tick one of the two boxes, namely

☐ Visually not unsatisfactory or

☐ Unsatisfactory, significant damage, deterioration and/or defects being evident.

The declaration must be consistent with the observations and recommendations made. A list of observations and recommendations for urgent remedial work and corrective action(s) necessary to restore the installation to a satisfactory condition should be given. But, given the limitations of a visual inspection, these recommendations may be incomplete and in such a case, a recommendation should be given that a full periodic inspection be performed to determine the full extent of the remedial action required.

Where the second box *'Unsatisfactory, significant damage, deterioration, defects being evident'* is ticked a list of corrective action(s) necessary to maintain the installation in a safe working order should be given. For further guidance on the recommendations to be given, see the reverse of page 1 of the Domestic Visual Condition Report.

Space is provided to insert the appropriate time interval before re-inspection of the installation becomes due. IEE Guidance Note 3 gives guidance on the frequency of inspection of electrical installations in various types of premises, but due account must be taken of factors such as the present condition of the installation and its use and operation. For domestic electrical installations, the maximum time interval from initial inspection is normally 10 years or upon change of occupancy. Your recommendation for the interval to the next inspection is to be conditional on all items that have attracted a recommendation

Code 1 and Code 2 in the Section *Observations and recommendations for actions to be taken* being remedied without delay and as soon as practical respectively. Additionally, your recommendation for the interval to the next inspection is also to be conditional on all items which have attracted a recommendation Code 3 being remedied as soon as practicable.

Observations and recommendations for actions to be taken includes two boxes at the top, in one of which the inspector is required to enter a 'Yes' or a '✓' to indicate, as appropriate, that *There are no visually-evident items affecting electrical safety* or *'The following observations and recommendations are made'*. In the latter case, the observations and recommendations are to be listed with a Recommendation Code 1, 2, 3 or 4 (see reverse of page 2 of the report forms for further guidance on the recommendations). **Only one Recommendation Code is to be given for each recorded observation**. At the bottom of the Section, two boxes are provided for recording the items which, in the opinion of the inspector, need urgent remedial action and those items requiring corrective action(s), respectively.

Where an NICEIC Domestic Installer/Approved Contractor classifies a recommendation as 'Urgent remedial action recommended', the client is to be advised immediately, in writing, to satisfy the duties imposed by the Electricity at Work Regulations 1989. It should be noted that, where an existing or a potential danger is observed that may put the safety of those using the installation at risk, Recommendation Code 1 (requires urgent attention) must be used.

If the space available on the form for recording observations and recommendations is insufficient, additional numbered pages are to be provided as necessary. Additional pages must be identified by the unique Domestic Visual Condition Report serial number.

Page 2, Schedule

All unshaded boxes should be completed either by insertion of the relevant details or by entering:

A '✓' meaning a particular inspection has been carried out and the result is, as far as can be ascertained from a visual-only inspection, **not unsatisfactory.**

A 'X' meaning a particular inspection has been carried out and the result is **unsatisfactory,**

or

'N/A' meaning **'Not Applicable'**, where appropriate. It is unlikely that all items will apply, and the range of applicable inspections will depend on the particular installation covered by the report. If an inspection is not applicable, 'N/A' should be recorded in the box.

Note that for every 'X' meaning 'unsatisfactory', an observation should be made in the Section *Observations and recommendations for actions to be taken.*

Further guidance

For further guidance on inspection and testing of electrical installations, refer to the practical advice and guidance in the NICEIC Inspection, Testing and Certification book, the NICEIC guide to Domestic Periodic Inspection, Testing and Reporting, the current edition of BS 7671, and IEE Guidance Note 3.

Published by NICEIC Group Limited © Copyright The Electrical Safety Council (Jan 2008)

DVP2-GB

Domestic Visual Condition Report

DVM2

DOMESTIC VISUAL CONDITION REPORT

Original (To the person ordering the work)

This safety report is an important and valuable document which should be retained for future reference.

DETAILS OF THE CLIENT AND INSTALLATION

Client:

Type of dwelling:

Address:

Postcode:

PARTICULARS OF CONTRACTOR

Trading Title:

Address:

Postcode:

Telephone No:

SUMMARY OF THE CONDITION OF THE INSTALLATION † See note

General condition of the installation:

Approximate age of the installation:

Evidence of alterations or additions:

DECLARATION

I being the person responsible for the visual inspection of the electrical installation (as indicated by my signature below, particulars of which are described above, having exercised reasonable skill and care when carrying out the inspection, hereby declare that the information in this report, including the observations and the attached schedules, provides an accurate assessment of the condition of the electrical installation taking into account the limitations of a visual-only inspection.

I further declare that in my judgement the condition of the said installation is ✱. ✦ Tick as appropriate

☐ Visually not unsatisfactory, or ☐ Unsatisfactory, significant damage, deterioration and/or defects being evident.

Signature:

Name (CAPITALS):

Date:

OBSERVATIONS AND RECOMMENDATIONS FOR ACTION TO BE TAKEN § See note

Referring to the attached schedule of inspection results:

☐ There are no visually-evident items affecting electrical safety

or

The following observations and recommendations are made.

Item No		Code §
1		

§ Please see the reverse of this page for guidance regarding the recommendations.

Urgent remedial action recommended for Items:

Corrective action(s) recommended for Items:

NEXT INSPECTION

† Enter interval in terms of years months or weeks as appropriate

I recommend that this installation is further inspected after an interval of not more than:

and that the inspection is: Please tick one box

Full periodic ☐

or

Visual condition ☐

Please see the 'Notes for Recipients' on the reverse of this page.

Page 1 of

DVM2 / 1

'Note. If necessary, continue on additional page(s) which must be referenced specifically to this report.

© Copyright The Electrical Safety Council (Jan 2008)

DVM2

Domestic Visual Condition Report

NOTES FOR RECIPIENT

THIS DOMESTIC VISUAL CONDITION REPORT IS AN IMPORTANT AND VALUABLE DOCUMENT WHICH SHOULD BE RETAINED FOR FUTURE REFERENCE

The purpose of a visual-only inspection of a domestic electrical installation is to determine, so far as is reasonably practicable, whether the installation has any visually-evident defects or has suffered any damage or deterioration which may affect safety. This domestic visual condition report provides an assessment of the condition of the electrical installation identified overleaf at the time it was inspected, taking into account the limitations of a visual-only inspection.

Whilst a visual inspection may reveal defects, damage or deterioration which may present electrical safety hazards, such an inspection alone cannot fully determine whether an installation is safe for continued use.

Furthermore, due to the significant limitations, it is not appropriate to report that an installation is in a satisfactory condition on the basis of visual inspection only.

Visual inspections do not include items that can only be checked with test instruments, such as the adequacy of earthing arrangements.

The contractor performing the visual inspection will recommend that a full inspection and test be performed if it is suspected that the installation is in an unsafe condition.

Also for safety reasons, the electrical installation will need to be re-inspected at appropriate intervals by a competent person. The recommended maximum time interval to the next inspection and the type of inspection is stated overleaf in the section: *Next Inspection*. The recommendation for the interval to the next inspection is conditional on all items which have attracted a Recommendation Code 1 and Code 2 in the section *Observations and recommendations for actions to be taken* being remedied without delay and as soon as practice respectively. Additionally, the recommendation given for the interval to the next inspection and Recommendation Code 3 being remedied as soon as practicable. It is recommended that you engage the services of an electrical contractor registered with one of the government approved Part P scheme operators for this purpose. There should be a notice at or near the consumer unit indicating the latest date by which a full periodic inspection and test of the installation is due.

Where the installation incorporates a residual current device (RCD), there should be a notice at or near the consumer unit stating that the device should be tested at quarterly intervals. For safety reasons, it is important that you carry out the test regularly.

Note that consumer units fitted with cartridge or rewirable fuses may be suitable for continued use provided the consumer unit is in a satisfactory condition and each fuse is correctly rated.

GUIDANCE FOR RECIPIENTS ON THE RECOMMENDATION CODES

Only one Recommendation Code should have been given for each recorded observation.

Recommendation Code 1

Where an observation has been given a Recommendation Code 1 (requires urgent attention), the safety of those using the installation may be at risk.

The person responsible for the maintenance of the installation is advised to take action without delay to remedy the observed deficiency in the installation, or to take other appropriate action (such as switching off and isolating the affected part(s) of the installation) to remove the potential danger. The contractor issuing this report will be able to provide further advice.

Recommendation Code 2

Recommendation Code 2 (requires improvement) indicates that, whilst the safety of those using the installation may not be at immediate risk, remedial action should be taken as soon as possible to improve the safety of the installation. The contractor issuing this report will be able to provide further advice.

Items which have been attributed Recommendation Code 2 should be remedied as soon as possible.

Recommendation Code 3

Where an observation has been given a Recommendation Code 3 (requires further investigation), the inspection has revealed an apparent deficiency which could not, due to the extent or limitations of this inspection, be fully identified. Items which have been attributed Recommendation Code 3 should be investigated by a competent person as soon as possible.

The person responsible for the maintenance of the installation is advised to arrange for the contractor issuing this report (or other competent person) to undertake further inspection and/or testing of the installation to determine the nature and extent of the apparent deficiency.

Recommendation Code 4

Recommendation Code 4 (does not comply with BS 7671 (as amended)) will have been given to observed non-compliance(s) with the current safety standard which do not warrant one of the other Recommendation Codes. It is not intended to imply that the electrical installation inspected is unsafe, but careful consideration should be given to the benefits of improving these aspects of the installation. The contractor issuing this report will be able to provide further advice.

It is important to note that the recommendation given at *Next Inspection* of this report for the maximum interval until the next inspection is conditional upon all items which have been given a Recommendation Code 1 and Code 2 being remedied without delay and as soon as possible respectively.

It would not be reasonable to indicate a 'visually not unsatisfactory' assessment if any observation in the report had been given a Code 1 or Code 2 recommendation.

Continued on the reverse of page 2

DVM2 / 1&2B

The NICEIC guide to
Domestic Periodic Inspection, Testing and Reporting

Domestic Visual Condition Report

DVM2

DOMESTIC VISUAL CONDITION REPORT

Original (to the person ordering the work)

ORIGIN OF INSTALLATION

System type(s)
TN-S:
TN-C-S:
TT:

Primary supply overcurrent protective device
BS EN:
Type and no. of poles:
Rated current: A
Rated short-circuit capacity: kA

Means of earthing
Distributor's facility:
Earth electrode:
Type:
Location:

Earthing system
Earthing conductor condition:
MET condition:

Bonding of extraneous-conductive-parts
Water service:
Gas service:
Other:

CONSUMER UNIT

Main switch type:

Overcurrent protective devices
Circuit-breakers:
BS 3036:
BS 1361:
BS 88 / BS EN 60269:
RCD (BS):
RCD (Iun):

Schedule of circuit details:
Label for RCD protection:
Label for next inspection:
Label for mixed wiring:
Overall condition:

FINAL CIRCUITS

	Satisfactory	Urgent attention required	Improvement required	Further investigation needed	Does not comply with standard	Observations
Lighting upstairs						
Lighting downstairs						
Socket-outlets						
Socket-outlets						
Cooker						
Immersion heater						
Shower unit						
Heating circuit						
Smoke detector(s)						
Equipment outdoors						
Other						
Other						

WIRING SYSTEM

Type:
Condition:

LOCATION CONTAINING BATH OR SHOWER – ADDITIONAL PROTECTION

Supplementary equipotential bonding
All final circuits protected by RCD

OPERATIONAL TESTS

RCD test button
Functional tests
Main switch
Smoke detector(s)

Please see the 'Notes for Recipients' on the reverse of this page:

Page 2 of

DVM2 / 3

© Copyright The Electrical Safety Council (Jan 2008)

NOTES FOR RECIPIENT (continued)

The visual-only inspection report

This report is intended to be issued only for the purpose of reporting on the condition of an existing electrical installation. The report should identify, so far as is reasonably practicable, any damage, deterioration and visually-evident defects which:

- may give rise to danger,
- require improvement,
- require further investigation or
- do not comply with the latest edition of the national standard for electrical safety BS 7671: *Requirements for Electrical Installations*

The report consists of at least two numbered pages. Additional numbered pages may have been provided to permit further relevant information concerning the installation to be reported. The report is invalid if any of the identified pages are missing.

The report should not have been issued to certify a new electrical installation. A 'Domestic Electrical Installation Certificate' or 'Electrical Installation Certificate' (where appropriate) should be issued for the certification of new installation work.

You should have received the report marked 'Original' and the contractor should have retained the report marked 'Duplicate'.

If you were the person ordering the work, but not the user of the installation, you should pass this report, or a full copy of it including these notes and additional pages (if any), immediately to the user.

The 'Original' report form should be retained in a safe place and shown to any person inspecting or undertaking further work on the electrical installation in the future. If you later vacate the property, this report will provide the new user with an assessment of the condition of the electrical installation at the time the inspection was carried out.

Understanding the report

Page 1

In the *Summary of the conditions of the installation* box, the inspector should have put a brief summary of the overall condition of the installation, taking into account the specific observations made.

In the *Declaration* box the inspector should have ticked one of the two boxes, namely:

☐ Visually not unsatisfactory, or

☐ Unsatisfactory, significant damage, deterioration and/or defects being evident.

The declaration should reflect the observations and recommendations made. A list of observations and recommendations for urgent remedial work and corrective action(s) necessary to restore the installation to a satisfactory condition should be given in the box at the bottom of page 1. But, given the limitations of a visual inspection, these recommendations may be incomplete and a full periodic inspection report may be necessary to determine the full extent of the required remedial action.

For further guidance on the recommendations, please see the reverse of page 1.

In the box entitled *Next Inspection* the inspector should have made a recommendation as to the time interval to the next inspection and the type of inspection, such as a visual inspection or a full periodic inspection. This recommendation will depend on circumstances such as the age of the installation or if it is subject to more rapid deterioration.

Page 2, Schedules:

All unshaded boxes should have been completed either by insertion of the relevant details or by entering:

A ✓ meaning a particular inspection has been carried out and the result, as far as can be ascertained from a visual-only inspection, is **not unsatisfactory**

or

A '**X**' meaning a particular inspection has been carried out and the result is **unsatisfactory**

or

'**N/A**' meaning '**Not Applicable**', where appropriate.

Note that for every '**X**' meaning '**unsatisfactory**', an observation should have been made in the Section *Observations and recommendations for actions to be taken*.

Should the person ordering the domestic visual condition inspection (eg the client, as identified on Page 1 of this report), have reason to believe that the report issued by the contractor does not reasonably reflect the condition of the electrical installation reported on given the limitations of a visual only inspection, the person should raise the specific concerns in writing with the contractor.

Jan 2008

DVM2 / 3A49

Domestic Visual Condition Report Continuation Sheet

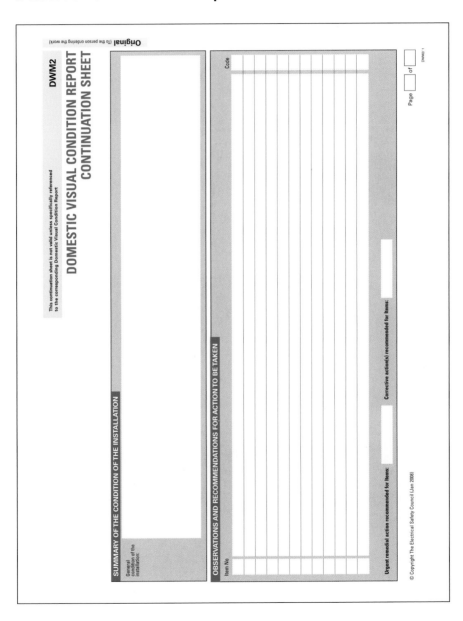

Guidance for Electrical Contractors

DOMESTIC VISUAL CONDITION REPORT
GUIDANCE FOR CONTRACTORS

A record of each report used should be made on the record sheet provided. Unused sets of obsolete reports must be destroyed to prevent their misuse.

General

The purpose of a visual-only inspection of a dwelling is to determine, so far as is reasonably practicable, whether an electrical installation has suffered any damage or deterioration or has any visually-evident defects which affect, or may affect, safety. The Domestic Visual Condition Report is intended to be used only for the purpose of reporting on the condition of an existing electrical installation. The report should identify, so far as is reasonably practicable, any damage, deterioration or defects which may give rise to danger.

The practice of 'visual inspection only' is **not non-compliant** with the requirements of the national standard for electrical safety, BS 7671: *Requirements for Electrical Installations,* **provided that:**

- The visual inspection is carried out in accordance with all the requirements of BS 7671 that are applicable to visual inspection.

- The limitations of 'visual inspection only' which are stated in the Notes for Recipients on the reverse of the report form are made clear in writing to the person ordering the work.

- It is **not** claimed that a 'visual inspection only' can or will fully determine whether an installation is **safe for continued use.**

- An objective report of the findings of the visual inspection is given to the person ordering the work, whether or not specifically requested by that person.

- It is made clear to the person ordering the work that a visual inspection does not include items that can only be checked with test instruments (such as the adequacy of earthing arrangements).

- Any quotation for proposed remedial work is given separately from the visual inspection report.

- A full periodic inspection is recommended to the customer if it is suspected that the installation is in an unsafe condition, or if it is believed that other significant defects cannot be determined, but may be revealed by testing.

The entire electrical installation should be inspected including the loft space(s) and any outside garage, workshop, greenhouse, conservatory etc.

A certain amount of dismantling is normally necessary even though the inspection is 'visual-only'. For example, after appropriate isolation, the cover of the consumer unit should be removed to permit the checking of electrical equipment such as the condition and suitability of the cables employed. In addition, equipment such as socket-outlets, light switches and luminaires should be inspected for signs of deterioration, damage, overheating etc.

The report must not be used instead of an Electrical Installation Certificate or a Domestic Electrical Installation Certificate for certifying a new electrical installation, or in place of a full Periodic Inspection Report for certifying that an electrical installation may continue to be used in safety.

The Domestic Visual Condition Report may be used only where all the following conditions apply:

- The inspection is limited to the installation in a single dwelling (house or individual flat).

- The supply to the installation is single-phase, 50 Hz, and the nominal voltage does not exceed 230 V.

- The installation forms part of a TN-S, TN-C-S (PME) or TT system.

- The protective measure against electric shock is provided by Automatic Disconnection of Supply (ADS).

- The installation is supplied from one source only.

The report form marked 'Original', including any additional pages, is to be given to the person ordering the inspection. The report form marked 'Duplicate' is to be retained by the contractor.

It is the responsibility of the compiler of the report to ensure that the information provided in the report is factual, and that the declaration of the condition of the electrical installation to which the report relates is fair and reasonable in all the circumstances, given the limitations of visual inspection only.

The total number of pages which make up the report must be inserted in the box provided at the foot of each of the pages on the right-hand side.

Completing the report

Page 1

The box entitled *Details of the client and the installation* provides space for the client's name, address and the type of dwelling being inspected; such as a house, flat or bungalow.

continued on reverse

DVM2

DVM2

Guidance for Electrical Contractors

In the box *Summary of the condition of the installation* the inspector should insert a brief description of the condition of the installation. The summary should adequately describe the overall condition of the installation having considered, for example:

- whether the earthing and bonding is likely to be adequate
- the condition of the consumer unit and the protective devices
- the type of wiring system and its condition
- the serviceability of equipment including accessories
- the presence of adequate identification and notices including a schedule of circuit details
- the extent of any wear and tear, damage or other deterioration.

Where the visual inspection has identified damage or deterioration to an installation or visually-apparent defects which may significantly affect electrical safety, the condition of that installation must be recorded as unsatisfactory. If the space available on the form for the summary of the inspection is insufficient, additional numbered pages are to be provided as necessary. Additional pages must be referenced specifically to this report.

In the box *Particulars of Contractor*, the Inspector should enter the appropriate details.

A *Declaration* of the overall condition of the installation must be given in this section of the report. The inspector should tick one of the two boxes, namely

☐ Visually not unsatisfactory or

☐ Unsatisfactory, significant damage, deterioration and/or defects being evident.

The declaration must be consistent with the observations and recommendations made. A list of observations and recommendations for urgent remedial work and corrective action(s) necessary to restore the installation to a satisfactory condition should be given. But, given the limitations of a visual inspection, these recommendations may be incomplete and in such a case, a recommendation should be given that a full periodic inspection be performed to determine the full extent of the remedial action required.

Where the second box *'Unsatisfactory, significant damage, deterioration, defects being evident'* is ticked a list of corrective action(s) necessary to maintain the installation in a safe working order should be given. For further guidance on the recommendations to be given, see the reverse of page 1 of the Domestic Visual Condition Report.

Space is provided to insert the appropriate time interval before re-inspection of the installation becomes due. IEE Guidance Note 3 gives guidance on the frequency of inspection of electrical installations in various types of premises, but due account must be taken of factors such as the present condition of the installation and its use and operation. For domestic electrical installations, the maximum time interval from initial inspection is normally 10 years or upon change of occupancy. Your recommendation for the interval to the next inspection is to be conditional on all items that have attracted a recommendation Code 1 and Code 2 in the Section *Observations and recommendations for actions to be taken* being remedied without delay and as soon as practical respectively. Additionally, your recommendation for the interval to the next inspection is also to be conditional on all items which have attracted a recommendation Code 3 being remedied as soon as practicable.

Observations and recommendations for actions to be taken includes two boxes at the top, in one of which the inspector is required to enter a 'Yes' or a '✓' to indicate, as appropriate, that *'There are no visually-evident items affecting electrical safety'* or *'The following observations and recommendations are made.'* In the latter case, the observations and recommendations are to be listed with a Recommendation Code 1, 2, 3 or 4 (see reverse of page 2 of the report forms for further guidance on the recommendations). **Only one Recommendation Code is to be given for each recorded observation.** At the bottom of the Section, two boxes are provided for recording the items which, in the opinion of the inspector, need urgent remedial action and those items requiring corrective action(s), respectively.

Where a contractor classifies a recommendation as *'Urgent remedial action recommended'*, the client is to be advised immediately, in writing, to satisfy the duties imposed by the **Electricity at Work Regulations 1989.** It should be noted that, where an existing or a potential danger is observed that may put the safety of those using the installation at risk, Recommendation Code 1 (requires urgent attention) must be used.

If the space available on the form for recording observations and recommendations is insufficient, additional numbered pages are to be provided as necessary. Additional pages must be referenced specifically to the report.

Page 2, Schedule

All unshaded boxes should be completed either by insertion of the relevant details or by entering:

A '✓' meaning a particular inspection has been carried out and the result is, as far as can be ascertained from a visual-only inspection, **not unsatisfactory.**

or

A 'X' meaning a particular inspection has been carried out and the result is **unsatisfactory.**

or

'N/A', meaning **'Not Applicable'**, where appropriate. It is unlikely that all items will apply, and the range of applicable inspections will depend on the particular installation covered by the report. If an inspection is not applicable, 'N/A' should be recorded in the box.

Note that for every 'X' meaning 'unsatisfactory', an observation should be made in the Section *Observations and recommendations for actions to be taken.*

Further guidance

For further guidance on inspection and testing of electrical installations, refer to the practical advice and guidance in the NICEIC Inspection, Testing and Certification book, the NICEIC guide to Domestic Periodic Inspection, Testing and Reporting, the current edition of BS 7671, and IEE Guidance Note 3.

Jan 2008

DVM2

DOMESTIC ELECTRICAL INSTALLATION PERIODIC INSPECTION REPORTS

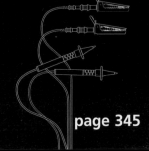

Domestic Electrical Installation Periodic Inspection Report

The form content (shown rotated) reads:

Original (To the person ordering the work)

DOMESTIC ELECTRICAL INSTALLATION PERIODIC INSPECTION REPORT (FOR A SINGLE DWELLING)

Issued in accordance with British Standard 7671 - Requirements for Electrical Installations by an Approved Contractor or Conforming Body enrolled with NICEIC, Warwick House, Houghton Hall Park, Houghton Regis, Dunstable LU5 5ZX.

NICEIC APPROVED CONTRACTOR

This report is not valid if the serial number has been defaced or altered

DPN4/

A DETAILS OF THE CLIENT
Client / Address:

B ADDRESS AND DETAILS OF THE INSTALLATION
Address:

Estimated age of the electrical installation: ___ years
If yes, estimated age: ___ years
Evidence of alterations or additions:
Date of previous inspection:
Electrical Installation Certificate number or previous Periodic Inspection Report number:
Records of installation available:
Records held by:

C PURPOSE OF THE REPORT † (see note below)
Purpose for which this report is required:

D EXTENT OF THE INSTALLATION AND LIMITATIONS OF THE INSPECTION AND TESTING ‡ (see note below)
Extent of the electrical installation covered by this report:
Agreed limitations (including the reasons), if any, on the inspection and testing

E PARTICULARS OF THE APPROVED CONTRACTOR
Trading Title:
Address:
Postcode:
Branch No: (if applicable)
NICEIC Enrolment No: (Essential Information)

F DECLARATION
I/We, being the person(s) responsible for the inspection and testing of the electrical installation (as indicated by my/our signatures below), particulars of which are described above (see B), having exercised reasonable skill and care when carrying out the inspection and testing, hereby declare that the information in this report, including the observations (see K) and the attached schedules (see K and L), provides an accurate assessment of the condition of the electrical installation taking into account the stated extent of the installation and the limitations of the inspection and testing (see D).
I/We further declare that in my/our judgement, the said installation was overall in ___ condition (see H) at the time the inspection was carried out, and that it should be further inspected as recommended (see I).

* (insert 'a satisfactory' or 'an unsatisfactory', as appropriate)

INSPECTION, TESTING AND ASSESSMENT BY:
Signature:
Name: (CAPITALS)
Position:
Date:

REPORT REVIEWED AND CONFIRMED BY: *See note below
Signature:
Name: (CAPITALS)
Date:
(Registered Qualified Supervisor for the Approved Contractor at E)

Please see the 'Notes for Recipients' on the reverse of this page.

Page 1 of ___

DPN4/1

† This Domestic Periodic Inspection Report must be used only for reporting on the condition of an existing installation.
‡ The inspection and testing have been carried out in accordance with BS 7671, as amended. Cables concealed within trunking and conduits, or cables and conduits concealed under floors, in inaccessible roof spaces and generally within the fabric of the building or underground, have not been visually inspected.
* This Domestic Periodic Inspection Report should be reviewed and confirmed by the registered Qualified Supervisor of the Approved Contractor responsible for issuing it.

This form is based on the model Periodic Inspection Report shown in Appendix 6 of BS 7671: 2008. Published by NICEIC Group Limited © Copyright The Electrical Safety Council (Jan 2008)

Domestic Electrical Installation Periodic Inspection Report

NOTES FOR RECIPIENT

THIS REPORT IS AN IMPORTANT AND VALUABLE DOCUMENT WHICH SHOULD BE RETAINED FOR FUTURE REFERENCE

The purpose of periodic inspection is to determine, so far as is reasonably practicable, whether an electrical installation is in a satisfactory condition for continued service. This report provides an assessment of the condition of the electrical installation identified overleaf at the time it was inspected, taking into account the stated extent of the installation and the limitations of the inspection and testing.

The report has been issued in accordance with the national standard for the safety of electrical installations, British Standard 7671 (as amended) - Requirements for Electrical Installations.

If you were the person ordering the work, but not the user of the installation, you should pass this report, or a full copy of it including these notes, the schedules and additional pages (if any), immediately to the user.

The 'Original' report form should be retained in a safe place and shown to any person inspecting or undertaking further work on the electrical installation in the future. If you later vacate the property, this report will provide the new user with an assessment of the condition of the electrical installation at the time the periodic inspection was carried out.

Where the installation incorporates a residual current device (RCD), there should be a notice at or near the main switchboard or consumer unit stating that the device should be tested at quarterly intervals. For safety reasons, it is important that you carry out the test regularly.

Also for safety reasons, the electrical installation will need to be re-inspected at appropriate intervals by a competent person. The recommended maximum time interval to the next inspection is stated on page 2 in Section I (Next Inspection). NICEIC* recommends that you engage the services of an Approved Contractor for this purpose. There should be a notice at or near the main switchboard or consumer unit indicating when the next inspection of the installation is due.

Only an NICEIC Approved Contractor or Conforming Body is authorised to issue this NICEIC Domestic Electrical Installation Periodic Inspection Report form.

The report consists of at least four numbered pages. Additional numbered pages may have been provided to permit further relevant information concerning the installation to be recorded. The report is invalid if any of the identified pages are missing. The report has a printed seven-digit serial number, which is traceable to the Approved Contractor to which it was supplied by NICEIC.

This report is intended to be issued only for the purpose of reporting on the condition of an existing electrical installation. The report should identify, so far as is reasonably practicable and having regard to the extent and limitations recorded in Section D, any damage, deterioration, defects, dangerous conditions and any non-compliances with the requirements of the national standard for the safety of electrical installations which may give rise to danger. It should be noted that the greater the limitations applying to a report, the less its value.

Published by NICEIC Group Limited © Copyright The Electrical Safety Council (Jan 2008)

This report should not have been issued to certify that a new electrical installation complies with the requirements of the national safety standard. A 'Domestic Electrical Installation Certificate' or Electrical Installation Certificate' should be issued for the certification of a new installation.

You should have received the report marked 'Original' and the Approved Contractor should have retained the report marked 'Duplicate'.

Section D addresses the extent and limitations of the report by providing boxes for the *Extent of the electrical installation covered by this report* and the *Agreed limitations, if any, on the inspection and testing*. Information given here should fully identify the scope of the inspection and testing and of the report. The Approved Contractor should have agreed all such aspects with the person ordering the work and other interested parties (eg insurance company, landlord, mortgagee etc) before the inspection was carried out.

A declaration of the overall condition of the installation should have been given by the inspector in Section F of the report. The declaration must reflect that report issued by the Approved Contractor does not reasonably reflect the observations and recommendations made in Section G. A list of observations and recommendations for urgent remedial work and corrective action(s) necessary to maintain the installation in a safe working order should have been given in Section G, where appropriate. For further guidance on the recommendations, please see the reverse of page 2.

Should the person ordering the periodic inspection (eg the client, as identified on Page 1 of this report) have reason to believe that the report issued by the Approved Contractor does not reasonably reflect the condition of the electrical installation reported on, the person should in the first instance raise the specific concerns in writing with the Approved Contractor. If the concerns remain unresolved, the client may make a formal complaint to NICEIC, for which purpose a standard complaint form is available on request.

The complaints procedure offered by NICEIC is subject to certain terms and conditions, full details of which are available upon application and from the website. NICEIC does not investigate complaints relating to the operational performance of electrical installations (such as lighting levels), or to contractual or commercial issues (such as time or cost).

Irrespective of the method of compilation of the form, all unshaded boxes should have been completed either by insertion of the relevant details or by entering 'N/A', meaning 'Not Applicable', where appropriate.

* NICEIC is a trading name of NICEIC Group Limited, a wholly owned subsidiary of The Electrical Safety Council. Under licence from The Electrical Safety Council, NICEIC acts as the electrical contracting industry's independent voluntary regulatory body for electrical installation safety matters throughout the UK, and maintains and publishes registers of electrical contractors that it has assessed against particular scheme requirements (including the technical standard of electrical work).

For further information about electrical safety and how NICEIC can help you, visit www.niceicgroup.com

DPN41635

Continued on the reverse of page 3

**The NICEIC guide to
Domestic Periodic Inspection, Testing and Reporting**

Domestic Electrical Installation Periodic Inspection Report

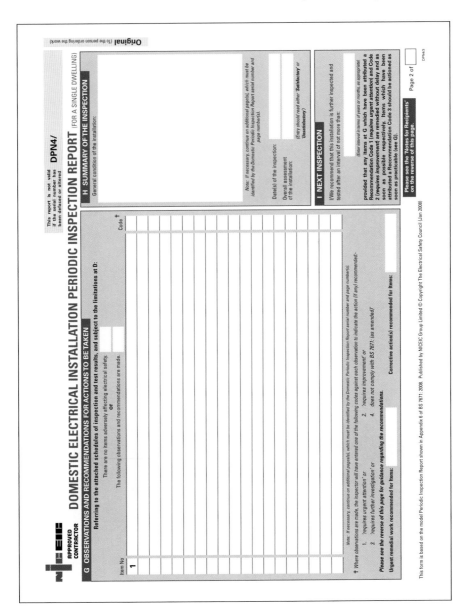

Domestic Electrical Installation Periodic Inspection Report

Jan 2008
DPN4/3449

It is important to note that the recommendation given at Section I *Next Inspection* of this report for the maximum interval until the next inspection is conditional upon all items which have been given a Recommendation Code 1 and Code 2 being remedied **without delay and as soon as possible respectively** (see Section G).

It would not be reasonable to indicate a 'satisfactory' assessment if any observation in the report had been given a Code 1 or Code 2 recommendation (see Section H).

GUIDANCE FOR RECIPIENTS ON THE RECOMMENDATION CODES

Only one Recommendation Code should have been given for each recorded observation.

Recommendation Code 1

Where an observation has been given a Recommendation Code 1 (requires urgent attention) a danger exists, and urgent remedial action is necessary as the safety of those using the installation may be at risk.

The person responsible for the maintenance of the installation is advised to take action without delay to remedy the observed deficiency in the installation, or to take other appropriate action (such as switching off and isolating the affected part(s) of the installation) to remove the potential danger.

NICEIC make available 'dangerous condition' notification forms to enable inspectors to record, and then to communicate to the person ordering the report, any dangerous condition discovered.

Recommendation Code 2

Recommendation Code 2 (requires improvement) indicates that, whilst the safety of those using the installation may not be at immediate risk, remedial action should be taken as soon as possible to remove potential danger, and improve the safety of the installation to the level provided by the national standard for the safety of electrical installations, BS 7671. The Contractor issuing this report will be able to provide further advice.

Items which have been given a Recommendation Code 2 should be remedied as soon as possible (see Section G).

Recommendation Code 3

Where an observation has been given a Recommendation Code 3 (requires further investigation), the inspection has revealed an apparent deficiency which could not, due to the extent or limitations of this inspection, be fully identified. Items which have been given a Recommendation Code 3 should be investigated as soon as possible (see Section G).

The person responsible for the maintenance of the installation is advised to arrange for the Contractor issuing this report (or other competent person) to undertake further examination of the installation to determine the nature and extent of the apparent deficiency.

Recommendation Code 4

Recommendation Code 4 [does not comply with BS 7671(as amended)] will have been given to observed non-compliance(s) with the **current** safety standard which do not warrant one of the other Recommendation Codes. It is not intended to imply that the electrical installation inspected is unsafe, but careful consideration should be given to the benefits of improving these aspects of the installation. The Contractor issuing this report will be able to provide further advice.

The NICEIC guide to
Domestic Periodic Inspection, Testing and Reporting

Domestic Electrical Installation Periodic Inspection Report

DOMESTIC ELECTRICAL INSTALLATION PERIODIC INSPECTION REPORT (FOR A SINGLE DWELLING)

Original (To the person ordering the work)

This report is not valid if the serial number has been defaced or altered

DPN4/

J SUPPLY CHARACTERISTICS, EARTHING AND BONDING ARRANGEMENTS

Supply Characteristics
- Nominal voltage: $U^{(1)}$ V
- Nominal voltage: $U_0^{(1)}$ V
- Nominal frequency: $f^{(1)}$ Hz
- Prospective fault current: $I_{pf}^{(2)}$ kA
- External earth fault loop impedance, $Z_e^{(2)}$ Ω

Notes:
(1) by enquiry
(2) by enquiry or by measurement
(3) by measurement

No. and type of live conductors (✓)
- 1-phase (2wire)
- 1-phase (3wire)
- 3-phase (3wire)
- 3-phase (4wire)
- Other (please state)

System Type(s) (✓)
- TN-S
- TN-C-S
- TT

Characteristics of Primary Supply Overcurrent Protective Device(s)
- BS(EN)
- Type
- Rated current A
- Short-circuit capacity kA

Main Switch or Circuit-Breaker *Enter details, as appropriate*
- Type: BS(EN)
- No of Poles
- Supply conductors material
- Supply conductors csa mm²
- Voltage rating V
- Rated current, I_n A
- RCD operating current, $I_{Δn}$* mA
- RCD operating time (at $I_{Δn}$)* ms

Applicable only where an RCD is used as a main circuit-breaker

Means of Earthing
- Distributor's facility
- Installation earth electrode
- Type: (eg rod(s), tape etc)
- Electrode resistance, R_A: Ω
- Location:
- Method of measurement:

Earthing and Protective Bonding Conductors

Main protective bonding conductors
- Earthing conductor: Conductor material / Conductor csa mm² / Continuity check (✓)
- Conductor material / Conductor csa mm² / Continuity check (✓)

Bonding of extraneous-conductive-parts (✓)
- Water service
- Gas service
- Oil service
- Structural steel
- Lightning protection
- Other incoming service(s)

K SCHEDULE OF ITEMS INSPECTED †See note below

Protective measures against electric shock

Basic and fault protection
- Extra low voltage
  - SELV
- Double or reinforced insulation
  - Double or reinforced insulation

Basic protection
- Insulation of live parts
- Barriers or enclosures

Fault protection
- Automatic disconnection of supply
  - Presence of earthing conductor
  - Presence of circuit protective conductors
  - Presence of main protective bonding conductors
  - Choice and setting of protective devices (for fault protection and/or overcurrent)

Electrical separation
- For one item of current-using equipment

Additional protection
- Presence of residual current device(s)
- Presence of supplementary bonding conductors

Prevention of mutual detrimental influence
- Proximity of non-electrical services and other influences
- Segregation of Band I and Band II circuits or Band II insulation used
- Segregation of safety circuits

Identification
- Presence of diagrams, instructions, circuit charts and similar information
- Presence of danger notices
- Presence of other warning notices, including presence of mixed wiring colours
- Labelling of protective devices, switches and terminals
- Identification of conductors

Cables and conductors
- Selection of conductors for current carrying capacity and voltage drop
- Erection methods

Cables and conductors (cont)
- Routing of cables in prescribed zones
- Cables incorporating earthed armour or sheath or run in an earthed wiring system, or otherwise protected against nails, screws and the like
- Additional protection by 30mA RCD (where required, in premises not under the supervision of skilled or instructed persons)
- Connection of conductors
- Presence of fire barriers, suitable seals and protection against thermal effects

General
- Presence and correct location of appropriate devices for isolation and switching
- Adequacy of access to switchgear and other equipment
- Particular protective measures for special installations and locations
- Connection of single-pole devices for protection or switching in line conductors only
- Correct connection of accessories and equipment
- Selection of equipment and protective measures appropriate to external influences
- Selection of appropriate functional switching devices

L SCHEDULE OF ITEMS TESTED
- External earth fault loop impedance, Z_e
- Installation earth electrode resistance, R_A
- Continuity of protective conductors
- Continuity of ring final circuit conductors
- Insulation resistance between live conductors
- Insulation resistance between live conductors and earth
- Polarity
- Earth fault loop impedance, Z_s
- Verification of phase sequence
- Operation of residual current device(s)
- Functional testing of assemblies
- Verification of voltage drop

† See note below

† All boxes must be completed. '✓' indicates that an inspection or a test was carried out and that the result was satisfactory. 'X' indicates that an inspection or a test was carried out and that the result was unsatisfactory. 'LIM' indicates that, exceptionally, a limitation agreed with the person ordering the work (as recorded in Section L) prevented the inspection or test being carried out. 'N/A' indicates that an inspection or a test was not applicable to the particular installation.

This form is based on the model Periodic Inspection Report shown in Appendix 6 of BS 7671: 2008. Published by NICEIC Group Limited © Copyright The Electrical Safety Council (Jan 2008)

Page 3 of

Domestic Electrical Installation Periodic Inspection Report

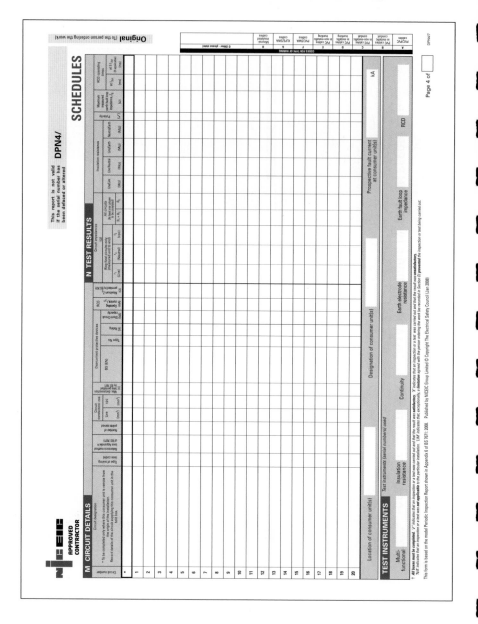

The NICEIC guide to
Domestic Periodic Inspection, Testing and Reporting

Domestic Electrical Installation Continuation Sheet

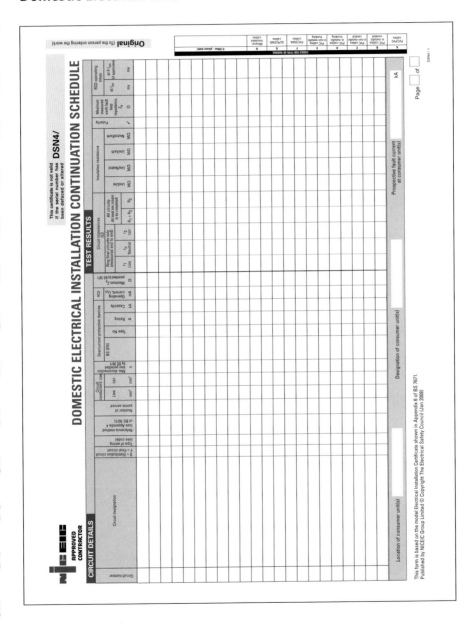

Guidance for Approved Contractors and Conforming Bodies

NICEIC DOMESTIC ELECTRICAL INSTALLATION PERIODIC INSPECTION REPORT
GUIDANCE FOR APPROVED CONTRACTORS AND CONFORMING BODIES

NICEIC certificates and reports are accountable documents. Unused copies should be kept secure by the Qualified Supervisor. A record of each report issued should be made on the record sheet provided. Unused sets of obsolete reports must be destroyed to prevent their misuse.

General

Detailed guidance on the completion of NICEIC forms for certification and reporting is included in the NICEIC Inspection, Testing and Certification book.

The NICEIC Domestic Electrical Installation Periodic Inspection Report is intended to be used only for the purpose of reporting on the condition of an existing electrical installation in a domestic property. The report should identify, so far as is reasonably practicable and having regard to the extent and limitations recorded in Section D, any damage, deterioration, defects, dangerous conditions and any non-compliances with the requirements of the current issue of BS 7671 which may give rise to danger. It should be noted that the greater the limitations applying to a report, the less is value to the recipient.

The report must not be used instead of an Electrical Installation Certificate or a Domestic Electrical Installation Certificate for certifying a new electrical installation, or as a substitute for a Minor Electrical Installation Works Certificate for certifying an addition or an alteration to an existing installation.

The Domestic Electrical Installation Periodic Inspection Report may be used only where all the following conditions apply:

☐ the inspection and testing work relates to a **single dwelling** (house or individual flat)

☐ the installation forms part of a TT, TN-S or TN-C-S (PME) system

☐ the distributor's cut-out incorporates an HBC fuse to BS 88, or a BS 1361 Type II fuse, rated at 100 A or less

☐ the protective measure against electric shock is by Automatic Disconnection of Supply (ADS).

The report form marked 'Original', including any additional pages, is to be given to the person ordering the inspection, as required by Regulation 631.2. The report form marked 'Duplicate' is to be retained by the Approved Contractor and made available for review by the NICEIC.

Published by NICEIC Group Limited © Copyright The Electrical Safety Council (Jan 2008)

This report form has been designed for compilation by hand or with the aid of computer software.

Irrespective of the method of compilation of the report, it remains the responsibility of the compiler of the report to ensure that the information provided in the report is factual, and that the declaration of the condition of the electrical installation to which the report relates is objective, fair and reasonable in all the circumstances.

The total number of pages which make up the report must be inserted in the box provided at the foot of each of the pages on the right-hand side.

Completing the report

Page 1

Section A (*Details of the Client*) provides space for the client's name and address.

Section B (*Address and Details of the Installation*) provides space for recording the details of the installation, including the address, if different from the address in A.

Section C (*Purpose of the Report*) is to enable the purpose of the report to be clearly identified. The main purpose of the report is to identify, so far as is practicable, any factors impairing the safe functioning of the electrical installation. This section may also identify the purpose in terms of expectations of interested parties such as a mortgage, landlord, or insurance company.

Section D (*Extent of the Installation and Limitations of the Inspection and Testing*) must fully identify the extent of the installation covered by the report and any agreed limitations on the inspection and testing. The Approved Contractor should have agreed all such aspects with the client and other interested parties before carrying out the inspection and testing. NICEIC will assume that comprehensive inspection and testing of the whole of the electrical installation, without limitations, has been carried out unless otherwise clearly indicated (including the reasons for these limitations) in Section D.

Section E (*Particulars of the Approved Contractor*) only NICEIC Approved Contractors are authorized to issue these reports.

Section F (*Declaration*) A declaration of the overall condition of the installation must be given by the inspector, reiterating that given in Section H which should summarise the observations and recommendations made in Section G. The inspection, testing and assessment by the inspector must be reviewed and confirmed by the registered NICEIC Qualified Supervisor. The signatures are to be those of the competent person undertaking the inspection of the installation and of the Qualified Supervisor of the NICEIC Approved Contractor or Conforming Body, who should review each report. Where the Qualified Supervisor carries out the inspection personally, the Qualified Supervisor should sign in both places.

Continued overleaf

Guidance for Approved Contractors and Conforming Bodies

Page 2

Section G (*Observations and Recommendations for Actions to be Taken*)

Section G includes two boxes at the top, in one of which the report compiler is required to enter a 'Yes' or a '✓' to indicate, as appropriate, that 'there are no items adversely effecting electrical safety' or 'the following observations and recommendations are made'. In the latter case, the observations and recommendations are to be listed with a Recommendation Code 1, 2, 3 or 4 (see reverse of page 2 of the report form for further guidance on the recommendations). **Only one Recommendation Code is to be given for each recorded observation.** At the bottom of the Section, two boxes are provided for recording the items which, in the opinion of the report's compiler, need urgent remedial work and those items requiring corrective action, respectively.

Where an Approved Contractor classifies a recommendation as '*requires urgent attention*', the client is to be advised immediately, in writing, to satisfy the duties imposed by the Electricity at Work Regulations 1989. It should be noted that, where an existing or a potential danger is observed that may put the safety of those using the installation at risk, Recommendation Code 1 (requires urgent attention) must be used.

If the space available on the form for recording recommendations is insufficient, additional numbered pages are to be provided as necessary. Additional pages must also be identified by the unique Domestic Electrical Installation Periodic Inspection Report serial number.

Section H (*Summary of the Inspection*) must be completed with an accurate description of the general condition of the installation, together with the date(s) of the inspection and a one-word overall assessment of the installation ie 'satisfactory' or 'unsatisfactory'. If the space available on the form for the summary of the inspection is insufficient, additional numbered pages are to be provided as necessary. Additional pages must also be identified by the unique Domestic Electrical Installation Periodic Inspection Report serial number.

It would not be reasonable to indicate a 'satisfactory' assessment if any observation in the report had been given a Code 1 or Code 2 recommendation.

Section I (*Next Inspection*) provides a place to insert the appropriate time interval before re-inspection of the installation becomes due. IEE Guidance Note 3 gives guidance on the **maximum** recommended intervals for various types of premises, but due account must be taken of the present condition of the installation. For domestic premises, the maximum initial interval to the next periodic inspection is normally ten years or upon change of occupancy. Your recommendation for the interval to the next inspection is conditional upon all items which have been given a Recommendation Code 1 and Code 2 being remedied without delay and as soon as possible respectively (see Section G). Additionally, your recommendation for the interval to the next inspection is also to be conditional on all items which have attracted a Recommendation Code 3 being remedied as soon as practicable.

Page 3

Section J (*Supply Characteristics, System Type, Earthing and Bonding Arrangements*) provides places to enter details of the supply characteristics, the type of system, the characteristics of the primary supply overcurrent protective device(s), the main switch or circuit-breaker, the means of earthing and the the main bonding conductors.

All boxes on the **Schedule of Items Inspected** and the **Schedule of Items Tested** are to be completed, as appropriate for the particular installation. To indicate that an inspection or test has been carried out and that the result is **satisfactory**, insert a '✓'. To indicate that an inspection or test has been carried out and that the result is **unsatisfactory**, insert a '✗'. It is unlikely that all items will apply, and the range of applicable inspections and tests will depend on the particular installation covered by the report. If an inspection or a test is not applicable, '**N/A**' should be recorded in the box. Exceptionally, where a limitation on a particular inspection or test has been agreed with the client, and has been recorded in Section D, the appropriate box(es) must be completed by inserting '**LIM**' indicating that an agreed limitation has **prevented** the inspection or test being carried out.

Page 4

Entries for circuit details and associated test results should be made for all installation circuits covered by the report. Boxes are provided for the 'Location of consumer unit(s)' and 'Designation of consumer unit(s)' to be recorded. The test instruments used to obtain test results should be identified by serial number in the boxes provided for the purpose.

Further Guidance

For further guidance on completing the report, refer to the practical advice and guidance in the NICEIC Inspection, Testing and Certification book, the current edition of BS 7671, and IEE Guidance Note 3.

Jan 2008

DPN4GB

Published by NICEIC Group Limited © Copyright The Electrical Safety Council (Jan 2008)

Domestic Electrical Installation Periodic Inspection Report

DOMESTIC ELECTRICAL INSTALLATION PERIODIC INSPECTION REPORT (FOR A SINGLE DWELLING)

Issued in accordance with *British Standard 7671–Requirements for Electrical Installations* by a Domestic Installer registered with NICEIC, Warwick House, Houghton Hall Park, Houghton Regis Dunstable LU5 5ZX

This report is **not valid** if the serial number has been defaced or altered   DPP2/

Original (To the person ordering the work)

A DETAILS OF THE CLIENT
Client/Address:

B ADDRESS AND DETAILS OF THE INSTALLATION
Address:

Estimated age of the electrical installation: _____ years

Evidence of alterations or additions: If yes, estimated age: _____ years

Date of previous inspection:

Electrical Installation Certificate number or previous Periodic Inspection Report number.

Records of installation available: Records held by:

C PURPOSE OF THE REPORT † (see note below)
Purpose for which this report is required:

D EXTENT OF THE INSTALLATION AND LIMITATIONS OF THE INSPECTION AND TESTING ‡ (see note below)
Extent of the electrical installation covered by this report:

Agreed limitations (including the reasons), if any, on the inspection and testing.

E PARTICULARS OF THE DOMESTIC INSTALLER † (see note below)
Trading Title:

Address:

Postcode

Registration Number (The registration number is essential information)

F DECLARATION
I/We, being the person(s) responsible for the inspection and testing of the electrical installation (as indicated by my/our signatures below), particulars of which are described above (see B), having exercised reasonable skill and care when carrying out the inspection and testing, hereby declare that the information in this report, including the observations (see G) and the attached schedules (see K and L), provides an accurate assessment of the condition of the electrical installation taking into account the stated extent of the installation and the limitations of the inspection and testing (see D).

I/We further declare that in my/our judgement, the said installation was overall in **+** _____ condition (see H) at the time the inspection was carried out, and that it should be further inspected as recommended (see I).

+ (Insert a 'satisfactory' or 'an unsatisfactory', as appropriate)   *See note below

INSPECTION, TESTING AND ASSESSMENT BY:

Signature:
Name: (CAPITALS)
Position:
Date:

REPORT REVIEWED AND CONFIRMED BY: *See note below

Signature:
Name: (CAPITALS)   (Registered Qualified Supervisor for the Domestic Installer at E)
Date:

Please see the 'Notes for Recipients' on the reverse of this page.

Page 1 of ____

DPP2 / 1

† This Domestic Periodic Inspection Report must be used only for reporting on the condition of an existing installation.
‡ The inspection and testing have been carried out in accordance with BS 7671, as amended. Cables concealed within trunking and conduits, or cables and conduits concealed under floors, in inaccessible roof spaces and generally within the fabric of the building or underground, have not been visually inspected.
* This Domestic Periodic Inspection Report should be reviewed and confirmed by the registered Qualified Supervisor of the Domestic Installer responsible for issuing it.

This form is based on the model Periodic Inspection Report shown in Appendix 6 of BS 7671: 2008. Published by NICEIC Group Limited (© Copyright The Electrical Safety Council (Jan 2008)

Domestic Electrical Installation Periodic Inspection Report

NOTES FOR RECIPIENT

THIS REPORT IS AN IMPORTANT AND VALUABLE DOCUMENT WHICH SHOULD BE RETAINED FOR FUTURE REFERENCE

The purpose of periodic inspection is to determine, so far as is reasonably practicable, whether an electrical installation is in a satisfactory condition for continued service. This report provides an assessment of the condition of the electrical installation identified overleaf at the time it was inspected, taking into account the stated extent of the installation and the limitations of the inspection and testing.

The report has been issued in accordance with the national standard for the safety of electrical installations, British Standard 7671 (as amended) - Requirements for Electrical Installations.

If you were the person ordering the work, but not the user of the installation, you should pass this report, or a full copy of it including these notes, the schedules and additional pages (if any), immediately to the user.

The 'Original' report form should be retained in a safe place and shown to any person inspecting or undertaking further work on the electrical installation in the future. If you later vacate the property, this report will provide the new user with an assessment of the condition of the electrical installation at the time the periodic inspection was carried out.

Where the installation incorporates a residual current device (RCD), there should be a notice at or near the main switchboard or consumer unit stating that the device should be tested at quarterly intervals. For safety reasons, it is important that you carry out the test regularly.

Also for safety reasons, the electrical installation will need to be re-inspected at appropriate intervals by a competent person. The recommended maximum time interval to the next inspection is stated on page 2 in Section I (Next Inspection). NICEIC* recommends that you engage the services of an NICEIC approved company registered for Domestic Periodic Inspection Reporting work for this purpose. There should be a notice at or near the main switchboard or consumer unit indicating when the next inspection of the installation is due.

Only an NICEIC approved company registered for Domestic Periodic Inspection Reporting work is authorised to issue this NICEIC Domestic Electrical Installation Periodic Inspection Report form.

The report consists of at least four numbered pages. Additional numbered pages may have been provided to permit further relevant information concerning the installation to be recorded. The report is invalid if any of the identified pages are missing. The report has a printed seven-digit serial number, which is traceable to the Domestic Installer to which it was supplied by NICEIC.

This report is intended to be issued only for the purpose of reporting on the condition of an existing electrical installation. The report should identify, so far as is reasonably practicable and having regard to the extent and limitations recorded in Section D, any damage, deterioration, defects, dangerous conditions and any non-compliances with the requirements of the national standard for the safety of electrical installations which may give rise to danger. It should be noted that the greater the limitations applying to a report, the less its value.

This report should not have been issued to certify that a new electrical installation complies with the requirements of the national safety standard. A 'Domestic Electrical Installation Certificate' or 'Electrical Installation Certificate' should be issued for the certification of a new installation.

Published by NICEIC Group Limited © Copyright The Electrical Safety Council (Jan 2008)

You should have received the report marked 'Original' and the Domestic Installer should have retained the report marked 'Duplicate'.

Section D addresses the extent and limitations of the report by providing boxes for the *Extent of the electrical installation covered by this report* and the *Agreed limitations, if any, on the inspection and testing*. Information given here should fully identify the scope of the inspection and testing and of the report. The Domestic Installer should have agreed all such aspects with the person ordering the work and other interested parties (eg insurance company, landlord, mortgagee etc) before the inspection was carried out.

A declaration of the overall condition of the installation should have been given by the inspector in Section F of the report. The declaration must reflect that given in Section H, which summarises the observations and recommendations made in Section G. A list of observations and recommendations for urgent remedial work and corrective action(s) necessary to maintain the installation in a safe working order should have been given in Section G, where appropriate. For further guidance on the recommendations, please see the reverse of page 2.

Should the person ordering the periodic inspection (eg the client, as identified on Page 1 of this report) have reason to believe that the report issued by the Domestic Installer does not reasonably reflect the condition of the electrical installation reported on, the person should in the first instance raise the specific concerns in writing with the Domestic Installer. If the concerns remain unresolved, the client may make a formal complaint to NICEIC, for which purpose a standard complaint form is available on request.

The complaints procedure offered by NICEIC is subject to certain terms and conditions, full details of which are available upon application and from the website†. NICEIC does not investigate complaints relating to the operational performance of electrical installations (such as lighting levels), or to contractual or commercial issues (such as time or cost).

All unshaded boxes should have been completed either by insertion of the relevant details or by entering 'N/A', meaning 'Not Applicable', where appropriate.

For further information about electrical safety and how NICEIC can help you, visit **www.niceicgroup.com**

---

† For further information, see the website†.

* NICEIC is a trading name of the NICEIC Group Limited, a wholly owned subsidiary of The Electrical Safety Council. Under licence from The Electrical Safety Council, NICEIC acts as the electrical contracting industry's independent voluntary regulatory body for electrical installation safety matters throughout the UK, and maintains and publishes registers of electrical contractors that it has assessed against a particular scheme requirements (including the technical standard of electrical work).

NICEIC Domestic Installers have been assessed as having the technical capability to carry out electrical work in compliance with the national standard for the safety of electrical installations, British Standard 7671 - Requirements for Electrical Installations, in relation to electrical installation work in dwellings, and all electrical installation work carried out by them is required to comply with that standard.

DPP2 / 16J3

The NICEIC guide to
Domestic Periodic Inspection, Testing and Reporting

Domestic Electrical Installation Periodic Inspection Report

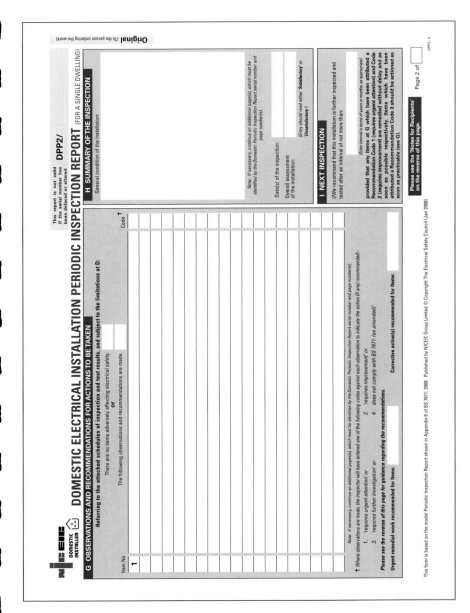

Domestic Electrical Installation Periodic Inspection Report

It is important to note that the recommendation given at Section I *Next Inspection* of this report for the maximum interval until the next inspection is conditional upon all items which have been given a **Recommendation Code 1 and Code 2 being remedied without delay and as soon as possible respectively** (see Section G).

It **would not** be reasonable to indicate a 'satisfactory' assessment if any observation in the report had been given a Code 1 or Code 2 recommendation (see Section H).

GUIDANCE FOR RECIPIENTS ON THE RECOMMENDATION CODES

Only one Recommendation Code should have been given for each recorded observation.

Recommendation Code 1

Where an observation has been given a Recommendation Code 1 (requires urgent attention) a danger exists, and urgent remedial action is necessary as the safety of those using the installation may be at risk.

The person responsible for the maintenance of the installation is advised to take action without delay to remedy the observed deficiency in the installation, or to take other appropriate action (such as switching off and isolating the affected part(s) of the installation) to remove the potential danger.

NICEIC make available 'dangerous condition' notification forms to enable inspectors to record, and then to communicate to the person ordering the report, any dangerous condition discovered.

Recommendation Code 2

Recommendation Code 2 (requires improvement) indicates that, whilst the safety of those using the installation may not be at immediate risk, remedial action should be taken as soon as possible to remove potential danger, and improve the safety of the installation to the level provided by the national standard for the safety of electrical installations, BS 7671. The Contractor issuing this report will be able to provide further advice.

Items which have been given a Recommendation Code 2 should be remedied as soon as possible (see Section G).

Recommendation Code 3

Where an observation has been given a Recommendation Code 3 (requires further investigation), the inspection has revealed an apparent deficiency which could not, due to the extent or limitations of this inspection, be fully identified. Items which have been given a Recommendation Code 3 should be investigated as soon as possible (see Section G).

The person responsible for the maintenance of the installation is advised to arrange for the Contractor issuing this report (or other competent person) to undertake further examination of the installation to determine the nature and extent of the apparent deficiency.

Recommendation Code 4

Recommendation Code 4 [does not comply with BS 7671(as amended)] will have been given to observed non-compliance(s) with the **current** safety standard which do not warrant one of the other Recommendation Codes. It is not intended to imply that the electrical installation inspected is unsafe, but careful consideration should be given to the benefits of improving these aspects of the installation. The Contractor issuing this report will be able to provide further advice.

Published by NICEIC Group Limited © Copyright The Electrical Safety Council (Jan 2008)

DPP2 / 3&4S

The NICEIC guide to
Domestic Periodic Inspection, Testing and Reporting

Domestic Electrical Installation Periodic Inspection Report

Original (To the person ordering the work)

This report is not valid if the serial number has been defaced or altered

DPP2/

DOMESTIC ELECTRICAL INSTALLATION PERIODIC INSPECTION REPORT (FOR A SINGLE DWELLING)

Page 3 of

DPP2 / 5

J SUPPLY CHARACTERISTICS, EARTHING AND BONDING ARRANGEMENTS

Supply Characteristics

		No. and type of live conductors (✓)	System Type(s) (✓)
Nominal voltage:	U(n)	V	1-phase (2wire)	TN-S
Nominal voltage:	U₀(n)	V	1-phase (3wire)	TN-C-S
Nominal frequency:	f(n)	Hz	3-phase (3wire)	TT
Prospective fault current:	I(pf)	kA	3-phase (4wire)	Other (please state)
External earth fault loop impedance: Z(e)		Ω		

Note:
(1) by enquiry
(2) by enquiry or by measurement
(3) by measurement

Characteristics of Primary Supply Overcurrent Protective Device(s)

BS(EN)

Type

Rated current

Short-circuit capacity — kA

Main Switch or Circuit-Breaker — *Enter details, as appropriate*

Type: BS(EN)

No of Poles

Supply conductors material

Supply conductors csa — mm²

Voltage rating — V

Rated current, I(n) — A

RCD operating current, I(Δn) — mA

RCD operating time (at I(Δn)) — ms

*Applicable only where an RCD is used as a main circuit-breaker

Means of Earthing

Distributor's facility:

Installation earth electrode:

Type: (eg rod(s), tape etc)

Electrode resistance, R(A) — (Ω)

Location:

Method of measurement

Earthing and Protective Bonding Conductors

Earthing conductor

	Conductor material		
Conductor csa — mm²		
Continuity check (✓)		

Main protective bonding conductors

	Conductor material		
Conductor csa — mm²		
Continuity check (✓)		

Bonding of extraneous-conductive-parts (✓)

Water service / Gas service / Oil service / Structural steel / Lightning protection / Other incoming service(s)

K SCHEDULE OF ITEMS INSPECTED †See note below

Protective measures against electric shock

Basic and fault protection

Extra low voltage — SELV

Double or reinforced insulation
- Double or reinforced insulation

Basic protection
- Insulation of live parts
- Barriers or enclosures

Fault protection

Automatic disconnection of supply
- Presence of earthing conductor
- Presence of circuit protective conductors
- Presence of main protective bonding conductors
- Choice and setting of protective devices (for fault protection and/or overcurrent)

Electrical separation
- For one item of current-using equipment

Additional protection
- Presence of residual current device(s)
- Presence of supplementary bonding conductors

Prevention of mutual detrimental influence
- Proximity of non-electrical services and other influences
- Segregation of Band I and Band II circuits or Band II insulation used
- Segregation of safety circuits

Identification
- Presence of diagrams, instructions, circuit charts and similar information
- Presence of danger notices
- Presence of other warning notices, including presence of mixed wiring colours
- Labelling of protective devices, switches and terminals
- Identification of conductors

Cables and conductors
- Selection of conductors for current carrying capacity and voltage drop
- Erection methods

Cables and conductors (cont)
- Routing of cables in prescribed zones
- Cables incorporating earthed armour or sheath or run in an earthed wiring system, or otherwise protected against nails, screws and the like
- Additional protection by 30mA RCD (where required, in premises not under the supervision of skilled or instructed persons)
- Connection of conductors
- Presence of fire barriers, suitable seals and protection against thermal effects

General
- Presence and correct location of appropriate devices for isolation and switching
- Adequacy of access to switchgear and other equipment
- Particular protective measures for special installations and locations
- Connection of single-pole devices for protection or switching in line conductors only
- Correct connection of accessories and equipment
- Selection of equipment and protective measures appropriate to external influences
- Selection of appropriate functional switching devices

L SCHEDULE OF ITEMS TESTED

- External earth fault loop impedance, Z(e)
- Installation earth electrode resistance, R(A)
- Continuity of protective conductors
- Continuity of ring final circuit conductors
- Insulation resistance between live conductors
- Insulation resistance between live conductors and earth
- Polarity
- Earth fault loop impedance, Z(s)
- Verification of phase sequence
- Operation of residual current device(s)
- Functional testing of assemblies
- Verification of voltage drop

†See note below

---

† *All boxes must be completed.* ✓ indicates that an inspection or a test was carried out and that the result was **satisfactory.** 'X' indicates that an inspection or a test was carried out and that the result was **unsatisfactory.** 'LIM' indicates that, exceptionally, a *limitation* agreed with the person ordering the work (as recorded in Section 12) *prevented* the inspection or test being carried out. N/A indicates that an inspection or a test was **not applicable** to the particular installation.

This form is based on the model Periodic Inspection Report shown in Appendix 6 of BS 7671: 2008. Published by NICEIC Group Limited © Copyright The Electrical Safety Council (Jan 2008)

DPP2

Domestic Electrical Installation Periodic Inspection Report

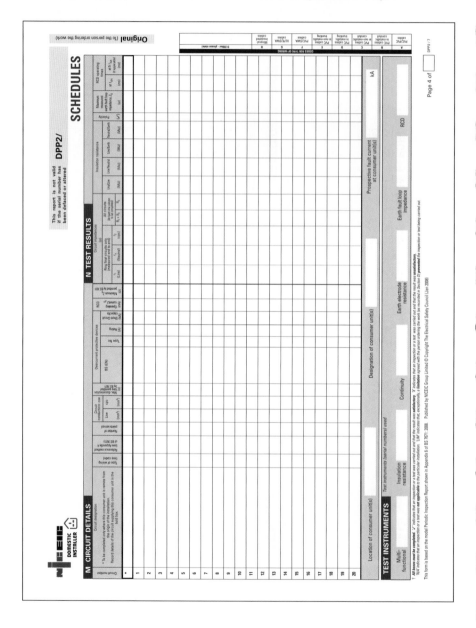

The NICEIC guide to
Domestic Periodic Inspection, Testing and Reporting

Guidance for Domestic Installers

NICEIC DOMESTIC ELECTRICAL INSTALLATION PERIODIC INSPECTION REPORT

GUIDANCE FOR DOMESTIC INSTALLERS

NICEIC certificates and reports are accountable documents. Unused copies should be kept secure by the Qualified Supervisor. A record of each report issued should be made on the record sheet provided. Unused sets of obsolete reports must be destroyed to prevent their misuse.

General

Detailed guidance on the completion of NICEIC forms for certification and reporting is included in the latest edition of the NICEIC Inspection, Testing and Certification book.

NICEIC Domestic Electrical Installation Periodic Inspection Report is intended to be used only for the purpose of reporting on the condition of an existing electrical installation in a domestic property. The report should identify, so far as is reasonably practicable and having regard to the extent and limitations recorded in Section D, any damage, deterioration, defects, dangerous conditions and any non-compliances with the requirements of the current issue of BS 7671 which may give rise to danger. It should be noted that the greater the limitations applying to a report, the less its value to the recipient.

The report must not be used instead of an Electrical Installation Certificate or a Domestic Electrical Installation Certificate for certifying a new electrical installation, or as a substitute for a Minor Electrical Installation Works Certificate for certifying an addition or an alteration to an existing installation.

The Domestic Electrical Installation Periodic Inspection Report may be used only where all the following conditions apply:

- the inspection and testing work relates to a **single dwelling** (house or individual flat)
- the installation forms part of a TT, TN-S or TN-C-S (PME) system
- the distributor's cut-out incorporates an HBC fuse to BS 88, or a BS 1361 Type II fuse, rated at 100 A or less
- the protective measure against electric shock is by Automatic Disconnection of Supply (ADS).

The report form marked 'Original', including any additional pages, is to be given to the person ordering the inspection, as required by Regulation 631.2. The report form marked 'Duplicate' is to be retained by the Domestic Installer and made available for review by NICEIC.

Published by NICEIC Group Limited © Copyright The Electrical Safety Council (Jan 2008)

This report form has been designed for compilation by hand or with the aid of computer software.

Irrespective of the method of compilation of the report, it remains the responsibility of the compiler of the report to ensure that the information provided in the report is factual, and that the declaration of the condition of the electrical installation to which the report relates is objective, fair and reasonable in all the circumstances.

The total number of pages which make up the report must be inserted in the box provided at the foot of each of the pages on the right-hand side.

Completing the report

Page 1

Section A (*Details of the Client*) provides space for the client's name and address.

Section B (*Address and Details of the Installation*) provides space for recording the details of the installation, including the address, if different from the address in A.

Section C (*Purpose of the Report*) is to enable the purpose of the report to be clearly identified. The main purpose of the report is to identify, so far as is practicable, any factors impairing the safe functioning of the electrical installation. This section may also identify the purpose in terms of expectations of interested parties such as a mortgagee, landlord, or insurance company.

Section D (*Extent of the Installation and Limitations of the Inspection and Testing*) must fully identify the extent of the installation covered by the report and any agreed limitations on the inspection and testing. The Domestic Installer should have agreed all such aspects with the client and other interested parties before carrying out the inspection and testing. NICEIC will assume that comprehensive inspection and testing of the whole of the electrical installation, without limitations, has been carried out unless otherwise clearly indicated (including the reasons for these limitations) in Section D.

Section E (*Particulars of the Domestic Installer*) only NICEIC approved companies registered for Domestic Periodic Inspection Reporting Work are authorized to issue these reports.

Section F (*Declaration*) A declaration of the overall condition of the installation must be given by the inspector, reiterating that given in Section H which should summarise the observations and recommendations made in Section G. The inspection, testing and assessment by the inspector must be reviewed and confirmed by the registered NICEIC Qualified Supervisor. The signatures are to be those of the competent person undertaking the inspection of the installation and of the Qualified Supervisor of NICEIC Domestic Installer, who should review each report. Where the Qualified Supervisor carries out the inspection personally, the Qualified Supervisor should sign in both places.

DPP2 GF

Continued overleaf

Guidance for Domestic Installers

Page 2

Section G (Observations and Recommendations for Actions to be Taken)

Section G includes two boxes at the top, in one of which the report compiler is required to enter a 'Yes' or a '✓' to indicate, as appropriate, that 'there are no items adversely effecting electrical safety' or 'the following observations and recommendations are made'. In the latter case, the observations and recommendations are to be listed with a Recommendation Code 1, 2, 3 or 4 (see reverse of page 2 of the report form for further guidance on the recommendations). **Only one Recommendation Code is to be given for each recorded observation.** At the bottom of the Section, two boxes are provided for recording the items which, in the opinion of the report's compiler, need urgent remedial work and those items requiring corrective action, respectively.

Where an Domestic Installer classifies a recommendation as 'requires urgent attention', the client is to be advised immediately, in writing, to satisfy the duties imposed by the Electricity at Work Regulations 1989. It should be noted that, where an existing or a potential danger is observed that may put the safety of those using the installation at risk, Recommendation Code 1 (requires urgent attention) must be used.

If the space available on the form for recording recommendations is insufficient, additional numbered pages are to be provided as necessary. Additional pages must also be identified by the unique Domestic Electrical Installation Periodic Inspection Report serial number.

Section H (Summary of the Inspection) must be completed with an accurate description of the general condition of the installation, together with the date(s) of the inspection and a one-word overall assessment of the installation ie 'satisfactory' or 'unsatisfactory'. If the space available on the form for the summary of the inspection is insufficient, additional numbered pages are to be provided as necessary. Additional pages must also be identified by the unique Domestic Electrical Installation Periodic Inspection Report serial number.

It would not be reasonable to indicate a 'satisfactory' assessment if any observation in the report had been given a Code 1 or Code 2 recommendation.

Section I (Next Inspection) provides a place to insert the appropriate time interval before re-inspection of the installation becomes due. IEE Guidance Note 3 gives guidance on the **maximum** recommended intervals for various types of premises, but due account must be taken of the present condition of the installation. For domestic premises, the maximum initial interval to the next periodic inspection is normally ten years or upon change of occupancy. Your recommendation for the interval to the next inspection is conditional upon all items which have been given a Recommendation Code 1 and Code 2 being remedied without delay and as soon as possible respectively (see Section G). Additionally, your recommendation for the interval to the next inspection is also to be conditional on all items which have attracted a Recommendation Code 3 being remedied as soon as practicable.

Page 3

Section J (Supply Characteristics, System Type, Earthing and Bonding Arrangements) provides places to enter details of the supply characteristics, the type of system, the characteristics of the primary supply overcurrent protective device(s), the main switch or circuit-breaker, the means of earthing and the the main protective bonding conductors.

All boxes on the **Schedule of Items Inspected** and the **Schedule of Items Tested** are to be completed, as appropriate for the particular installation. To indicate that an inspection or test has been carried out and that the result is **satisfactory**, insert a '✓'. To indicate that an inspection or test has been carried out and that the result is **unsatisfactory**, insert a '✗'. It is unlikely that all items will apply, and the range of applicable inspections and tests will depend on the particular installation covered by the report. If an inspection or a test is not applicable, **'N/A'** should be recorded in the box. Exceptionally, where a limitation on a particular inspection or test has been agreed with the client, and has been recorded in Section D, the appropriate boxes) must be completed by inserting **'LIM'**, indicating that an agreed limitation has **prevented** the inspection or test being carried out.

Page 4

Entries for circuit details and associated test results should be made for all installation circuits covered by the report. Boxes are provided for the 'Location of consumer unit(s) and 'Designation of consumer units(s)' to be recorded. The test instruments used to obtain test results should be identified by serial number in the boxes provided for the purpose.

Further Guidance

For further guidance on completing the report, refer to the practical advice and guidance in NICEIC Inspection, Testing and Certification book, the current edition of BS 7671, and IEE Guidance Note 3.

Jan 2008

DPP2 / 08

The NICEIC guide to
Domestic Periodic Inspection, Testing and Reporting

Domestic Electrical Installation Periodic Inspection Report

Original (To the person ordering the work)

DPM2

DOMESTIC ELECTRICAL INSTALLATION PERIODIC INSPECTION REPORT (FOR A SINGLE DWELLING)

Issued in accordance with British Standard 7671 – *Requirements for Electrical Installations*

A DETAILS OF THE CLIENT

Client / Address:

B ADDRESS AND DETAILS OF THE INSTALLATION

Address:

Evidence of alterations or additions:

Estimated age of the electrical installation: ___ years

If yes, estimated age ___ years

Date of previous inspection:

Electrical Installation Certificate number or previous Periodic Inspection Report number:

Records of installation available:

Records held by:

C PURPOSE OF THE REPORT † (see note below)

Purpose for which this report is required:

D EXTENT OF THE INSTALLATION AND LIMITATIONS OF THE INSPECTION AND TESTING

Extent of the electrical installation covered by this report

Agreed limitations (including the reasons), if any, on the inspection and testing

‡ (see note below)

E PARTICULARS OF THE CONTRACTOR

Trading Title:

Address:

Postcode

F DECLARATION

I/We, being the person(s) responsible for the inspection and testing of the electrical installation (as indicated by my/our signatures below), particulars of which are described above (see B), having exercised reasonable skill and care when carrying out the inspection and testing, hereby declare that the information in this report, including the observations (see G) and the attached schedules (see K and L), provides an accurate assessment of the condition of the electrical installation taking into account the stated extent of the installation and the limitations of the inspection and testing (see D).

I/We further declare that in my/our judgement, the said installation was overall in its ___ condition (see H) at the time the inspection was carried out, and that it should be further inspected as recommended (see I).

✦ *Insert 'a satisfactory' or 'an unsatisfactory', as appropriate*)

INSPECTION, TESTING AND ASSESSMENT BY:

Signature:

Name: (CAPITALS)

Position:

Date:

Please see the 'Notes for Recipients' on the reverse of this page.

Page 1 of ___

DPM2 / 1

† This Domestic Periodic Inspection Report must be used only for reporting on the condition of an existing installation.

‡ The inspection and testing have been carried out in accordance with BS 7671, as amended. Cables concealed within trunking and conduits, or cables and conduits concealed under floors, in inaccessible roof spaces and generally within the fabric of the building or underground, have not been visually inspected.

This form is based on the model Periodic Inspection Report shown in Appendix 6 of BS 7671: 2008. © Copyright The Electrical Safety Council (Jan 2008)

DPM2 📄

Domestic Electrical Installation Periodic Inspection Report

NOTES FOR RECIPIENT

THIS REPORT IS AN IMPORTANT AND VALUABLE DOCUMENT WHICH SHOULD BE RETAINED FOR FUTURE REFERENCE

The purpose of periodic inspection is to determine, so far as is reasonably practicable, whether an electrical installation is in a satisfactory condition for continued service. This report provides an assessment of the condition of the electrical installation identified overleaf at the time it was inspected, taking into account the stated extent of the installation and the limitations of the inspection and testing.

The report has been issued in accordance with the national standard for the safety of electrical installations, British Standard 7671 (as amended) – Requirements for Electrical Installations.

If you were the person ordering the work, but not the user of the installation, you should pass this report, or a full copy of it including these notes, the schedules and additional pages (if any) immediately to the user.

The 'Original' report form should be retained in a safe place and shown to any person inspecting or undertaking further work on the electrical installation in the future. If you later vacate the property, this report will provide the new user with an assessment of the condition of the electrical installation at the time the periodic inspection was carried out.

Where the installation incorporates a residual current device (RCD), there should be a notice at or near the main switchboard or consumer unit stating that the device should be tested at quarterly intervals. For safety reasons, it is important that you carry out the test regularly.

Also for safety reasons, the electrical installation will need to be re-inspected at appropriate intervals by a competent person. The recommended maximum time interval to the next inspection is stated on page 2 in Section I (Next Inspection). There should be a notice at or near the main switchboard or consumer unit indicating when the next inspection of the installation is due.

The report consists of at least four numbered pages. Additional numbered pages may have been provided to permit further relevant information concerning the installation to be recorded. The report is invalid if any of the identified pages are missing.

This report is intended to be issued only for the purpose of reporting on the condition of an existing electrical installation. The report should identify, so far as is reasonably practicable and having regard to the extent and limitations recorded in Section D, any damage, deterioration, defects, dangerous conditions and any non-compliances with the requirements of the national standard for the safety of electrical installations which may give rise to danger. It should be noted that the greater the limitations applying to the report, the less its value.

This report should not have been issued to certify that a new electrical installation complies with the requirements of the national safety standard. A 'Domestic Electrical Installation Certificate' or 'Electrical Installation Certificate' should be issued for the certification of a new installation.

You should have received the report marked 'Original' and the Contractor should have retained the report marked 'Duplicate'.

Section D addresses the extent and limitations of the report by providing boxes for the *Extent of the electrical installation covered by this report* and the *Agreed limitations, if any, on the inspection and testing*. Information given here should fully identify the scope of the inspection and testing and of the report. The Contractor should have agreed all such aspects with the person ordering the work and other interested parties (e.g. insurance company, landlord, mortgagee etc) before the inspection was carried out.

A declaration of the overall condition of the installation should have been given by the inspector in Section F of the report. The declaration must reflect that given in Section H, which summarises the observations and recommendations made in Section G. A list of observations and recommendations for urgent remedial work and corrective action(s) necessary to maintain the installation in a safe working order should have been given in Section G, where appropriate. Please see the reverse of page 2.

All unshaded boxes should have been completed either by insertion of the relevant details or by entering 'N/A', meaning 'Not Applicable', where appropriate.

© Copyright The Electrical Safety Council (Jan 2008)

DPM2 / 1&2B

The NICEIC guide to
Domestic Periodic Inspection, Testing and Reporting

Domestic Electrical Installation Periodic Inspection Report

DPM2

Original (To the person ordering the work)

DOMESTIC ELECTRICAL INSTALLATION PERIODIC INSPECTION REPORT (FOR A SINGLE DWELLING)

G OBSERVATIONS AND RECOMMENDATIONS FOR ACTIONS TO BE TAKEN

Referring to the attached schedules of inspection and test results, and subject to the limitations at D:

There are no items adversely affecting electrical safety.

OR

The following observations and recommendations are made.

Item No		Code †
1		

Note: If necessary, continue on additional page(s), which must be identified by the Domestic Periodic Inspection Report serial number and page number(s).

† Where observations are made, the inspector will have entered one of the following codes against each observation to indicate the action (if any) recommended:-

1. 'requires urgent attention' or
2. 'requires improvement' or
3. 'requires further investigation' or
4. does not comply with BS 7671 (as amended)'

Please see the reverse of this page for guidance regarding the recommendations.

Urgent remedial work recommended for Items:

Corrective action(s) recommended for Items:

H SUMMARY OF THE INSPECTION

General condition of the installation:

Note: If necessary, continue on additional page(s), which must be identified by the Domestic Periodic Inspection Report serial number and page number(s).

Date(s) of the inspection:

Overall assessment of the installation:

(Entry should read either 'Satisfactory' or 'Unsatisfactory')

I NEXT INSPECTION

I/We recommend that this installation is further inspected and tested after an interval of not more than:

(Enter interval in terms of years or months, as appropriate)

provided that any Items at G which have been attributed a Recommendation Code 1 requires urgent attention and Code 2 'requires improvement' are remedied without delay and as soon as possible respectively. Items which have been attributed a Recommendation Code 3 should be actioned as soon as practicable (see G).

Please see the 'Notes for Recipients' on the reverse of this page.

Page 2 of

DPM2 : 3

This form is based on the model Periodic Inspection Report shown in Appendix 6 of BS 7671: 2008. © Copyright The Electrical Safety Council (Jan 2008)

Domestic Electrical Installation Periodic Inspection Report

GUIDANCE FOR RECIPIENTS ON THE RECOMMENDATION CODES

Only one Recommendation Code should have been given for each recorded observation.

Recommendation Code 1

Where an observation has been given a **Recommendation Code 1 (requires urgent attention)** a danger exists, and urgent remedial action is necessary as the safety of those using the installation may be at risk.

The person responsible for the maintenance of the installation is advised to take action without delay to remedy the observed deficiency in the installation, or to take other appropriate action (such as switching off and isolating the affected part(s) of the installation) to remove the potential danger.

NICEIC make available 'dangerous condition' notification forms to enable inspectors to record, and then to communicate to the person ordering the report, any dangerous condition discovered.

Recommendation Code 2

Recommendation Code 2 (requires improvement) indicates that, whilst the safety of those using the installation may not be at immediate risk, remedial action should be taken as soon as possible to remove potential danger, and improve the safety of the installation to the level provided by the national standard for the safety of electrical installations, BS 7671. The Contractor issuing this report will be able to provide further advice.

Items which have been given a Recommendation Code 2 should be remedied as soon as possible (see Section G).

Recommendation Code 3

Where an observation has been given a Recommendation Code 3 (requires further investigation), the inspection has revealed an apparent deficiency which could not, due to the extent or limitations of this inspection, be fully identified. Items which have been given a Recommendation Code 3 should be investigated as soon as possible (see Section G).

The person responsible for the maintenance of the installation is advised to arrange for the Contractor issuing this report (or other competent person) to undertake further examination of the installation to determine the nature and extent of the apparent deficiency.

Recommendation Code 4

Recommendation Code 4 (does not comply with BS 7671 (as amended)) will have been given to observed non-compliance(s) with the **current** safety standard which do not warrant one of the other Recommendation Codes. It is not intended to imply that the electrical installation inspected is unsafe, but careful consideration should be given to the benefits of improving these aspects of the installation. The Contractor issuing this report will be able to provide further advice.

It is important to note that the recommendation given at Section I *Next Inspection* of this report for the maximum interval until the next inspection is conditional upon all items which have been given a Recommendation Code 1 and Code 2 being remedied without delay and as soon as possible respectively (see Section G).

It would not be reasonable to indicate a 'satisfactory' assessment if any observation in the report had been given a Code 1 or Code 2 recommendation (see Section H).

Jan 2008

DPM2 / 3&4B

Domestic Electrical Installation Periodic Inspection Report

Original (To the person ordering the work)

DPM2

DOMESTIC ELECTRICAL INSTALLATION PERIODIC INSPECTION REPORT (FOR A SINGLE DWELLING)

J SUPPLY CHARACTERISTICS, EARTHING AND BONDING ARRANGEMENTS

Enter details, as appropriate

Supply Characteristics

No. and type of live conductors (✓)	System Types (✓)
1-phase (2-wire)	TN-S
1-phase (3-wire)	TN-C-S
3-phase (3-wire)	TT
3-phase (4-wire)	Other (please state)

Nominal voltage: $U^{(1)}$ V

Nominal voltage: $U_0^{(1)}$ V

Nominal frequency, $f^{(1)}$ Hz

Prospective fault current, $I_{pf}^{(2)}$ kA

External earth fault loop impedance, $Z_e^{(2)}$ Ω

Note:
(1) by enquiry
(2) by enquiry or by measurement
(3) by measurement

Characteristics of Primary Supply Overcurrent Protective Device(s)

BS(EN)
Type
Rated current A
Short-circuit capacity kA

Main Switch or Circuit-Breaker

Type: BS(EN)
No. of Poles
Supply conductors material
Supply conductors csa mm²
Voltage rating V
Rated current, I_n A
RCD operating current, $I_{\Delta n}$ * mA
RCD operating time $I_{\Delta n}$ * ms

*applicable only where an RCD is used as a main circuit-breaker

Means of Earthing

Distributor's facility:
Installation earth electrode:
Type: (eg rod(s), tape etc)
Electrode resistance, R_A: Ω
Location:
Method of measurement:

Earthing and Protective Bonding Conductors

Earthing conductor:
Conductor material
Conductor csa mm²
Continuity check (✓)

Main protective bonding conductors:
Conductor material
Conductor csa mm²
Continuity check (✓)

Bonding of extraneous-conductive-parts (✓)
Water service
Gas service
Lightning protection
Structural steel
Oil service
Other incoming service(s)

K SCHEDULE OF ITEMS INSPECTED †See note below

Protective measures against electric shock

Basic and fault protection
Extra low voltage — SELV

Double or reinforced insulation
Double or reinforced insulation

Basic protection
Insulation of live parts
Barriers or enclosures

Fault protection

Automatic disconnection of supply
Presence of earthing conductor
Presence of circuit protective conductors
Presence of main protective bonding conductors
Choice and setting of protective devices for fault protection and/or overcurrent)

Electrical separation
For one item of current-using equipment

Additional protection †See note below
Presence of residual current device(s)
Presence of supplementary bonding conductors

Prevention of mutual detrimental influence
Proximity of non-electrical services and other influences
Segregation of Band I and Band II circuits or Band II insulation used
Segregation of safety circuits

Identification
Presence of diagrams, instructions, circuit charts and similar information
Presence of danger notices
Presence of other warning notices, including presence of mixed wiring colours
Labelling of protective devices, switches and terminals
Identification of conductors

Cables and conductors
Selection of conductors for current carrying capacity and voltage drop
Erection methods

Cables and conductors (cont)
Routing of cables in prescribed zones
Cables incorporating earthed armour or sheath or run in an earthed wiring system, or otherwise protected against nails, screws and the like
Additional protection by 30mA RCD (where required, in premises not under the supervision of skilled or instructed persons)
Connection of conductors
Presence of fire barriers, suitable seals and protection against thermal effects

General
Presence and correct location of appropriate devices for isolation and switching
Adequacy of access to switchgear and other equipment
Particular protective measures for special installations and locations
Connection of single-pole devices for protection or switching in line conductors only
Correct connection of accessories and equipment
Selection of equipment and protective measures appropriate to external influences
Selection of appropriate functional switching devices

L SCHEDULE OF ITEMS TESTED
External earth fault loop impedance, Z_e
Installation earth electrode resistance, R_A
Continuity of protective conductors
Continuity of ring final circuit conductors
Insulation resistance between live conductors
Insulation resistance between live conductors and earth
Polarity
Earth fault loop impedance, Z_s
Verification of phase sequence
Operation of residual current device(s)
Functional testing of assemblies
Verification of voltage drop

†See note below

Please see the "Notes for Recipients" on the reverse of this page.

Page 3 of

DPM2 / 5

† *All boxes must be completed.* ✓ *indicates that an inspection or a test was carried out and that the result was satisfactory.* X *indicates that an inspection or a test was carried out and that the result was unsatisfactory.* LIM *indicates that, exceptionally, a* limitation *agreed with the person ordering the inspection or test being carried out.* N/A *indicates that an inspection or a test was* not applicable *to the particular installation.* (LIM *indicates that, exceptionally, a* limitation *shown in Appendix 6 of BS 7671: 2008.* © Copyright The Electrical Safety Council (Jan 2008))

This form is based on the model Periodic Inspection Report shown in Appendix 6 of BS 7671: 2008. © Copyright The Electrical Safety Council (Jan 2008)

Domestic Electrical Installation Periodic Inspection Report

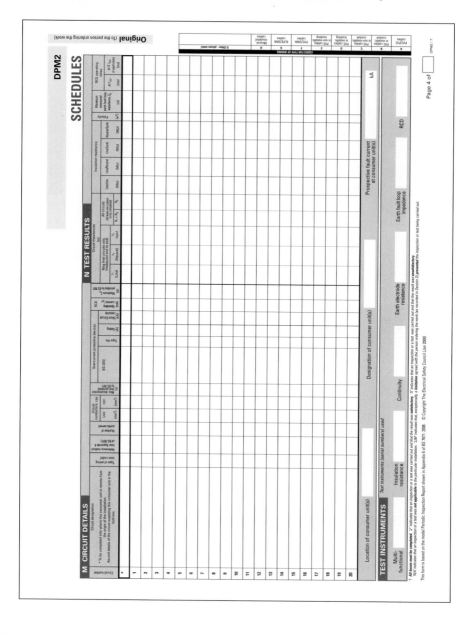

The NICEIC guide to
Domestic Periodic Inspection, Testing and Reporting

Domestic Electrical Installation Continuation Schedule

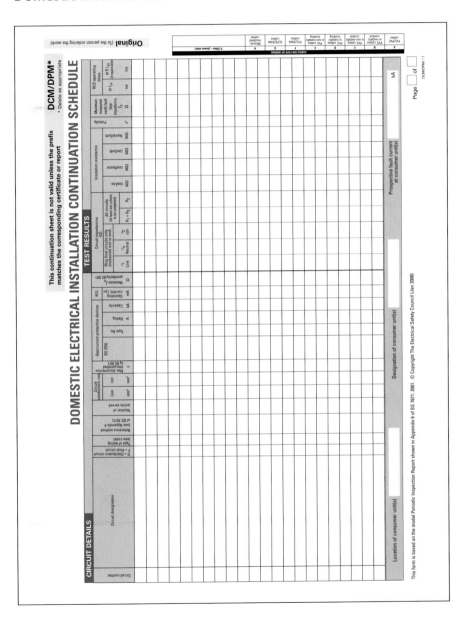

Guidance for Electrical Contractors

DOMESTIC ELECTRICAL INSTALLATION PERIODIC INSPECTION REPORT

GUIDANCE FOR CONTRACTORS

General

Relevant guidance on the completion of forms for certification and reporting may be found in the NICEIC Inspection, Testing and Certification book.

The Domestic Electrical Installation Periodic Inspection Report is intended to be used only for the purpose of reporting on the condition of an existing electrical installation in a domestic property. The report should identify, so far as is reasonably practicable and having regard to the extent and limitations recorded in Section D, any non-compliances with the requirements of the current issue of BS 7671 which may give rise to danger. It should be noted that the greater the limitations applying to a report, the less its value to the recipient.

The report must not be used instead of an Electrical Installation Certificate or a Domestic Electrical Installation Certificate for certifying a new electrical installation, or as a substitute for a Minor Electrical Installation Works Certificate for certifying an addition or an alteration to an existing installation.

The Domestic Electrical Installation Periodic Inspection Report may be used only where all the following conditions apply:

- ☐ the inspection and testing work relates to a **single dwelling** (house or individual flat)
- ☐ the installation forms part of a TT, TN-S or TN-C-S (PME) system
- ☐ the distributor's cut-out incorporates an HBC fuse to BS 88, or a BS 1361 Type II fuse, rated at 100 A or less
- ☐ the protective measure against electric shock is by Automatic Disconnection of Supply (ADS).

The report form marked 'Original', including any additional pages, is to be given to the person ordering the inspection, as required by Regulation 631.2. The report form marked 'Duplicate' is to be retained by the Contractor. The report form has been designed for compilation by hand.

Irrespective of the method of compilation of the report, it remains the responsibility of the compiler of the report to ensure that the information provided in the report is factual, and that the declaration of the condition of the electrical installation to which the report relates is objective, fair and reasonable in all circumstances.

© Copyright The Electrical Safety Council (Jan 2008)

The total number of pages which make up the report must be inserted in the box provided at the foot of each of the pages on the right-hand side.

Where an installation consists of more circuits than can be recorded on page 4, continuation sheets for circuit details and test results should be used. Contact NICEIC sales for pads of continuation sheets and ask for DSM. The prefix on the continuation sheet is labelled DCM/DPM. For the Periodic Report cross-out DCM, which does not apply.

Completing the report

Page 1

Section A (*Details of the Client*) provides space for recording the client's name and address

Section B (*Address and Details of the Installation*) provides space for recording the details of the installation, including the address, if different from the address in A.

Section C (Purpose of the Report) is to enable the purpose of the report to be clearly identified. The main purpose of the report is to identify, so far as is practicable, any factors impairing the safe functioning of the electrical installation. This section may also identify the purpose in terms of expectations of interested parties such as mortgagee, landlord, or insurance company.

Section D (*Extent of the Installation and Limitations of the Inspection and Testing*) must fully identify the extent of the installation covered by the report and any agreed limitations on the inspection and testing. The Contractor should have agreed all such aspects with the client and other interested parties before carrying out the inspection and testing. Unless otherwise indicated (including the reasons for the limitations), it will be assumed that a comprehensive inspection and testing of the whole of the electrical installation has been carried out.

Section E (*Particulars of the Contractor*)

Section F (*Declaration*) A declaration of the overall condition of the installation must be given by the inspector, reiterating that given in Section H which should summarise the observations and recommendations made in Section G.

Continued overleaf

DPM2 / GF

Page 2

Section G (Observations and Recommendations for Actions to be Taken)

Section G includes two boxes at the top, in one of which the report compiler is required to enter a 'Yes' or a '✓' to indicate, as appropriate, that 'there are no items adversely affecting electrical safety' or 'the following observations and recommendations are made'. In the latter case, the observations and recommendations are to be listed with a Recommendation Code 1, 2, 3 or 4 (see reverse of page 2 of the report for further guidance on the recommendations). **Only one Recommendation Code is to be given for each recorded observation.** At the bottom of the Section, two boxes are provided for recording the items which, in the opinion of the report's compiler, need urgent remedial work and those items requiring corrective action, respectively.

Where a Contractor classifies a recommendation as 'requires urgent attention', the client is to be advised immediately, in writing, to satisfy the duties imposed by the Electricity at Work Regulations 1989. It should be noted that, where an existing or a potential danger is observed that may put the safety of those using the installation at risk, Recommendation Code 1 (requires urgent attention) must be used.

If the space available on the form for recording recommendations is insufficient, additional numbered pages are to be provided as necessary.

Section H (Summary of the Inspection) must be completed with an accurate description of the general condition of the installation, together with the date(s) of the inspection and a one-word overall assessment of the installation i.e. 'satisfactory' or 'unsatisfactory'. If the space available on the form for the summary of the inspection is insufficient, additional numbered pages are to be provided as necessary.

It would not be reasonable to indicate a 'satisfactory' assessment if any observation in the report had been given a Code 1 or Code 2 recommendation.

Section I (Next Inspection) provides a place to insert the appropriate time interval before re-inspection of the installation becomes due. IEE Guidance Note 3 gives guidance on the **maximum** recommended intervals for various types of premises, but due account must be taken of the present condition of the installation. For domestic premises, the maximum initial interval to the next periodic inspection is normally ten years or upon change of occupancy. Your recommendation for the interval to the next inspection is conditional upon all items which have been given a Recommendation Code 1 and Code 2 being remedied without delay and as soon as possible respectively (see

Section G). Additionally, your recommendation for the interval to the next inspection is also to be conditional on all items which have attracted a Recommendation Code 3 being remedied as soon as practicable.

Page 3

Section J (Supply Characteristics, System Type, Earthing and Bonding Arrangements) provides places to enter details of the supply characteristics, the type of system, the characteristics of the primary supply overcurrent protective device(s), the main switch or circuit breaker, the means of earthing and the main protective conductors.

All boxes on the **Schedule of Items Inspected** and the **Schedule of Items Tested** are to be completed, as appropriate for the particular installation. To indicate that an inspection or test has been carried out and that the result is **satisfactory**, insert a '✓'. To indicate that an inspection or test has been carried out and that the result is **unsatisfactory**, insert a 'X'. It is unlikely that all items will apply, and the range of applicable inspections and tests will depend on the particular installation covered by the report. If an inspection or a test is not applicable, **'N/A'** should be recorded in the box. Exceptionally, where a limitation on a particular inspection or test has been agreed with the client, and has been recorded in Section D, the appropriate box(es) must be completed by inserting **'LIM'**, indicating that an agreed limitation has **prevented** the inspection or test being carried out.

Page 4

Entries for circuit details and associated test results should be made for all installation circuits covered by the report. Boxes are provided for the 'Location of consumer unit(s)' and 'Designation of consumer unit(s)' to be recorded. The test instruments used to obtain test results should be identified by serial number in the boxes provided for the purpose.

Further guidance

For further guidance on completing the report, refer to the practical advice and guidance in the NICEIC Inspection, Testing and Certification book, the current edition of BS 7671, and IEE Guidance Note 3.

Jan 2008

DPM2 / G8

The NICEIC guide to
Domestic Periodic Inspection, Testing and Reporting

ELECTRICAL DANGER NOTIFICATION FORMS

Electrical Danger Notification

Original (To the person responsible for the installation)

NICEIC APPROVED CONTRACTOR

XNN3/

ELECTRICAL DANGER NOTIFICATION

Issued by an Approved Contractor or Conforming Body enrolled with NICEIC, Warwick House, Houghton Hall Park, Houghton Regis, Dunstable LU5 5ZX.

DETAILS OF THE DANGEROUS CONDITION

While at the premises/location indicated below, an electrical condition has been observed which, in the opinion of the competent person issuing this Notification, constitutes a real and immediate danger to persons, property or livestock. **The person(s) having responsibility for the safety of the electrical installation or equipment concerned have a duty to ensure that appropriate action is taken without delay to remove the danger.** General information and advice is given overleaf. The competent person issuing this Notification will be able to provide further specific advice.

Dangerous condition

The dangerous condition detailed above may result in risk of injury or loss from

| Electric shock | Burns from hot surfaces | Mechanical movement of electrically-actuated equipment | Arcing or burning, excessive pressure and/or toxic gases |
| Fire | Burns from the passage of electric current | Explosion | Power supply interruptions and/or safety services |

ORGANIZATION AND/OR PERSON RESPONSIBLE

Organization and/or person responsible

Address

Postcode

ADDRESS AND SPECIFIC LOCATION OF DANGEROUS CONDITION

Address and specific location

Postcode

DETAILS OF THE APPROVED CONTRACTOR NOTIFYING THE DANGEROUS CONDITION

Trading title

NICEIC APPROVED CONTRACTOR

NICEIC Enrolment No (Essential information)

Trading address

Branch Number (if applicable)

Telephone No

Postcode

Signature

Position

Name (CAPITALS)

Date

Time

IMMEDIATE ACTION TAKEN

Time

FURTHER URGENT ACTION RECOMMENDED

RECEIPT   I acknowledge receipt of this dangerous condition notification.

Signature

Position

Name (CAPITALS)

Date

IF YOU ARE NOT A PERSON HAVING RESPONSIBILITY FOR THE SAFETY OF THE ELECTRICAL INSTALLATION/EQUIPMENT CONCERNED, IT IS IMPORTANT THAT YOU PASS THE NOTIFICATION TO SUCH A PERSON WITHOUT DELAY

This form is intended to be used to notify the existence of a dangerous electrical condition. It is not a detailed or comprehensive report on the condition of the installation /equipment concerned.

Published by NICEIC Group Limited © Copyright The Electrical Safety Council (Jan 2008).

Please see the 'Notes for Recipients' on the reverse of this page.

XNN3/1

Page 1 of

XNN3

Electrical Danger Notification

The NICEIC guide to
Domestic Periodic Inspection, Testing and Reporting

Guidance for Approved Contractors and Conforming Bodies

ELECTRICAL DANGER NOTIFICATION

GUIDANCE FOR APPROVED CONTRACTORS AND CONFORMING BODIES

> NICEIC Electrical Danger Notification forms are accountable documents. Unused forms should be kept secure by the Qualified Supervisor. A record of each form used should be made on the record sheet provided. Unused sets of obsolete forms must be destroyed to prevent their misuse.

The purpose of the Electrical Danger Notification form is to permit an Approved Contractor to:

    (i)   advise in writing a person responsible for the safety of an existing electrical installation of the location and nature of a dangerous condition discovered in that installation, and

    (ii)   provide a record of the immediate action taken to remove or minimize the danger, thereby assisting the Approved Contractor to discharge the duty imposed on competent persons by Regulations 4(1) and 4(2) of the Electricity at Work Regulations, and

    (iii)   provide a record of the advice given to remedy the deficiency as a matter of urgency.

The Electrical Danger Notification form is not intended to be used to notify danger arising from equipment not forming part of a fixed electrical installation, such as portable and transportable appliances. The removal of danger arising from such equipment should not warrant the formal notification procedure.

The Notification should identify only damage, deterioration, defects, dangerous conditions and any non-compliances with the requirements of the current issue national standard for the safety of electrical installations which give rise to real and immediate danger.

An Electrical Danger Notification should not be issued unless the competent person considers that real and immediate danger actually exists – Notifications are subject to challenge by duty holders, and NICEIC will investigate any complaint that the issue of a Notification was not justified.

The information given in the Notification must be clear, factual, and fair and reasonable in all the circumstances.

Where a real and immediate danger exists, with the agreement of a person having responsibility for the safety of the electrical installation, appropriate action should be taken to remove or minimize the danger immediately (such as switching off and isolating the affected part(s) of the installation). The action taken should be noted on the form in the box provided for this purpose.

Approved Contractors have no legal right to isolate or disconnect any part of an electrical installation without the owner's permission. If permission cannot be obtained to remove danger immediately, Approved Contractors should act without delay to minimise the danger so far as is reasonably practicable, such as by providing temporary barriers or enclosures for exposed live parts, posting danger notices etc.

In electrical installations, risk of injury may result from:

    (i)   electric shock

    (ii)   fire

    (iii)   burns from hot surfaces

    (iv)   burns from the passage of electric current

    (v)   mechanical movement of electrically-actuated equipment, in so far as such injury is intended to be prevented by electrical emergency switching or by electrical switching for mechanical maintenance of non-electrical parts of such equipment

    (vi)   explosion

    (vii)   arcing or burning, excessive pressure and/or toxic gases

    (viii)   power supply interruptions and/or safety services.

Continued overleaf

Published by NICEIC Group Limited © Copyright The Electrical Safety Council (Jan 2008)   XNN3/GF

Guidance for Approved Contractors

It is considered that real and immediate danger would arise from conditions such as:

- Live parts exposed to touch
- Connections or equipment showing evidence of arcing or overheating
- Safety devices removed or bypassed
- Overheating cables
- Inadequate switching arrangements for emergency or mechanical maintenance purposes
- Incorrectly selected, damaged or poorly maintained equipment in potentially explosive atmospheres (hazardous areas).

Note that not all conditions that would warrant a Code 1 recommendation ('requires urgent attention') in a Periodic Inspection Report necessarily constitute real and immediate danger, and therefore the issue of an Electrical Danger Notification.

If necessary to determine the full extent and nature of any dangerous conditions, a full periodic inspection and test of the installation should be recommended to a person having responsibility for the safety of the electrical installation.

The Electrical Danger Notification form marked 'Original' is to be given to a person having responsibility for the safety of the electrical installation. The form marked 'Duplicate' is to be retained by the Approved Contractor and made available for review by NICEIC.

Completing the Electrical Danger Notification form

The first box entitled *Details of the Dangerous Condition* should explain clearly the details of the dangerous condition, with reference to the regulations in the national standard for electrical safety, *BS 7671: Requirements for Electrical Installations*, and the *Electricity at Work Regulations*.

The second box *Organization and/or Person Responsible* provides space for recording details of the Client, the responsible person and the installation.

The boxes *Address and Specific Location of the Dangerous Condition* and *Details of the Approved Contractor Notifying the Dangerous Condition* are self-explanatory.

In the box *Immediate Action Taken*, the Approved Contractor must record the immediate action (such as switching off and isolating the affected part(s) of the installation) taken to remove the danger.

The box *Further Urgent Action Recommended* by the Approved Contractor is self-explanatory.

The final box *Receipt* enables the recipient to acknowledge receipt of the Notification and, if appropriate, that the Notification will be passed without delay to a person having responsibility for the safety of the electrical installation.

If the space available on the form is insufficient, additional numbered pages are to be provided as necessary. Any additional pages are to be given the same unique serial number as the Notification.

Jan 2008

Published by NICEIC Group Limited © Copyright The Electrical Safety Council (Jan 2008)

XNN3/GB

The NICEIC guide to
Domestic Periodic Inspection, Testing and Reporting

Domestic Electrical Danger Notification

	XNP2/
DOMESTIC INSTALLER 🏠	**DOMESTIC ELECTRICAL DANGER NOTIFICATION** Issued by a Domestic Installer registered with with NICEIC, Warwick House, Houghton Hall Park, Houghton Regis, Dunstable LU5 5ZX.

This electrical danger notification should not be ignored and the dangers identified rectified immediately

Original (To the person responsible for the installation)

DETAILS OF THE DANGEROUS CONDITION

While at the premises/location indicated below, an electrical condition has been observed which, in the opinion of the competent person issuing this Notification, constitutes a real and immediate danger to persons, property or livestock. **The person(s) having responsibility for the safety of the electrical installation or equipment concerned have a duty to ensure that appropriate action is taken without delay to remove the danger.** General information and advice is given overleaf. The competent person issuing this Notification will be able to provide further specific advice.

Dangerous condition

The dangerous condition detailed above may result in risk of injury or loss from

Electric shock		Burns from hot surfaces		Mechanical movement of electrically-actuated equipment		Arcing or burning, excessive pressure and/or toxic gases	
Fire		Burns from the passage of electric current		Explosion		Power supply interruptions and/or safety services	

ORGANIZATION AND/OR PERSON RESPONSIBLE

Organization and/or person responsible

Address

Postcode

ADDRESS AND SPECIFIC LOCATION OF DANGEROUS CONDITION

Address and specific location

Postcode

DETAILS OF THE DOMESTIC INSTALLER NOTIFYING THE DANGEROUS CONDITION

Trading title

Trading address

NICEIC Registration No

Postcode

Telephone No

Signature | Position

Name (CAPITALS) | Date | Time

IMMEDIATE ACTION TAKEN

Time

FURTHER URGENT ACTION RECOMMENDED

RECEIPT — I acknowledge receipt of this dangerous condition notification.

Signature | Position

Name (CAPITALS) | Date

IF YOU ARE NOT A PERSON HAVING RESPONSIBILITY FOR THE SAFETY OF THE ELECTRICAL INSTALLATION/EQUIPMENT CONCERNED, IT IS IMPORTANT THAT YOU PASS THE NOTIFICATION TO SUCH A PERSON WITHOUT DELAY

This form is intended to be used to notify the existence of a dangerous electrical condition. It is not a detailed or comprehensive report on the condition of the installation/equipment concerned.

Published by NICEIC Group Limited © Copyright The Electrical Safety Council (Jan 2008).

Please see the 'Notes for Recipients' on the reverse of this page.

XNP2/1

Page 1 of ☐

Domestic Electrical Danger Notification

NOTES FOR RECIPIENTS

IF YOU ARE NOT A PERSON HAVING RESPONSIBILITY FOR THE SAFETY OF THE ELECTRICAL INSTALLATION OR EQUIPMENT CONCERNED, IT IS IMPORTANT THAT YOU PASS THIS NOTIFICATION TO SUCH A PERSON WITHOUT DELAY.

The Domestic Installer registered with NICEIC issuing this Notification has found that a part or parts of the electrical installation identified overleaf are in a potentially dangerous condition. The safety of those using the installation may be at risk.

Appropriate action needs to be taken immediately to remove the danger. The action taken (such as switching off and isolating the affected part(s) until remedied) should be recorded overleaf.

Urgent remedial work is necessary to bring the installation up to the standard required by the current issue of the national standard for the safety of electrical installations, British Standard 7671 - *Requirements for Electrical Installations*. The Domestic Installer registered with NICEIC issuing this Notification will be able to provide further advice.

This Notification is intended to be issued only for the purpose of reporting a dangerous condition in an existing electrical installation. The Notification records only damage, deterioration, defects, dangerous conditions and any non-compliances with the requirements of the national standard for the safety of electrical installations which give rise to real and immediate danger. It is not a detailed or comprehensive report on the condition of the installation or equipment concerned. A periodic inspection of the installation may be necessary to determine the full extent of any deficiencies.

Only a Domestic Installer registered with NICEIC is authorised to issue this Domestic Electrical Danger Notification. A person having responsibility for the safety of the electrical installation should have received the copy marked 'Original' and the Domestic Installer should have retained the report marked 'Duplicate'. The Notification has a printed seven-digit serial number which is traceable to the Domestic Installer to which it was supplied by NICEIC.

Should a person having responsibility for the safety of the electrical installation have reason to believe that the issue of this Notification is unjustified, they should in the first instance raise the specific concerns in writing with the Domestic Installer registered with NICEIC. If the concerns remain unresolved, they may make a formal complaint to NICEIC, for which purpose a standard complaint form may be downloaded from the NICEIC website (www.niceicgroup.com), or is available from NICEIC on request.

* NICEIC is a trading name of NICEIC Group Limited, a wholly owned subsidiary of The Electrical Safety Council. Under licence from The Electrical Safety Council, NICEIC acts as the electrical contracting industry's independent voluntary regulatory body for electrical installation safety matters throughout the UK, and maintains and publishes registers of electrical contractors that it has assessed against particular scheme requirements (including the technical standard of electrical work).

For further information about electrical safety and how NICEIC can help you, visit **www.niceicgroup.com**

Published by NICEIC Group Limited © Copyright The Electrical Safety Council (Jan 2008)   XNP2/1&2B

Guidance for Domestic Installers

DOMESTIC ELECTRICAL DANGER NOTIFICATION
GUIDANCE FOR DOMESTIC INSTALLERS REGISTERED WITH NICEIC

NICEIC Domestic Electrical Danger Notification forms are accountable documents. Unused forms should be kept secure by the Qualified Supervisor. A record of each form used should be made on the record sheet provided. Unused sets of obsolete forms must be destroyed to prevent their misuse.

The purpose of the Domestic Electrical Danger Notification form is to permit a Domestic Installer registered with NICEIC to:

(i) advise in writing a person responsible for the safety of an existing electrical installation of the location and nature of a dangerous condition discovered in that installation, and

(ii) provide a record of the advice given to remedy the deficiency as a matter of urgency.

The Domestic Electrical Danger Notification form is not intended to be used to notify danger arising from equipment not forming part of a fixed electrical installation, such as portable and transportable appliances. The removal of danger arising from such equipment should not warrant the formal notification procedure.

The Notification should identify only damage, deterioration, defects, dangerous conditions and any non-compliances with the requirements of the current issue national standard for the safety of electrical installations which give rise to real and immediate danger.

A Domestic Electrical Danger Notification should not be issued unless the competent person considers that real and immediate danger actually exists – NICEIC will investigate any complaint that the issue of a Notification was not justified.

The information given in the Notification must be clear, factual, fair and reasonable in all the circumstances.

Where a real and immediate danger exists, with the agreement of a person having responsibility for the safety of the electrical installation, appropriate action should be taken to remove or minimize the danger immediately (such as switching off and isolating the affected part(s) of the installation). The action taken should be noted on the form in the box provided for this purpose.

Domestic Installers registered with NICEIC have no legal right to isolate or disconnect any part of an electrical installation without the owner's permission. If permission cannot be obtained to remove danger immediately, Domestic Installers should act without delay to minimise the danger so far as is reasonably practicable, such as by providing temporary barriers or enclosures for exposed live parts, posting danger notices etc.

In electrical installations, risk of injury may result from:

(i) electric shock

(ii) fire

(iii) burns from hot surfaces

(iv) burns from the passage of electric current

(v) mechanical movement of electrically-actuated equipment, in so far as such injury is intended to be prevented by electrical emergency switching or by electrical switching for mechanical maintenance of non-electrical parts of such equipment

(vi) explosion

(vii) arcing or burning, excessive pressure and/or toxic gases

(viii) power supply interruptions and/or safety services.

Continued overleaf

Published by NICEIC Group Limited © Copyright The Electrical Safety Council (Jan 2008)

XNP2/GF

Guidance for Domestic Installers

It is considered that real and immediate danger would arise from conditions such as:

- Live parts exposed to touch
- Connections or equipment showing evidence of arcing or overheating
- Safety devices removed or bypassed
- Overheating cables
- Inadequate switching arrangements for emergency or mechanical maintenance purposes
- Incorrectly selected, damaged or poorly maintained equipment in potentially explosive atmospheres (hazardous areas)

Note that not all conditions that would warrant a Code 1 recommendation ('requires urgent attention') in a Periodic Inspection Report necessarily constitute real and immediate danger, and therefore the issue of an Domestic Electrical Danger Notification.

If necessary to determine the full extent and nature of any dangerous conditions, a full periodic inspection and test of the installation should be recommended to a person having responsibility for the safety of the electrical installation.

The Domestic Electrical Danger Notification form marked 'Original' is to be given to a person having responsibility for the safety of the electrical installation. The form marked 'Duplicate' is to be retained by the Domestic Installer registered with NICEIC and made available for review by NICEIC.

Completing the Domestic Electrical Danger Notification form

The first box, entitled *Details of the Dangerous Condition,* should explain clearly the details of the dangerous condition, with reference to the regulations in the national standard for electrical safety, *BS 7671: Requirements for Electrical Installations.*

The second box, *Organization and/or Person Responsible,* provides space for recording details of the Client, the responsible person and the installation.

The boxes *Address and Specific Location of Dangerous Condition* and *Details of the Domestic Installer (registered with NICEIC) Notifying the Dangerous Condition* are self-explanatory.

In the box *Immediate Action Taken,* the Domestic Installer must record the immediate action (such as switching off and isolating the affected part(s) of the installation) taken to remove the danger.

The box *Further Urgent Action Recommended* by the Domestic Installer is self-explanatory.

The final box *Receipt* enables the recipient to acknowledge receipt of the Notification and, if appropriate, that the Notification will be passed without delay to a person having responsibility for the safety of the electrical installation.

If the space available on the form is insufficient, additional numbered pages are to be provided as necessary. Any additional pages are to be given the same unique serial number as the Notification.

Jan 2008

Published by NICEIC Group Limited © Copyright The Electrical Safety Council (Jan 2008)

XNP2/GB

**The NICEIC guide to
Domestic Periodic Inspection, Testing and Reporting**

RESISTANCE OF COPPER AND ALUMINIUM CONDUCTORS

ANNEX **E**

Information on the resistance of copper and aluminium conductors is given in *BS 6360 – Specification for conductors in insulated cables and cords*.

For ease of reference Table E1 (based on data from Table 1 of *BS 6360*) is shown below. It gives resistance per metre values of single-core and multicore cable plain copper or aluminium conductors at 20 °C, in units of milliohms per metre (m Ω per m).

Table E1 – Maximum resistance of conductors at 20 °C

Conductor cross-sectional area (mm²)	Resistance per metre of conductor (m Ω per m)	
	Copper	Aluminium
1	18.1	–
1.5	12.1	18.1
2.5	7.41	12.1
4	4.61	7.41
6	3.08	4.61
10	1.83	3.08
16	1.15	1.91
25	0.727	1.2
35	0.524	0.868
50	0.387	0.641

Data courtesy of British Standards Institution

RESISTANCE OF COPPER AND ALUMINIUM CONDUCTORS

Conductor resistance values at a conductor temperature other than 20 °C

Resistance values shown in Table E1 may be corrected to other resistance values, for conductor temperatures other than 20 °C, by using the formula:

$$R_x = R_{20} (1 + (0.004 \times (T_x - T_{20})))$$

Where:

R_x – is the corrected conductor resistance value, in mΩ, at x °C

R_{20} – is the conductor resistance value at 20 °C, in mΩ, (see table E1 for values)

0.004 – is the approximate resistance temperature coefficient for copper or aluminium

T_x – is the x °C conductor temperature

T_{20} – is the 20 °C conductor temperature.

Calculation of conductor resistance at 30 °C

An example follows, to calculate the resistance of a 6 mm² cross-sectional area (csa) copper conductor at a temperate of 30 °C, which demonstrates the use of the previous formula and the resistance values given in Table E1.

Example

T_{30} = 30 °C

R_{20} = 3.08mΩ for a 6 mm² csa copper conductor, at 20 °C. (The value of 3.08mΩ is taken from column 2 of table E1.)

Substituting the above values in the previous formula gives.

$$R_{30} = R_{20} (1 + (0.004 \times (T_{30} - T_{20})))$$

$$R_{30} = 3.08(1 + (0.004 \times (30-20))) = 3.08 (1 + (0.004 \times 10))$$

The NICEIC guide to
Domestic Periodic Inspection, Testing and Reporting

$$R_{30} = 3.08 \times (1 + 0.04)$$

$$R_{30} = 3.08 \times 1.04$$

$$R_{30} = 3.2 \text{ m}\Omega$$

It can be seen from the above calculation that the original value of conductor resistance at 20 °C is increased by a multiplication factor of 1.04 for a conductor temperature of 30 °C. (Out of interest, 30 °C is the 'assumed initial conductor temperature' used in Table 54.2 of *BS 7671*.)

Conductor resistance at 70 °C

By carrying out a calculation similar to that shown in the previous exercise, it can be shown that the resistance of a conductor at 70 °C is 1.2.times its resistance value at 20°C. (Out of interest, 70 °C is the 'assumed initial conductor temperature' given in Table 54.3 of *BS 7671*.)

The previous calculated commonly used conductor temperature correction factors are included in table E1, for ease of reference (since they are used, and referenced, elsewhere in this book).

Further information on conductor temperature correction multiplication factors

Further information on conductor temperature correction multiplication factors for temperatures other than 20 °C is given in Table 5 of *BS 6360*.

RESISTANCE OF COPPER AND ALUMINIUM CONDUCTORS

Table E2 – Resistance temperature multiplication correction factors for protective conductors with thermoplastic (pvc) insulation, which are protected by standard overcurrent devices (given in Tables 41.2, 41.3 and 41.4 of *BS 7671*)

Protective conductor with thermoplastic (pvc) insulation	Initial conductor temperature (see Tables 54.2 and 54.3 of *BS 7671*)	20°C conductor resistance correction multiplication factor (for applying to values in Table E1)
Applies where conductor is not incorporated in a cable or bunched with cables, or bare conductors in contact with cable covers	30 °C	1.04
Applies where conductor is incorporated in a cable or bunched with other cables	70 °C	1.2

**The NICEIC guide to
Domestic Periodic Inspection, Testing and Reporting**

Older installations may incorporate circuit-breakers that, although marked as 'Type B', pre-date the *BS EN 60898* product standard, first published in 1991. These earlier 'Type B' circuit-breakers, which have a push-button mechanism for manual switching, were made to the previous (now withdrawn) product standard *BS 3871*, and have different time/current characteristics to Type B circuit-breakers made to *BS EN 60898*.

BS 3871 Type B circuit-breaker with push button operation

The time-current characteristics for overload protection (thermal operation) of the 'old' and 'new' Type B circuit-breakers are understood to be similar. However, the same cannot be said of their respective time-current characteristics at fault current magnitudes (magnetic operation). The difference is particularly significant if the

earlier type of circuit-breaker is intended to provide automatic disconnection of the circuit under earth fault conditions (that is, fault protection), as the limiting earth fault loop impedance is likely to be less than for a Type B circuit-breaker to *BS EN 60898*.

The Type B circuit-breakers with push-button operation were manufactured between 1968 and 1980, and featured a plug-in mounting arrangement. It is estimated that some 12 million of these devices were produced, many of which will still be in use. Some of these circuit-breakers may have been installed after 1980, as wholesalers' and contractors' stocks were used up. These Type B circuit-breakers have time/current characteristics closely-related to Type 3, *BS 3871* circuit-breakers.

Inspectors carrying out the periodic inspection of installations incorporating push-button Type B circuit-breakers should refer to the limiting values of earth fault loop impedance, Z_S, given in the following table, which includes data for Type 3, *BS 3871* circuit-breakers that correspond to Type B circuit-breakers commonly used. Allowance for temperature differentials between ambient temperature and fully loaded conductor temperature must be made. The table also includes the '80% Rule of Thumb' values of the limiting values prescribed in *BS 7671*, for comparison with the corresponding measured values.

LIMITING AND 80% 'RULE OF THUMB' MEASURED VALES OF Z_S FOR 'TYPE B' CIRCUIT-BREAKERS (having a push-button mechanism for manual switching)						
Ratings (Amperes)	5	10	15	20	30	40
Limiting Z_s (Ω) (According to data published for Type 3 circuit-breakers to *BS 3871*)	4.6	2.3	1.53	1.15	0.76	0.57
80% 'Rule of Thumb' measured Z_s (Ω) (Rounded down)	3.68	1.84	1.22	0.92	0.6	0.45

ASSESSING THE MAXIMUM DEMAND OF A DOMESTIC ELECTRICAL INSTALLATION

ANNEX **G**

ASSESSING THE MAXIMUM DEMAND OF A DOMESTIC ELECTRICAL INSTALLATION

Maximum demand is one of the general characteristics of an electrical installation that Part 3 of *BS 7671* requires to be assessed. This article gives guidance on assessing the maximum demand for the installation of an individual dwelling (such as a house or flat).

G1 Requirement to assess the maximum demand

Regulation 313.1 requires the maximum demand of the installation, expressed in amperes or volt amperes, to be assessed.

The purpose of the assessment is to establish whether the supply of electricity to the installation will be of sufficient rated current for the purpose for which the installation is intended.

G2 Making the assessment

For assessing maximum demand, sufficient information is needed about the connected load, how the installation is likely to be used and any diversity factors that may be applied.

Failure to allow for diversity, where applicable, would normally lead to assessing the available supply capacity as inadequate for the load of the installation. In addition, the economic design of an installation almost always means that diversity must be taken into account for certain circuits.

For example, to comply with Regulation 553.1.7, an adequate number of suitably positioned socket-outlets are needed for portable electrical equipment. Without allowing for diversity, a circuit having (say) fifteen 13 A socket-outlets would have a potential load of approximately 196 A, which would exceed the rated current of the supply normally provided to a domestic installation (typically 60 to 100 A).

In fact, the load on the socket-outlet circuits in a dwelling does not depend on the number of socket-outlets, but on the particular items of current-using equipment connected to the socket-outlets and in use.

A variety of methods exist for estimating the maximum demand for a distribution system (or distribution circuit) of a dwelling. The method adopted will depend on the information available at the time the estimate is made. For most installations, the estimate will be approximate as there is no exact method for calculating maximum demand in all circumstances. The appropriate diversity factors may be known or can be estimated.

Where the diversity factor for a distribution system of a dwelling is not known, the inspector may wish to adopt one of the following two methods:

1. The method described in *IEE Guidance Note 1 – Selection and Erection* (see items A3 and A4) , or

2. Applying a judgmental approach based on engineering knowledge and experience (see item A5).

G3 The method described in IEE Guidance Note 1

The method described in *IEE Guidance Note 1* uses the information in Table H2 of that publication for estimating the maximum demand for the distribution circuit supplying all of the circuits of an individual household installation. Information from Table H2 is reproduced in Table G1 of this annex, for ease of reference.

Table G1 – Allowance for diversity to be applied to an individual household installation, including an individual dwelling in a block.

Purpose of final circuit fed from conductors or switchgear to which diversity applies	Diversity factor to be applied to the distribution circuit
Lighting	66 % of the connected lighting load
Heating appliances	The first 10 A of the connected load plus 50 % of the remainder of the connected load
Cooking appliance(s)	The first 10 A of the connected load plus 30 % of the remainder of the rated current in excess of 10 A plus 5 A if socket-outlet incorporated in the control panel

Table continued on next page

ASSESSING THE MAXIMUM DEMAND OF A DOMESTIC ELECTRICAL INSTALLATION

Purpose of final circuit fed from conductors or switchgear to which diversity applies	Diversity factor to be applied to the distribution circuit
Instantaneous water heaters (including electric shower heaters)	100 % full load (F.L.) of the largest appliance plus 100 % F.L. of the 2nd largest appliance plus 25 % F.L. of the remaining appliances
Storage water heaters	No diversity applied
Floor warming installations	No diversity applied
Thermal storage space heating	No diversity applied
Socket-outlet and stationary equipment supplied by a standard arrangement	100 % of current demand of largest socket-outlet circuit plus 40 % of current demand of every other socket-outlet circuit

G4 Worked example using the method described in IEE Guidance Note 1

Suppose that the electrical installation of an individual dwelling is to have a single-phase supply, provided by an electricity distributor, of nominal voltage 230 V and current-carrying capacity 100 A.

The maximum demand of the installation is to be calculated using the method described in *IEE Guidance Note 1*, in order to establish whether the 100 A current-carrying capacity of the distributor's proposed service is adequate for the installation.

Table G2 of this annex, details the current-using equipment and socket-outlet circuits of the installation, and the associated values of connected load. Also shown in the table is the application of diversity factors, taken from Table G1.

The calculation of the maximum demand for the installation, using these diversity factors, is shown in column 6 of the Table G2.

**The NICEIC guide to
Domestic Periodic Inspection, Testing and Reporting**

Table G2 – Calculation of the maximum demand of the installation of an individual dwelling by applying diversity factors to the connected loads of the individual final circuits

Description	Number of points served	Connected load per point	Total connected load of all points	Allowance for diversity (from Table G1)	Calculation to determine the maximum demand of the installation	
					Using the method described in IEE Guidance Note 1	Using the alternative method: applying a judgmental approach
1	2	3	4	5	6	7
Mains voltage tungsten halogen lighting	6	100 W	600 W ÷ 230 V = 2.61 A	90 % of the connected load	2.35 A	2.35 A
Mains voltage tungsten halogen lighting	7	100 W	700 W ÷ 230 V = 3.04 A	66 % of the connected load	2.01 A	2.01 A
Cooker (consisting of 4 rings, grill and oven) without a socket-outlet in the control panel	1	10 k W	10,000 W ÷ 230 V = 43.5 A	10 A of the connected load plus 30% of the remainder of the connected load	20.05 A	20.05 A
32 A ring final socket-outlet circuit	8	See Note 2	32 A	100% of current demand of largest socket-outlet circuit plus 40% of current demand of every other socket-outlet circuit	32.0 A	12.8 A
32 A ring final socket-outlet circuit	12	See Note 2	32A		12.8 A	12.8 A
Electric shower (instantaneous water heater)	1	10.8 k W	10,800 W ÷ 230 = 47 A	No diversity allowed	47.0 A	37.6 A

Table continued on next page

Description	Number of points served	Connected load per point	Total connected load of all points	Allowance for diversity (from Table G1)	Calculation to determine the maximum demand of the installation	
					Using the method described in IEE Guidance Note 1	Using the alternative method: applying a judgmental approach
1	2	3	4	5	6	7
Electric shaver socket-outlet	1	N/A	-	May be neglected	0 A	0 A
Security alarm	1	N/A	-	May be neglected	0 A	0 A
Smoke/ heat alarms	4	N/A	-	May be neglected	0 A	0 A
				Total for the installation	116.21 A	87.61 A

Notes to Table G2:

1   The diversity factors used in the table do not apply where the source of supply is a generator, such as a standby diesel-or-petrol-engine-driven generator.

2   The current demand associated with the ring final circuits to which diversity factors from Table G2 should be applied in order to estimate the maximum demand of the installation is the nominal current (I_n) of the circuit protective device.

As can be seen from the bottom row of column 6 of the Table G2, the calculated maximum demand is around 116 A. Therefore, the proposed 100 A current-carrying capacity of the supply is **inadequate** for the installation, on the basis of the method of calculation described in *IEE Guidance Note 1*.

G5 The alternative method: applying a judgmental approach

The installation designer may wish to adopt a different approach from that described in *IEE Guidance Note 1*, and make an assessment of maximum demand by applying engineering judgment. In this example, engineering judgment is applied to the same installation as described in the previous example.

The NICEIC guide to Domestic Periodic Inspection, Testing and Reporting

To make an engineering judgment, the inspector will need to consider the:

1. operating time profile of the load

2. coincidence or simultaneous operation of individual loads with other loads

3. seasonal demands of heating and cooling loads

4. allowance, if any, for spare load capacity.

The inspector may consider, for example, that the following allowances for diversity, which are different from those used in the method described in *IEE Guidance Note 1*, may be made with regard to socket-outlets and the electric shower:

A Socket-outlets

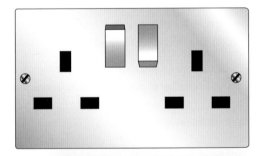

Assume that both ring final circuits will have similar operating profiles, such that a diversity factor of 40 % could reasonably be applied to both circuits.

B Electric shower

For the purpose of assessing the maximum demand of a household electrical installation supplied from the public electricity network, it is reasonable to take the average of the maximum demand occurring over a 15 minute period. This is because the service cable, service cut-out fuse and distribution circuit cable (meter tails) take a certain amount of time to be heated up by the load current, and

Photograph courtesy of Redring Electric Ltd

the additional heating effects on the source of supply (the distribution transformer) due to the peak maximum demand in an installation within a 15 minute period will be negligible.

As the shower is unlikely to used for more that (say) 12 minutes in a given 15 minute period, it is reasonable to apply a diversity factor of 80 % (12/15ths) to the connected load of the electric shower.

The allowances for diversity in this example are for illustrative purposes only and **must** be treated with some reservation. The actual allowances that the inspector makes must be based on his or her own judgment, taking account of the circumstances applying to the particular installation.

The calculation of the maximum demand for the installation, taking account of the allowances for diversity described above for the socket-outlets and electric shower, is given in column 7 of Table G2.

As can be seen from the bottom row of column 7 of Table G2, the calculated maximum demand is around 88 A. Therefore, the proposed 100 A current-carrying capacity of the supply is **adequate** for the installation, on the basis of this alternative method of calculation.

INDEX

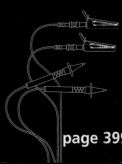

INDEX

**The NICEIC guide to
Domestic Periodic Inspection, Testing and Reporting**

INDEX

C

**The NICEIC guide to
Domestic Periodic Inspection, Testing and Reporting**

INDEX

E

F

G

H

The NICEIC guide to Domestic Periodic Inspection, Testing and Reporting

I

INDEX

**The NICEIC guide to
Domestic Periodic Inspection, Testing and Reporting**

M

N

O

P

INDEX

The NICEIC guide to Domestic Periodic Inspection, Testing and Reporting

INDEX

**The NICEIC guide to
Domestic Periodic Inspection, Testing and Reporting**